From Peat Bog to Conifer Forest

AN ORAL HISTORY OF WHITELEE, ITS COMMUNITY AND LANDSCAPE

From Peat Bog to Conifer Forest

AN ORAL HISTORY OF WHITELEE, ITS COMMUNITY AND LANDSCAPE

Ruth Tittensor

PACKARD PUBLISHING LIMITED
CHICHESTER

From Peat Bog to Conifer Forest

AN ORAL HISTORY OF WHITELEE, ITS COMMUNITY AND LANDSCAPE

© Ruth Tittensor, Countryside Management Consultancy

First published in 2009 by Packard Publishing Limited,
Forum House, Stirling Road, Chichester, West Sussex, PO19 7DN, UK.

Reprinted in 2010
by Countryside Management Consultancy
www.ruthtittensor.co.uk

ISBN: 978 185341 142 7
A cataloguing record for this edition may be obtained from the British Library.

Edited and indexed by Michael Packard
Design and layout by Susan Anderson, Eikon Graphics, Ayrshire: www.eikongraphics.co.uk
Printed and bound in Scotland by Twentyone Colour, Glasgow: www.twentyonecolour.co.uk

Half-title: Dickman's Glen looking north-east to East Kilbride — Photo: Bryan Simpson

Frontispiece: Harvested timber awaiting transport from Whitelee Forest — Photo: Ruth Tittensor

Contents

This book is for Andy
Who always stands by me

And for Penny
Who always understands me

Acknowledgements

All Contributors to the Whitelee Forest Oral History Project are acknowledged with huge thanks for their enthusiasm, interest, knowledge, memories and personal accounts, as well as their friendship. There would be no project, no recordings, no writings and no book without them.

Caroline Earwood, Coordinator of the Welsh Oral History of Forestry Project (Hanes y Goed) left a superb set of archives telling the story of Welsh forestry and set me off on the right path. William Linnard, lately of the Welsh National History Museum, St Fagans, gave initial advice, and information on forest history in Wales. Hywel Evans of the Welsh National History Museum advised and helped with recording technology.

Pauline Cairns and Chris Robinson of Scottish Language Dictionaries recorded and transcribed speakers of Scots, and educated me on the Scots language. Colin Donati transcribed more recordings of Scots speakers with attentive understanding. Susan Hutton transcribed many hours of recordings of English speakers with great dedication.

Susan Anderson of Eikon Graphics designed the lovely project brochure, this book and its evocative cover. John Mackie prepared some ingenious artwork.

William Clark & Son (Parkgate) Ltd and James A. Cuthbertson Ltd (Biggar) provided expertise on early forestry ploughs and donated photographs. Alloway Publishing (Ayr) gave permission to use a quote from Malkin (1981), while Bill Sutherland gave permission to copy his hand-drawn acquisitions map. Air photographs are courtesy of the Royal Commission on the Ancient and Historical Monuments of Scotland (RAF Air Photograph Collection). Maps and two air photographs are published under Ordnance Survey Licence 100048944.

The following gave photographs for this book: Robin Chambers, Michael Cruise, Jim Currie, Derek Douglas, Alexander Fenton, Forestry Commission Picture Library, Robert Graham, Tom and Janet Grant, Franz Grimley, William Hunter Senior, John MacKinnon, Richard Marriott, Ian Murgatroyd, Grant Peter, Heather Saunders, Heather Scott, Brian Shaw and Stuart Brabbs (Ayrshire Rivers Trust), Bryan Simpson, John Speirs, Brian Speirs and Sean Tibbetts. Isobel Cameron and Keith Hobley took excellent informal photographs of contributors. Thank you to all these people.

I am very grateful to contributors who donated items and old photographs: Robert Allan, Norman Davidson, Jim Kennedy, Morag Gillett, Roy Harvey, Jim Leitch, Jim Loudoun, Christine McWhirter, Stan Share, John R. Speirs, John Struthers.

Malcolm Crosby, Frank Jackson, Jim Newall, Jim Smalls and Rena Tarwinska of the Forestry Commission Scottish Lowlands District helped in many practical ways, while Marcus Sangster of the Forestry Commission, Edinburgh, gave ongoing background support.

Michael Chalton gave data from Saughall Meteorological Station. Jim Watson, of The Meteorological Office, Edinburgh, provided further weather information and introduced me to his mother Mrs Elizabeth Watson, the oldest contributor.

Penny Wooding commented on an early, unrecognizable draft of this book, while John Walters edited the completed draft with a fine-tooth comb. Andrew Tittensor accompanied me and took photographs on hazardous treks to Whitelee Forest.

Elizabeth-Ann Dickie, Aileen Ferrier, Gillian Findlay, Margaret Richards and Elizabeth Worthington gave office and computer help. John Andrews was a wizard with multi-media through arduous hours of work at the computer with the recording-machine, recordings and CDs. Ralph Tittensor also gave multi-media support and took photographs, while Derek and Rosemary Tittensor gave me moral support in times of need.

The Whitelee Forest Oral History Project was generously supported by the Forestry Commission with additional help from East Ayrshire Council, the Loudoun Valley Trust, the Russell Trust and South Lanarkshire Council. St Andrews University acted as administrator for the grants and provided facilities to collect information under the Data Protection Act.

I welcomed and appreciated the support and guidance of Professor Christopher Smout throughout the project, and his advice as this book developed.

I am especially grateful to Michael Packard of Packard Publishing for taking on this unusual and complex book and getting it through publication.

I thank all these people and organizations for supporting the Whitelee Forest Oral History Project and the preparation of this book. I also thank those unnamed people who gave support in their own ways. Recorded discussions and writings are reproduced with permission from contributors. They are listed in Appendix 1.

I take responsibility for mistakes: please excuse them. **RT**

Foreword

The establishment of the Forestry Commission in 1919 was to prove to be a turning-point in the history of the British uplands. Within 70 years, hundreds of thousands of hectares of open country had been transformed into dense woodland. Blankets of conifers stretched over Wales, North Yorkshire, Northumberland and parts of the Peak District. In the Lake District it evoked, as early as the inter-war years, a rare and partly successful response to a perceived threat to natural beauty. In Norfolk and Suffolk, however, planting impinged on the lowlands and destroyed much of the ancient Breckland.

But it was in Scotland that afforestation went further. As late as 1960 only six per cent of the country was woodland. By the end of the century this had become 17 per cent, and most of the new forest was concentrated on wet northern and western moorlands where it only became possible to drain and plough the peats after 1945. It was the biggest change in Scottish land-use history since the Highland Clearances. Much was expected of the trees by foresters, planners and politicians, but they mostly disappointed expectations. Many places, such as Whitelee, neither made a profit nor provided more than derisory levels of local employment, often being abandoned before felling. But they changed the land for better or worse, irreversibly.

When Ruth Tittensor began her study, no one had looked at the social and ecological history of all this change in Scotland, and very little had been done elsewhere apart from a pilot oral history project in Wales. Ruth's study is also oral history, but by its concentration on a single place it has achieved an enviable depth. The Whitelee Plateau in Ayrshire was never admired by the outside world as were the Trossachs or the English Lakes: it was bleak, wet and hard to access. It was wild and dangerous too; the workplace of farmers, the delight of boys and poachers, the habitat of hares, curlews and gulls, crossed by old and high moorland tracks between communities, a place of remembered history and of the archaeology of the forgotten. Yet it was bought from the farmers at a good price by the Forestry Commission, drained, planted and transformed amid great hopes for the future by the hard slog of dedicated and ingenious men.

Then it was left to grow, and the abandoned wood became a tangle of unthinned Sitka spruce, siskins and coal tits replaced the curlews, and people avoided it because it became impenetrable. Remarkably, some of the moorland flowers survived in the gaps and rides, and the mosses and lichens flourished exceedingly. Some trees were felled and made good money, but most were of trivial economic value, and thus, when the opportunity arose, the Forestry Commission made over the ground for a very large wind farm. Nobody asked the local community for their consent, either to the afforestation or to the wind turbines. But local people were affected and had an opinion. This book is the story of those who made the forest and those who were affected by its planting, growth and transformation. It is told in their own words by someone who listened to them for the first time.

One can only say: *'those who have ears, let them hear'*

Christopher Smout

Now and Then

The old ones read the land and the sea like books;
They understood the skies, they listened to the rain,
They did what the winter told them.

Now almost all of them have gone.
Those that are left glint like the odd gold grain
Swirled from a stream – rare and precious.

By Kenneth C. Steven

Pogiven Linn at time of spate   Photo: Ruth Tittensor

CHAPTER 1

Introduction

A flat boulder, crusty with lichens, lies at an important meeting-place on a bleak, remote, heather-moorland plateau in south-west Scotland. Covenanters met here and held their unseen services, the preacher using the boulder as a pulpit. Three centuries and more ago, the Covenanters were hounded by troops for retaining their Scottish form of Protestantism against the wishes of successive monarchs.

The bleak moorland in 1948, looking from Pogiven Bridge north to Low Overmoor and High Overmuir   Photo: Morag Gillett

The meeting point of the counties of Ayrshire, Lanarkshire and Renfrewshire is also remote, amongst the heather, swathes of grass and clumps of rushes. It is close to the source of the Glen Water which has cut deep ravines through the plateau. The story of this moorland plateau during the twentieth century is to be told here in the words of the people who lived and live there, worked or walked it, or who had fun there.

Meeting point of Ayrshire, Lanarkshire and Renfrewshire near the source of Glen Water   Photo: Ruth Tittensor

The bleak, remote, heather moorland plateau
Photo: Ruth Tittensor

In the first half of the twentieth century, the oats started to ripen on moorland farms in late summer each year; purple heather stretched away on the dense, black, peaty land. Large patches of fluorescent-green bog-moss formed plant mats over wide holes of black, liquid, peat. People knew they dare not walk over such green patches, else they would sink (to the waist at least), companion to dozens of sheep which mistook the bog-moss for growing grass, never to reappear except as skulls and bones when the peat came to be dug in later years for farmhouse and village fires.

The scent of heather nectar and musty peat hung on the air. A shepherd whistled to his collies as he tramped the plateau checking his living flock on their self-ordained hefts, hoping not to find any ewes on their backs, or signs of disease like 'blue-arse flies' whose grubs gnaw at a sheep's gut.

With few trees, this wide-open moorland gave little shelter to people, plants or animals: workers and walkers felt the heat of the afternoon sun, the prickle of flesh on seeing an adder sunning itself amongst the warm heather, and the clouds of midges and fat clegs which attacked their skin. To farmers the moorland was their factory-floor, and to walkers it was a well-worn local route or a haven of wilderness and harmonious sounds.

The typical wide-open moorland with few trees at Fore Hareshaw
Photo: Ruth Tittensor

'Fluorescent-green bog-moss'   Photo: Ruth Tittensor

Ailsa Craig from Whiteleehill steading
Photo: Ruth Tittensor

There was a phenomenal view both across the open plateau and far beyond. To the north could be seen the industry and tenements of Glasgow, with Ben Lomond beyond. The wide Firth of Clyde and the high, hazy peaks of the Isle of Arran provided spiritual uplift to the west. South of Arran, the cone of Ailsa Craig rose clearly from the seas between Scotland and Ireland. Turning south, the rounded mountains of the Southern Uplands stretched far into the distance. The Pentland Hills and Edinburgh were visible to the east before finally returning to Glasgow via Tinto and other Lanarkshire hills: a stupendous 360° panorama.

As summer became autumn, salmon swam against the flow up the burns, to spawn, a few caught by hand by knowing chaps. Thick clusters of orange berries hung from occasional rowan trees. Gunshots signalled that it was the season for shooting grouse and blackcock. Mountain hares, in blue fur at this season, rushed away at the disturbance. Sudden mists formed more frequent white girdles around the scarp of the

'**Thick clusters of orange berries hung from rowan trees**'
Photo: Ruth Tittensor

plateau. The moorland turned red-brown with white patches as swathes of moor grass and jointed rushes turned deep red, while tufted hair-grass bleached.

At each year's end, the plateau was lashed by seemingly constant heavy rains, giving a total annual rainfall of at least 1727mm (68 inches). Shooters of pheasant and grouse struggled with their gear in the wet, and boy-beaters sat outdoors on the open plateau at lunchtime to eat their 'piece', blasted by the winter winds, while 'the guns' lorded it in a warm, toileted, lodge.

This miserable weather was followed in the New Year by snowfalls which could lie until May. The Blackface sheep and hardy, rough-coated Blue-gray cattle survived with the help of the farmers, shepherds, collies and their wool. Plateau-edge farms with plump Ayrshire dairy cattle struggled to supply their daily milk to nearby towns.

As spring came, crows might peck out the eyes or tongues of new-born lambs if shepherds were not quick enough. Sometimes, shepherds mistook the still-white mountain hares for new lambs. White clouds of black-headed gulls came to nest on the wettest, softest, peat, called 'hags'. Skylarks trilled unforgettably high in the sky and the calls of numerous curlews and lapwings – known to the local Scots' speakers as whaups and peezers – floated outwards from above the rushes and short grass. As spring became summer, the sheep were marked, dipped and clipped. Peats were dug laboriously by hand and dried against the winter wet and snow.

This place, described above by the people who lived, worked and walked there, is the Whitelee Plateau, 20 km (13 miles) south of Glasgow (Map 1). Its rounded hills stretch from east to west 15 kilometres or so in the triangle between Kilmarnock (Ayrshire), Strathaven (Lanarkshire) and Eaglesham (Renfrewshire) and rise to 376 metres (1,230 feet).

Whitelee Hill is one of the highest points and Whiteleehill steading was one of the farm holdings which made a living from the peat lands and difficult climate.

Map 1: Location

During the second half of the twentieth century the wild and beautiful Whitelee Plateau experienced enormous changes resulting from the long-term effects of two World Wars and the rural policies of successive British governments.

By the century's turn, the millennium, it was still possible for people to experience some of the scents, sounds and sights of that high plateau. But a huge shock awaited anyone who had not visited the area for several decades, because it was no longer either 'open' or 'moorland'.

The sheep, shepherds and their collies are almost gone from the plateau; skylarks, curlews and lapwings are rarely heard or seen. Ubiquitous purple heather grows as occasional leggy patches on rocky outcrops or on the tops of hummocks

Conifer forest: Sitka spruce on Moss Mulloch   Photo: Ruth Tittensor

along soggy tracks. These tracks are 'brakes' which provide access and fire insurance to thick blocks of tall, dark-blue-green, prickly, conifer trees packed close together, their orange-brown cones hanging down decoratively.

The panoramic views are visible only from a few, bare hilltops, projecting above the huge blanket of forest or from the forest edge. For that is what it is: in forty years, the heather and grassy moorland has been changed into 6000 hectares (14,280 acres) of quick-growing, dark-green coniferous forest. Millions of conifers and some broadleaved trees have been planted as part of the British government's 'afforestation' programme for the whole country.

The wildlife has not gone, but changed: crossbills, mistle thrushes and siskins call, instead of skylarks and curlews. Groups of roe deer browse and graze within glades and rest under the tree canopy, where once there were mountain hares and grouse. Forty years without sheep flocks has allowed the development of massive moss and lichen hummocks, thigh-high along brakes. Grouse and pheasants hardly frequent the Forest habitats, so the increasing roe deer are the shooters' quarry nowadays. The midges are still there – of course!

There is now the murmur of wind in branches and the whine of diesel machinery harvesting whole trees. Instead of shepherds whistling to collies on the moors, walkers call to their golden retrievers along the forest road. There are no sheep bleating, but foxes bark. Forest workers and contractors have taken the place of many farmers and shepherds.

The moorland at Craigendunton in May looking north
Photo: Aileen Ferrier

The young forest on Corse Hill with heather and blanket bog in the foreground, 1980s
Photo: Bryan Simpson

20th Century Changes in Scotland's Countryside

The enormous changes experienced on this one moorland plateau mirror similar profound changes throughout the Scottish landscape during the twentieth century. Just over 5 per cent of mainland Scotland was covered with trees at the start of the 20th century; at the end of the century it had increased to 17 per cent. Most of the millions of trees were planted in Scotland from the 1960s onwards, usually on open, peaty moorland, but sometimes on sites of birch and oak woodlands. Conifers, from outside Britain originally, were the main types of trees planted, as they were expected to produce the necessary marketable crop and quick economic return on the huge investments required. The most important species planted in Scotland was Sitka spruce (*Picea sitchensis*) from western North America, whose ecological requirements most closely matched the parameters provided by the high rainfall and cool, peaty environment of the Scottish uplands.

This surge of afforestation has probably been the biggest change in land use since the 'Clearances'. The appearance of the Scottish countryside has altered more, and more quickly, than for two centuries: since the medieval cultivation system of open 'runrig' was enclosed into modern fields and farms between 1750 and 1830. The statutory Forestry Commission drove this woodland expansion of the 1960s and 1970s at the behest of governments wishing to produce much more home-gown timber and to reduce rural unemployment. Its own huge tree-planting programme and the provision of financial incentives to private landowners wishing to invest in trees and timber were the methods it used.

Yet no one has ever asked those people who planted the new forests – who afforested 12 per cent of Scotland in less than a century – how they did it or what they thought about it. Neither have the people who sold or lost their land or their livelihood, been asked what happened to them or how it affected their lives. Who did sell, or did not sell, their land for forestry? What became of their working lives? What technology and tools were used to afforest 12 per cent of Scotland? What was life like in and around the new forests? What were the effects on families and the rural economy? How did ecology, soils, and landscapes change?

Now is a good time to seek answers to these questions. The people who were involved from the beginning are becoming elderly, and their recollections need to be captured so that we, and posterity, may understand what really happened. The Forestry Commission and forestry itself are changing. The emphasis has moved away from the mass production of wood and timber and assisting rural employment. The current Forestry Commission remit and practice is still to encourage timber production, but with more and easier direct use of forests for recreation, education and health and a changed potential for flora and fauna. Forest landscapes, both internal and external, are more closely considered during forest management, harvesting and replanting.

So it is a suitable moment to look back at the birth and growth of today's conifer forests in Scotland.

This book presents the story of one particular forest, Whitelee Forest, as told by the people actually involved in its birth and growth to maturity. Oral History, the name given to history as told by the people who made that history, is an ideal way of finding out what happened. The participants themselves have the opportunity to discuss and describe the situations in which they took part, in as much or as little detail as they wish. It is an important way of learning the dynamics of what happened in the past: at the time, the people concerned were not usually consulted officially, nor their knowledge and feelings documented.

This one project – which took from 2004 to 2007 – can only be a case study providing a window into the wider question of how the Scottish people experienced twentieth-century afforestation, and what people saw and experienced of simultaneous changes in flora, fauna and the landscape.

The Whitelee Forest Oral History Project

The Whitelee Forest Oral History Project set out to obtain factory-floor detail from people involved in as many aspects of the Forest as possible, as well as people who knew or worked in the locality beforehand, and people looking on.

Information was recorded or written during informal discussion sessions with people who offered to participate in the project (Table 1).

Table 1: Topics of Discussion

The Whitelee Plateau Before 1960: farm management, other land-uses, uses by local communities; environment, ecology and landscape.

The National Context for Whitelee Forest: why the Forestry Commission was buying land & planting large forests in the UK/Scotland. Reasons for choice of Whitelee locality.

Acquiring the Land: approaching landowners, prices paid, reasons for selling; prior surveys by FC: soil, weather, access, markets; practicalities of the changeover from farming to forestry.

Practical Aspects of the Forestry: how tasks were carried out, for instance removing stock, fencing, ploughing, draining, tree planting, positioning of rides & fire-breaks, manufacture of roads; targets; siting of fire towers; tree species chosen, who chose, where the seedlings came from, their provenance; silvicultural methods.

Machinery: tools, other technology and their level of sophistication, types of manual work.

Where the Forestry Workers Came From: were there any women workers, how many workers, how were they trained, did they work long-term, where did they stay, what time did work start and finish, when was the tea-break, how far away was home, was their pay satisfactory, did they enjoy the work?

The Work of the Managers: head foresters, foresters and assistant foresters: their backgrounds, their training and careers; what was included in their work at Whitelee Forest.

Effects of Forestry Plantings: on landscape, farming, ecology, economy, past uses, people; what people saw & remember of the changes; the scale of change.

Reactions of Local Communities to the Changes: land use, species, landscape, climate, the view, ecology; the benefits or problems caused; effects on land prices.

Whitelee Forest in the 21st Century: contributors' feelings about recent and current changes.

The background to the oral history methods and ethics of the Whitelee Forest Oral History Project are discussed elsewhere (Tittensor 2006, Tittensor 2008) as this book concentrates on the results of the project.

The Whitelee Forest story is told here through transcripts of recordings, by the personal writings of contributors and by evidence written by me during spoken discussions (if contributors did not wish to be recorded). All material presented here has been agreed by the contributors concerned. As Scots is the native language of some contributors, they were given the option of being recorded by a native Scots speaker. Their recordings were then transcribed from the spoken to the written word by native Scots-speaking transcribers. The other recordings were transcribed by native English-speaking transcribers.

The testimonies of 59 people, both recorded and written, are the main data and results of the project. Photographs and objects were also donated. The archives – copies of all this material – are deposited in the Scottish Life Archive of the National Museums of Scotland, Edinburgh and at the Forestry Commission's Research Station at Alice Holt Lodge, Farnham, Surrey: they are available for public use in both places. There will be an archive close to Whitelee Forest: local as well as national depositories are needed if the resource is to have meaning and be used by nearby communities as well as academic researchers.

The archive resource is the testimony of the contributors kept safe for us and posterity. This book is written entirely from the orally-derived material of this project, or from participants' written contributions. Documentary sources from the Forestry Commission or elsewhere have not been used to provide information; printed sources have been used sparingly, only where a context is needed. The history presented here is an 'alternative' history provided by living people who experienced up to 50 years of change for themselves.

The Locality and Its Contributors

Whitelee Forest was chosen because it is not too large a coniferous state forest, forming a discrete, cohesive unit in south-west Scotland about 20 km (13 miles) south of Glasgow (Map 1). It is typical of the large-scale twentieth century afforestation of sheep-grazed moorland carried out by the Forestry Commission. Small, contiguous areas were planted by private firms at the same time, and competition between state and business was one of the interesting facets of Whitelee Forest.

When the Project started in 2004, there was still great population stability in the area surrounding Whitelee Forest. Families remained in the area all their lives. The resulting close network of marriage relationships meant people knew each other and several generations of families could be found in the locality. There were still people of an age to remember the beginning of the Forest in the 1960s and its subsequent development, and there appeared to be an exceptional number of elderly people aged 70 to 100 who had lived in the locality all their lives. These features suggested it would be possible to discover potential contributors.

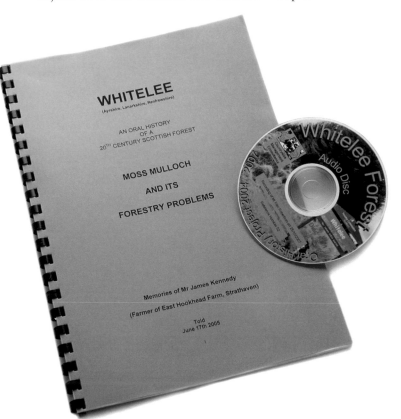

There are a limited number of discrete communities to contact in the surrounding area (Map 2). The five small towns are Darvel, Eaglesham, Galston, Newmilns and Strathaven; the five hamlets are Chapelton, Drumclog, Fenwick, Moscow and Waterside. The two larger towns of East Kilbride and Kilmarnock are too distant to participate to the same extent.

Whitelee Forest is a wild and feelingly-remote place, just as wild, remote and peaceful a haven as the preceding moorland. Its total area is 5953 hectares (14,704 acres). About 10 million trees were planted there between 1961 and 1994, but 112 hectares (277 acres) of very soft peat, ravines and waterways were left without trees. Whitelee Forest has gaps of privately-owned moorland and enclosed farmland protruding into it. It is planted from 210 metres (701 feet) altitude at Blood Moss on Burnfoot farm, to 376 metres (1,230 feet) at Corse Hill.

Despite its closeness to Glasgow and local settlements, Whitelee Forest is difficult to find and to access. One remote, minor road runs through it, along its eastern extremity. A few very minor roads skirt it or end at farms with no further access. Vehicles can be left at two tiny car-parking sites, and access is available at two other sites. But these four places are remote from main roads and difficult to find unless you have a map or good local knowledge. Otherwise, access needs permission from surrounding landowners and the ability to get over a fence into deep, soft peat. The internal forest road sits on soft peat. Walkers, horse-riders and cyclists keep to the security of this road, as the hummocky brakes are difficult and dangerous to walk along. Moving under the mature tree-cover is possible, though open forestry drains are a major hazard, and the monotony of the mature tree canopy means that people can, and do, get lost.

The isolated, discrete plateau on which Whitelee Forest grows makes it almost invisible to unknowing tourists and local residents in the valleys and plains below. The few people who now know the Forest well are some who live in adjoining upland farms, the forest rangers, shooting tenants and avid naturalists and ecologists who think nothing of wandering off the beaten track into the wet wilderness.

Contributors to the Whitelee project are listed in Appendix 1. The Latin names of flora and fauna mentioned

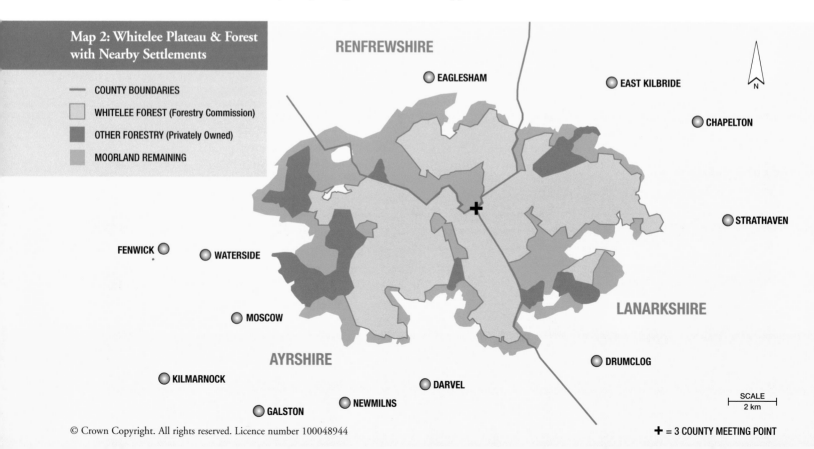

Map 2: Whitelee Plateau & Forest with Nearby Settlements

— COUNTY BOUNDARIES
WHITELEE FOREST (Forestry Commission)
OTHER FORESTRY (Privately Owned)
MOORLAND REMAINING

RENFREWSHIRE

EAGLESHAM
EAST KILBRIDE
CHAPELTON
STRATHAVEN
LANARKSHIRE
FENWICK
WATERSIDE
MOSCOW
AYRSHIRE
DRUMCLOG
KILMARNOCK
DARVEL
NEWMILNS
GALSTON

N

SCALE
2 km

✛ = 3 COUNTY MEETING POINT

by contributors, whether in Scots or English, are listed in Appendix 2. Words which may be unfamiliar in either Scots or English are explained in the Glossary in Appendix 3.

The large number of keen contributors to the Whitelee project suggests a high level of interest in the local cultural and natural heritage, in local history and in the changing politics and practices of rural land-use.

At the time this book is being written in 2008, the Whitelee Plateau is undergoing further huge change. The largest wind-farm in Europe, with over 200 turbines, is being built within the Forest and on moorland to the north. The provision of easy access via a 50 km (31 miles) network of hardcore roads to the turbines and to a visitor centre will open up the area for varied outdoor recreation. However, the developing wind-farm story will be a new chapter in the history of land-use and landscape change in Scotland, for others to tell in due course.

Reading the Evidence

The memories of all contributors are presented in this book in their native language, which may be (for example) Ayrshire, Renfrewshire or Doric Scots; Glaswegian; Yorkshire, Liverpool or Durham English; a native Welsh speaker spoke in English. There were no Gaelic speakers amongst the contributors.

Spoken language is quite different from written language. People speak neither in grammatically-correct sentences, nor even in sentences at all! So, recorded discussions transcribed into written text may look and feel strange as you read them. But transcribers do their work without imposing grammar on what was a freely-spoken discussion – it is the only way to present verbal discussion accurately as writing. I hope you find the result is more personal, more colourful, has more feeling and gives more points of view than you would get from just my personal interpretation of what was said.

I hope that you will also enjoy the wide range of language and dialect of contributors, which has been so ably and accurately caught in writing by the transcribers. As the transcribers have not corrected any grammar, the oral evidence presented here is as close to the original as possible.

Participants' written contributions have also been reproduced faithfully. In cases where I wrote participants' oral (verbal) contributions, my own form of English has been used.

In the transcriptions you will find that transcribers have used ( ) for non-verbal noises emitted by people during the discussion, for instance: (laughs), (hoasts), (pause). But square brackets are used for three purposes. First, if the transcriber cannot hear a word or passage precisely, then she uses [ ] for instance: [indistinct], [inaudible 1–2 words], [?yock], [?worsened]. She also uses [ ] if there are outside noises: [phone rings], [noises from the kitchen], [geese call from the garden]. Thirdly, transcribers use square brackets to comment on or explain a partial word or other happening: [fiddles with map], [imitates a partridge by growling in his throat], [19]61, ye['d].

During most of the recorded discussions there were only two people present. These were the contributor whose memories and knowledge were being recorded, and the 'interviewer'. The 'interviewer' was either Pauline Cairns of Scottish Language Dictionaries or me, Ruth Tittensor. When you read the transcripts, it should be clear who is speaking, because the interviewer's words are in normal typface, while the contributor's words are in italics. However, the name of the speakers is given at the start of each discussion. If spouses or relatives were also present and took part in the conversation, their name also precedes what they said. Thinking words like 'Eh', 'Er', 'Uhm' and 'Mm' are included because they are part of the conversation.

If parts of the conversation have not been included here, this is shown by . . . while… means that the speaker tailed off into nothing without finishing the sentence, a common occurrence in spoken compared with written language. Verbatim quotes or extracts from writings are also in italics, to highlight them from the rest of the text. To help enjoy the Scots contributions, it might be helpful to know that 'A' and 'Ah' mean 'I' in English, 'o' means 'of' and 'Ken' means 'YeKnow'.

Please read on and enjoy the story which follows.

CHAPTER 2

A Landscape of Peat Bogs and Mosses

Peat Formation

Brown peat of Brownhill Moss Photo: Andrew Tittensor

Peat links landscape and people of the Whitelee Plateau. Peat is very important in archaeology, ecology, economy, farming, forestry and landscape amenity. It has been studied in detail during the past century. Hundreds of publications describe every conceivable aspect of this brown or black substance which covers so much of the surface of Britain and which is so beloved by walkers and garden-centres. Because of its relevance to past and present land-use of the Whitelee Plateau, I give a short introduction to the origins and development of peat using books listed in the Bibliography under 'Peat'.

Peat is not true soil, as it contains no mineral particles from the underlying rock; neither is it true rock, as it is organic, meaning formed only from once-living things. It is a deposit which is of mainly plant origin with some animal remains. Under suitable conditions it accumulates slowly.

The type of rock underneath a layer of peat is largely irrelevant to peat's structure, because it is the growing vegetation (past and present) which determines this. Peat is formed from dead but undecomposed remains of what had been growing vegetation. In Scotland, vegetation communities growing on peat are usually dominated by 'bog mosses', which are species of *Sphagnum*. These and other mosses, sedges and grasses give peat an amorphous matrix, while remains of plants like heathers and cotton-grass give it some fibrous texture.

A green species of Sphagnum or Bog Moss
Photo: Ruth Tittensor

A red species of Sphagnum
Photo: Andrew Tittensor

Small 'Raised Bog' on Whatriggs
Photo: Ruth Tittensor

Cool ground is needed for peat to accumulate. It also requires poorly-drained rock or soil below it, so that surface-water cannot drain downwards — causing constant waterlogging with no air. Fungi and other microbes (which would normally decompose dead plants and animals) are inactive or absent in the cool, airless conditions. So plants barely decompose when they die, resulting in a brown, accumulating mass. One centimetre in height is a good annual growth rate for peat. Bits of invertebrate animal (like legs or wings of beetles) which once lived in the peat ecosystem also remain within the peat. As the peat grows higher, the lower levels are under increasing pressure, are more squashed and often wetter and black. Rain, mist and fog, from the atmosphere above are the only sources of water for most peat ecosystems. Groundwater, from below, is usually inaccessible to plants growing in peat.

'Moss' or 'Bog' are the common names for a peat ecosystem, while 'Mire' is the scientific term. 'Blanket Bog' ('Blanket Moss' or 'Blanket Mire') is a formation which develops over large areas of flat ground or shallow, convex hills up to about 457m (1,500 ft) in Scotland. Blanket bog is acid and very poor in plant nutrients (mineral particles derived from the underlying rocks). Generally cool air and

Black peat is dense, Myres Hill
Photo: Ruth Tittensor

ground temperatures, high rainfall, with frequent mist and fog, mean that large areas of Scotland are very suitable for peat growth!

'Raised Bogs' are another peat formation, with similar vegetation to blanket bogs. As they usually start to develop within wet hollows, they do receive drainage water from the surrounding higher ground. So in their lower layers they may contain mineral particles from underlying rocks. As raised bogs rise in height, they extend above the surrounding land: then their vegetation no longer receives any groundwater with mineral nutrients. Like blanket bogs, they then rely entirely upon atmospheric precipitation for their water supply. Raised bogs can gradually build up into a mound several metres higher than the surrounding land.

Functioning raised bogs have similar vegetation to blanket bogs, but can be recognised by their smaller size, their convex (mound) shape and situation in hollows. Being 90 per cent water, they can be thought of as mounds of water held together by peat!

Peat ecosystems are not entirely natural features of the Scottish landscape. They first developed after the latest Ice Age, during the period called by archaeologists the Mesolithic (Middle Stone Age) 8,500 to 5,500 years Before the Present (BP). Hunting people of this prehistoric period burned trees, shrubs, heather and the margins of forests. Fire created open glades in which wild plant-eating animals collected to forage for fresh plant growth. Humans could then catch them more easily for food.

People of the Neolithic (New Stone Age) 5,500 years BP onwards, continued to burn and clear the increasingly open forests. Domestic cattle and sheep were probably allowed to feed in the glades too, extending them by constantly nibbling back the growing shoots of bushes and trees. Time went on, and by about 4,000 BP, humans of the Bronze Age continued to alter and open the once-wooded environment. But the weather worsened as far as they were concerned, turning wetter and cooler. Rushes, sedges and mosses began to spread over the ever bigger and damper woodland glades and peat started to form and continued to accumulate in what were now cooler and wetter environmental conditions.

Scotland's early forests, containing natural openings, were gradually changed (during decades and centuries) into open landscapes with large expanses of peat mires and islands of relict woodland. This opened-up landscape was cultivated and grew crops or was grazed by domestic stock more intensively

Typical peat pool, Low Overmoor
Photo: Ruth Tittensor

Loch Burn flows through black peat on Lochfield
Photo: Ruth Tittensor

and extensively; some wild herbivores became extinct. The incoming Romans met this changed, well-used landscape and not a wilderness of forest.

Over the centuries, methods of using the landscape changed, changed again and again. Sometimes weather, famine or social conditions caused people to abandon land, on which peat might then grow. Peat continued to expand over whatever land was suitable, probably until about one thousand years ago.

Peat mires have been with us since prehistoric times, used by people to hunt wild game, graze domestic stock, cut for fuel, as a source of wild plant foods, as spiritual places and sometimes for burying bodies. More recently, peat has been afforested with trees or machine-dug and sold to garden-centres. It is highly regarded by archaeologists and ecologists for its cultural value, while grouse-moor owners appreciate its recreational and economic value.

'Moss Stock': the Forest Archive in the Peat

The topography and climate of the Whitelee Plateau make it a typical place for blanket and raised bogs to develop. The hills have shallow convex slopes with hollows and form a plateau.

Poorly-drained clay lies on top of the bedrock, annual rainfall is high, there is frequent mist, the mean annual temperature is low, while summer and winter weather are not differentiated as much as in the south and east of Britain. These conditions are all are conducive to peat formation over 80 per cent of the Plateau, where it can be up to seven metres (23 feet) deep.

Within Whitelee's deep peat, there is an archive, a record, of earlier, different, Whitelee forests which could have been growing hundreds or thousands of years ago.

Contributors to this project frequently discovered evidence of these earlier forests in the Whitelee peat. For instance, the difficulties of horse-ploughing in the 1940s and 1950s were described **Jim Leitch**.

> *Moss Stock. These were very hard tree trunks inside the peat they were also found in fields being ploughed, especially if the field was mossy. Then - poor plough!*

Archie Mitchell wrote about Moss Stock on his farm.

> *Much of Whatriggs farm has peat as its land surface (soil) - which is why it needs draining constantly and grows rushes. 'Moss Stock' (trunks of trees once growing in the peat surface, but which have become partly fossilised in the wet peat conditions) are often found in the Whatriggs peats. They can be up to 1 foot in diameter and with long trunks. Where the fields have been drained and are reasonably dry, the Moss Stock have become really hardened and have to be dug out and taken away.*

Farmer Archie Mitchell and naturalist Bryan Simpson with a big moss stock ploughed from Whatriggs peat   Photo: Ruth Tittensor

Hummocky peat on Back Hareshaw
Photo: Ruth Tittensor

He also mentioned an incident which happened when he was a young man.

An elderly farm worker was ploughing with his horse on ground a bit higher up the farm towards the High Bowhill March Fence. He was walking behind the plough, guiding the horse. The ploughman said [to the young Archie Mitchell] how the plough-share hit a Moss Stock and became stuck in it. Not only that, the plough-shaft with the stuck Moss Stock flew backwards and hit him hard on the forehead and he fell down and lost consciousness – for about an hour he thought.

Even modern steel ploughs drawn by big tractors still plough up Moss Stock: Jim Boswell was lucky enough (!) to plough up yet another oak trunk on his farm near Loudoun Hill, while Archie Mitchell recently ploughed up six Moss Stock from his land. They were stored out of the way near a farm track, and despite shrinkage since, they now measure up to 253 cm long and 37 cm across at the base. Four root plates ploughed up at the same time were up to 85 cm across. These measurements suggest they had once been big living trees.

Brian Speirs discussed the problems with Moss Stock during draining operations on the peat.

Ruth: . . . did you ever come across these Moss Stock – I think if that's what you call them, Moss Stock or Bog Oaks, any, um, ancient trees or tree trunks in the peat?

Brian: *We did. In some areas quite a lot, eh, [ul] some o them recognised as birch, rowan or pine. Some o them that way.*

And were they big, I mean were they, were they, uh, trunks and proper trunks, or branch bits?

Both

The, the trunk, or the base o the trunk, was quite big, was quite big, and then . . . Sort of six inches across? Nine inches?

Six – nine inches. Eh, a lot o the time, ye would come across at the bottom o the, the drain ye were clearing and it wes quite a job cutting through this to have the bottom

o the drain level. But mostly the, they ploughed, the plough drew in the furra, brought the, the old wood up tae be exposed, so that you could see them.

How did you, how did you manage to identify them as birch, rowan or pine?

By the bark.

The bark was still on it?

The bark was still on most ae them, yes, yes.

Small moss stock piled by the farm track
Photo: Ruth Tittensor

These Moss Stock, and others still being dug up, are the archive of past forests on the Whitelee plateau. They are the remains of shrubs and tree canopies of past Whitelee forests, while the peat surrounding them is the remains of former herbaceous flora. They are exceedingly difficult to identify, but oak, Scots pine, rowan, birch and willow have been identified so far. They may not have all been growing at the same time in one forest: they are found at varying depths, suggesting woodlands grew at different times on the past Whitelee Plateau. It would be possible in the future to date the Moss Stock by dendrochronology (tree-ring dating) and radio-carbon methods, while analysis of pollen and semi-fossilised animals in the peat could tell us more about the vegetation and fauna which lived in Whitelee's past landscapes.

The Modern Peat Landscape at Whitelee

Earlier Whitelee forests in the peat are interesting enough, but the twentieth century peat landscape of the Whitelee Plateau has other exciting features.

Firstly, it sinks! And people and animals sink in it!

Brian Speirs ran a Forest Workers Holding at Craigendunton for ten years. He described what happened to the view in that decade.

> *. . . when you looked out from Craigendunton to the south, you could see Ailsa Craig and the sea in the distance.*
>
> *In the foreground, Airtnoch was the nearest farm and dwelling, about one mile away. But there was a hill in the peat between Craigendunton and Airtnoch, so you could not actually* **see** *the steading itself.*
>
> *But when we left ten years later, the hill had sunk and we could see the chimneys of Airtnoch. The farmer at Airtnoch had not drained the hill or done anything to it – that's just how the peat was!*

In the 1930s and 1940s, **Jim Currie** learned the dangers of the Whitelee hills, which he has frequented ever since.

> *It wis… A mean ye('d) sink up… They aye. Everyone aye said there wis horse an cairts in them. Ken a horse went in there an it gote buried. A mean, a've been up ti ma knees in it. But. But, e, if ah wis up ti the knees ah wis panickin. Ah wantid oot. Ken. An [if he]. When I used ti go, the twa o us, wee Froggie an I went wursel, I wid gae oot. I always hud a. I cairried a rope wi us. An a'd gae oot. If ah sunk too faur, he poued me oot. Ken. We used ti strip doun ti*

wur. Eh. Y-fronts or. It wisnae y-fronts in thae days, it wis juist yir drawers, ken. (Laughs) If ye wur lucky.

Hugh Hendry wrote about the deep sinks of liquid peat called 'Peat Hags' which he learned about in the same period.

> *They consist of areas of more or less long, parallel, deep gullies. These gullies are 3 to 5 feet deep and 5 to 10 feet across. The gullies or ditches have sides which are bare peat, but in the ditch bottoms there is Sphagnum moss and sometimes short grass in shallow water. The Sphagnum in the ditch bottoms does not form mounds in any way at all. Sometimes, there are also sheep bones or carcases, where sheep have fallen in and been unable to climb out, as their wool becomes wet, heavy and sticky. The gully walls of bare peat are either very steep or vertical.*
>
> *Between the gullies normal heather moorland forms the vegetation surface. If you walk across the moorland in the dark you could easily fall into the gullies of these hags. Hugh's Pond (alias Pley Lochan) and the wet area forming the main 'Gulls' Hag' just north of Lochfield Loch are two examples of Peat Hags.*

There was plenty of experience of peat hags on the family farm for the young **Iain Hamilton**.

Artist's impression of peat hags
Graphic: John Mackie

If you moved oot tae-dward Whitelee Hill then ye get moass haggs, ye'll no need tae ken whit a moass hagg is ye only need tae see it tae believe it, it's where the waater fae the burns gaither an cut their wey through the peat an leaves these banks, oh, fifteen, twenty feet high some o them an a loat o the peat haggs have nae vegetation oan them, ken they were bare and in some cases a daith trap ye juist needed tae ken where ye were gaun.

It's the same wi Sphagnum moass an if ye were ever oan the hill an ye were ever unsure aye go where a sheep goes because it'll ken better than you. Usually the brighter the green, the healthier lookin o the moss the deeper the waater an the mair danger ye were in.

Jim Kennedy repeated the tale of a farm tragedy experienced by an elderly farm worker, on an infamous area called Moss Mulloch, when a lad, just before 1920.

Right. He wis up there workin as a boy. Which were a lot more labour on the farms, then. He wis tae go out ontae Moss Mulloch an check some young heifers that wis there while the boss wis away at a Sheeps Sale an the rest of, the rest o the neighbors – it wis a big Sheeps Sale apparently, ah juist got this handit down tae me but it's a true story. Now he got. One ae his heifers, one o his young stock, wis amissin an he got it in one ae these ditches. But he couldnae get it oot himself. So he decidit tae go intae the stable an get a horse and ropes, and take it out, an tie ropes ontae the beast an, an, an, eh, pull it out, get it out the ditch, because he wis feart it would be drowned bi the time... Well, the young boy wouldnae huv any experience of horses – Clydesdale horse or whatever type o horse it was – but a mean, cattle-beasts ull sorta find their way out through it. But ah don't know whether any o the two o yese hae any experience wi horses, but a mean if a horse gets ontae a saft bit, it panics. Ye know. An then. He never. He got so far out. Didnae even get near where the beast was, an the horse panicked an it went down – hit, the horse went down. An [did the]. An. When they come home at night, whether the horse wis dead or no when they come home at night ah don't know – the boss – but eh, a'm led

tae believe that they hud tae shoot the horse because the horse wis really strugglin an there were no way they could get it out. Eh, an then the, the neighbours come an helped an one hing an anither, which we do in the farmin line, an they, they manhandelt the, the heifer out the ditch, eventually. If the, if the young boy hud – he juist kinnae, wis over energetic, or over anxious tae get it out. But. That must've been the late teens possibly that that happent.

Well, in nineteen... eighty, when they were ploughin that, they ploughed up that, the horse – that skeleton.

A sunk tractor in the peat on Craigends, 1950s
Photo: John Struthers

The peat of Moss Mulloch provided **Jim Kennedy** with his own difficulties later in the twentieth century.

It wis so bad that when ah looked this farm – inspected it in the first place – we went tae the side ae the fence and the previous owner says a'm not even taikin ye over that, because, cause he says, ye can forget about it, for it, for it*, it's useless. An he, he didn't tell us then that it wis actually dangerous, but eh – thay h-, they hud it, they hud it fenced off tae keep any livestock from gaun ontae it . . .

Ah never went, ah never went over that ground maself, wuthout tellin ma wife where ah wis goin. It wis actually... Actually it wasn't safe for one person tae go out there an walk on their own because if ye went-, if ye went down, eh, there were no, there were no, mobile telephones in these days if ye got stuck sumwhere an ye – a person could get stuck very easy. * [that is, the land over the fence]

On Whatriggs they lost a foal drowned in the liquid peat, as **Archie Mitchell** remembered in his writings.

> *Once, they lost a foal in a drain. Mr Mitchell's father put a washing pole (about 8 feet long) down into the drain, but the pole never got near the drain bottom! He explained that drains on the farm might be vegetated on top but below the vegetation is usually liquid peat.*

Madge Andrew (who was then Madge Bell) was a Land Army Girl at Whatriggs from 1946 to 1948 and she told her memories of peat cutting there (the Mr Mitchell she mentions was Archie Mitchell's father).

> **Ruth:** You remember Mr Mitchell digging peat?

> **Madge:** *Oh yes. I eh peat field there'd still be a peat field but there's. I eh it fascinated me it did. It was like well to me it was like digging as if you're digging well there's a cutters of some sort. An they dig so much an then they cut it into oblongs.*

Right. Like a brick?

> *A bricks a bit longer mebe a bigun but an then they they had peat stacks you know eh an then in in the house of course they'd a ehm is it a basket thing and that filled up with peat I just loved it was in the fire but I don't actually know where the peat storage was. I think it was in one of the sheds you know like the byre because there was the hay shed (pause) I can't remember exactly where the the peat the eh that'd be stacked as well but the eh oh! that was I thought that was marvellous thing, the peat.*

Yes, yes. What colour was the peat?

> *Eh eh it wes just like oh just like peat I was going to say that sounds daft it was like black. It was a lovely smell. Oh! A super thing y'know.*

Peat-digging for fuel had been a tradition and a need for local farms and residents. **Archie Mitchell** described how it came to an end for his family.

Piles of peat bricks awaiting winter fires on Fair Isle
Photo: Andrew Tittensor

In the 1960s he decided that at peat-cutting time there was too much work lifting turnips, labour was getting scarce, and there was insufficient time for peat-cutting. It was a very busy time of year on the farm – always too much to do. He decided that they would stop peat-cutting on Whatriggs farm and buy in coal or get wood for the fire. However he does think that in the future, when coal and oil have gone, that the peat may be a very good resource again.

And **James Mair** told a story of the disappearance of a local weaver.

There's a famous tale of, this is the handloom weaving time when they used to carry their webs across to Glasgow, with their finished webs and collect their yarn for their next . . . And there's the story of, what is known as Jenny Ge's man, her husband disappeared forever, was never ever found. Could have been all sorts of reasons for that though, he might have been skedaddling, but . . . He was, they thought that he'd been lost in the moor. Ge being, well before Gebbie, the local language at that time, you used to cut off the names of people when you were saying them.

Comment

This was and is the peat landscape of the Whitelee Plateau: a soft, sometimes liquid, and often dangerous base for the factory-floor of farming, a blunter of ploughs, a grave for beasts, a place where lads soon learned to take care, and a provider of fuel for winter fires. It is also an archive centuries older than our documents and cathedrals, a difficult but much-loved place to live, a plateau of blanket bog and of growing 'mounds' of rainwater held in shape by the vegetation growing and dying in it.

Place-names reflect the peaty nature of the terrain. There are 22 areas with the name 'Moss', 'Muir' or 'Bog', for instance, Dinnafind Moss, Wallacegill Muir and Honey Bog. Farm names also reflect the peaty terrain, for instance Laigh Blackmoss, Mosside and High Overmuir.

Contributors' descriptions of the many resources provided by the peat landscape will be in later chapters.

Digging peat for winter fires at High Hapton, 1930s
Graphic: John Mackie

AY 1 1932

1.

4.

2.

3.

1933 PEATS
AWAITING
CUTTING

1932 (CURRENT)
PEAT TO CUT

1930 SURFACE
PEAT CUT

1931 SURFACE
PEAT CUT

AYS 2 AND 3
1932

1.

4.

2.

3.

PEAT HAG

PEAT TO BE
CUT IN 1933

PEAT CUT
IN 1930

PEAT CUT
IN 1931

1932 PEAT
BEING CUT

CHAPTER 3

Environment and Ecology Before the Forest

'Basalt' bedrock on Corse Hill   Photo: Ruth Tittensor

'Trachytic' bedrock outcropping in Dickman's Glen
Photo: Andrew Tittensor

'Gowk Stane member' bedrock altered by heat
Photo: Andrew Tittensor

The Rocks Beneath the Peat

The soft, organic peat sits directly on top of mineral rocks, both formed during the last one million years. They sit on top of very old, deep, extremely hard rocks which were extruded from volcanoes as thick liquids, including lava, over 400 million years ago in the 'Carboniferous' era. The basic physical structure of the area was produced by these ancient, hardest rocks. They are called the 'Bedrock', whereas the rocks and peat on top are together called 'Superficial' deposits. The Superficial deposits come from two time-zones.

First they formed during the latest 'Ice Age' or 'Devensian Glaciation' which lasted from 80,000 to 13,000 years ago. The whole of this part of Scotland was covered with thick ice towards the end of this period. The ice scraped away any previous superficial deposits. It froze, melted and moved around, and pulverised the surface of the ancient bedrocks. Meltwater from the ice deposited this detritus as clay, sand and gravel in river valleys and lake hollows. At Whitelee, moving ice and meltwater deposited a layer up to 5 m deep of red-brown clay-with-stones sediment called 'Glacial Till' over the Plateau top. Glacial Till is visible where burns or drains have cut through the peat.

Second after the Ice Ages (the 'Post-glacial' 13,000 BP to the present), the most recent deposits have been laid down and some continue to form. 'Moraines' are low hills of debris left by glaciers when they melted away, and they occur on the north-east of the Plateau, for instance at East Browncastle and Moss Mulloch. Running water did and still does deposit 'Alluvium': fine-grained layers of silt, mud and sand without stones. It is found along the valley bottoms of burns which flow in a southerly direction from the Whitelee plateau – in particular, the Calder Water, Glen Water and Dunton Water.

'Glacial Erratic' moved by
ice to Hole Craig
Photo: Ruth Tittensor

The Covenanters' Stone, Gowk Stane and other boulders formerly used as preaching stones are 'Glacial Boulders' moved and then deposited by melting ice.

80 per cent of the surface of the Whitelee Plateau is Peat, which sits directly on top of the glacial till on top of the ancient lavas. These surface as volcanic knobs in only a few high places such as Drumduff Hill and Corse Hill. Only about 20 per cent of Whitelee Plateau surface is free of peat.

The Whitelee Plateau lies at altitudes of 250m to 376m but most is undulating between 275 m and 335 m. A walk to a high point or a quick look at a map shows the nearest hills of comparable height are Dungavel and Distinkhorn eight miles away to the south-west.

Dunton Cove, an artificial cave adjoining Dunton Water, used as
a hiding place by Covenanters   Photo: John Struthers

'Glacial Till' of clay and stones by Pogiven Water
Photo: Andrew Tittensor

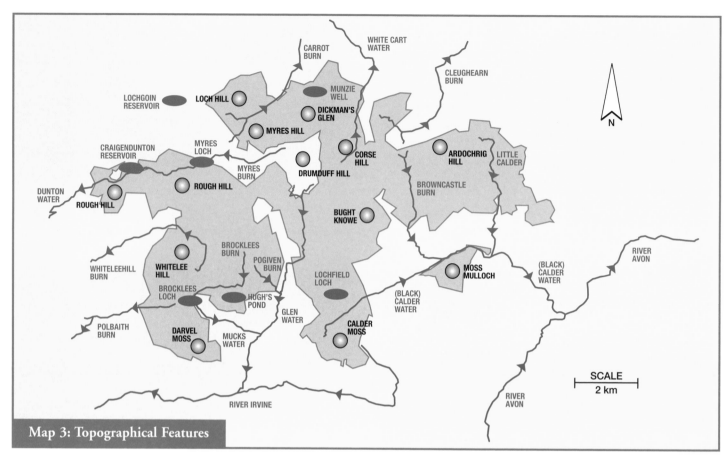

Map 3: Topographical Features

The ravine of the Glen Water, which bisects Whitelee Plateau
Photo: Ruth Tittensor

Soils

The Forestry Commission carried out a survey of the soils of part of the Whitelee Plateau in 1972, to discover whether aerial photographs could provide as much information as tramping the hills. **Richard Toleman** carried it out and contributed his written report to the project (see Bibliography), and it is summarized here.

Although glacial and post-glacial sediments cover the bedrocks, the most widespread soils of the Whitelee Plateau are mainly derived from the peat sitting on the very top of them all. Seven main types of Peat Soil have developed. 'Hill Peats' and 'Unflushed Bog' grow mainly heathers and related small shrubs; 'Flushed Bogs' grow big grasses such as Tufted hair-grass and Purple Moor-grass, but no heathers. The other peaty soils have various mixtures of grasses, mosses and lichens. 'Bog mosses' (Sphagnum species) grew on most peaty soils but not on 'Eroded Peat'.

Mineral Soils derived from the underlying Glacial Till are very scarce on the Whitelee Plateau, occurring where peat is absent from the land surface. Most mineral soils have been used for cultivated farmland (the inbye lands), but some occur along waterway and valley sides. The mineral soils were classified as 'Upland Brown Earths' and 'Poorly Drained Brown Earths', which are the best soils of the area for agriculture. 'Ironpan' and 'Gley' soils tend to be lacking in air due to an impervious iron layer or waterlogging. The mineral soils, if not cultivated, do not grow heather but support smaller, more varied grasses than the big tufted grasses of peaty soils. Different soil types intergrade and develop over small areas and so complexes of many types occur close together.

Whitelee Plateau soils have not been left alone to develop naturally. Descriptions by contributors tell of fertilizing (with animal manure and artificial chemicals such as ash and slag), draining, ploughing and harrowing the mineral soils before planting crops. Peat soils were drained on a huge scale, burned to promote heather growth for sheep and grouse feed, and dug for fuel.

25

Mucks Water looking downstream
Photo: Ruth Tittensor

Myres Burn flowing from an old barytes mine to Flow Moss
Photo: Ruth Tittensor

A drain joins Cleughearn Burn at Burnhouse
Photo: Ruth Tittensor

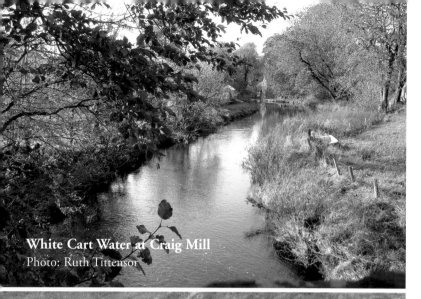

White Cart Water at Craig Mill
Photo: Ruth Tittensor

Hareshawmuir Water near Tayburn
Photo: Ruth Tittensor

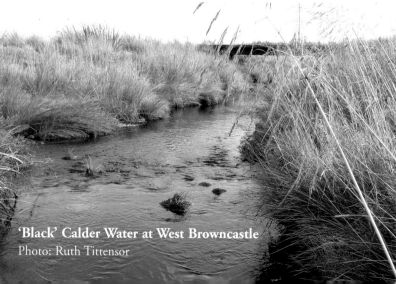

'Black' Calder Water at West Browncastle
Photo: Ruth Tittensor

Waterways and Lochs

The margin of the Whitelee Plateau is broken up into mainly long, even slopes with gently convex hill-tops and depressions. Deep ravines contain larger burns such as Pogiven Burn and Dunton Water and – by far the largest and most spectacular - the Glen Water, which cuts the plateau in two from north to south. The Plateau has a scarp-like slope between Carrot and Ardochrig on its north, and here the smaller Munzie and Carrot Burns flow north with waterfalls on the way.

There are several wide, shallow valleys with slower moving burns such as the Black Calder Water, which flows into the River Avon, and Hareshawmuir Water which flows west towards Waterside from Craigends.

There are 90 or more Waterways traversing the Whitelee Plateau. They flow into the Rivers Avon, Irvine and Clyde. Most of them are Burns (streams). Small watercourses in boggy ground drying up in the summer are Sikes while Gills are gully waterways. Delightful Waterfalls or Linns and dark, peaty Pools occur along the Glen Water and bigger burns. There are numerous Springs on and around the Whitelee Plateau: some farms obtain their water from springs or burns. Derelict Wells occur in or near steadings, for instance at High Hapton and Brocklees. Munzie Well produces orange chalybeate water in a field at the bottom of Dickman's Glen. Huge systems of Parallel Drains were once dug into the peat for drainage and are still visible.

Lochs include: Brocklees (alias Burnfoot) Loch built as a fishing lake; Myres Loch a feeder for Craigendunton Reservoir; Pley Lochan (alias Hugh's Pond alias Gateside Loch) was made in the 1950s, by damming a peat hag on Pley Moss for duck shooting. The almost-drained Lochfield Loch is between Braidley Moss and Loch Hill. Heads Loch and others have gone. On Dunton Water, there is a cave once used by Covenanters as a hiding place, called Dunton Cove.

This summary of Whitelee's geology and topography has been compiled from observations, from contributors' knowledge and from maps listed in the Bibliography.

Brocklees (Burnfoot) Loch in open moorland in the 1960s
Photo: Jim Currie

Hugh's Pond, formed in Pley Moss by damming Stagmire Burn with sleepers and heather
Photo: Ruth Tittensor

The orange water of Munzie Well
Photo: Ruth Tittensor

Craigendunton Reservoir, which supplied Kilmarnock with water
Photo: Ruth Tittensor

A dark spring near Hole Craig
Photo: Ruth Tittensor

The old peat-diggings of High Hapton
Photo: Ruth Tittensor

Moorland drainage on Gateside and Long Green Farms was described in detail by **Jim Leitch**.

Between the 1930s and 1950s, drains on the moors were dug by hand, often by Irish labourers. The farmer decided the position of the rows of drains in the landscape, bearing in mind the slope of the ground, and where he wanted the main Carrier Drain to be.

The labourers dug open drains using three tools. Firstly, they used a 'Ripping Spade' which had a short stem and a very wide handle at the top with a very large, curved and sharp blade. They put one foot on the blade and pushed hard and down, so cutting vertically downwards. They could do this hardly stopping to pull the spade out of the ground, so it seemed like one continuous movement along and into the ground. With the ripping spade, they formed the long, parallel sides of the drain which were about 18 inches deep.

With a more normal 'Garden Type Spade', they also cut vertically downwards about 18 inches, but across from side to side of the drain so blocks of peat were formed all along the drain.

Thirdly, the labourers used a 'Curved Prong Fork', and dug out the soil to a depth of 18 inches. The sides of the drain would be 6 inches apart at the bottom and 12 inches apart at the top, so that the sides sloped inwards towards the base. The soil and turf (vegetation) pulled out would be laid down in a long heap along both sides of the new drain. Open drains dug by labourers on the moorlands took 10 to 20 years to silt up and infill. Then they would have to be redug. Long, parallel, open drains on the peat moors were produced this way.

From the 1950s onwards, the moors were drained with a machine. By the time the Forestry Commission came along in the early 1960s, draining of moorland had already dwindled, as the profits from hill-farming were so poor and it was hardly worthwhile.

The mineral soils of the inbye were drained differently from the moorland, as **Archie Mitchell** explained.

The drains were about 8 yards apart. The land was ploughed towards the centre of the 8-yard strip between the drains, so that this became a ridge. Half the water therefore flowed from the ridge down either slope each side into the drains. This system was designed to drain the soil a foot or two down from the soil surface, a long way compared with farms on better land where only the top several inches might need draining. In each parallel drain, Mug Tiles were placed. The government and landlord usually paid half each for the drains; however, if the landlord was not wealthy, the drains were dug further apart. 5 yards apart, not the 8 yards apart as at Whatriggs, was the normal distance.

Archie Mitchell remembers ploughing the rigged area himself in his younger days – *'a long time ago'* he said!

Weather

Many contributors mentioned the weather in the past. There could be very hot days on top of the Whitelee hills in summer which were exacerbated by the lack of shelter from trees, hollows or adjoining hills. On the other hand, it could rain, rain, rain for weeks on end. Rain and damp made it difficult for cereals to ripen. Even when there was only a tiny puff of wind in the Irvine Valley, there could be a gale blowing on top of the Whitelee Plateau.

John Telfer spoke about the awful weather at Carrot on the Eaglesham side of the Whitelee hills in the 1970s.

Carrot Farm was 4,300 acres, an extremely large farm compared with others in the area. It was very wet, very misty. Everything in the house was damp and things got mouldy. It was easy to get lost in the mist on the hills, and the flatness of the hill-tops did not help, as it meant landmarks were few. The annual rainfall in the Carrot Farm area is 88 inches. Carrot is a dirty stinking wet hole.

Brian Speirs described an incident in the mist when he was a forest worker.

But there wes one occasion, we were up there workin away there, the trees theirself wad be about five-six foot high and the mist come down and we worked away, and this man and this young boy come along the brake.

"Hullo!"

Away they went. Half an hour later they come back.

"It's no very nice day."

"No, no." Away he went. The third time he come back.

"Please help me, I'm totally lost."

His, eh, well I assume it wes his son wes almost crawling at the time. And eventually, once he was (Laughs) finished this, we told him tae head up this brake. And he would come on ti the farm road. And away he would – he could go then. But that wes the only time we ever met anybody that wes lost in the mis.

It wes the only time. I mean, the like o the squad, we knew – mean, if you got an area that wes to be – all the work routine on. You were that used to gaun to that area.

Dairy farmers had a difficult time in the prolonged snow, as also told by **Jim Leitch**.

The Snow *During the 1940s there was a lot of hard weather, deep snow and hard frost that could last for weeks. This caused quite a few lives to be lost among the sheep. On the boundary between Low Overmoor and High Hapton there were a lot of deep peat hags, about seven feet deep, ten feet wide at the top with running water at the bottom. We had bridges across them, mainly old lorry bodies, they made a good bridge.*

When the snow came these hags became level full with snow and the frost made it hard. The sheep would then start walking across the snow and could fall through and drown in the water below when the thaw came.

The roads could be an average of five feet deep. I am told the road at West Heads was 11 feet deep at one time. The only way out with the milk from the dairy farms or to collect supplies was by horse and cart. I have ridden a Clydesdale horse through snow drifts to break them down and make it easier for the horse following with a cart load of milk. We went in company with other farms so as to

Blizzard conditions at the entrance to High Overmuir early 1980s
Photo: Grant Peter

help each other on the way. We cut fences as we went, farmers had no objections as long as we repaired them after the snow had gone.

Snow and freezing conditions in the 1950s were described by **John Struthers**.

There was much more snow than nowadays … There were sheep under the snow, which the dogs could sniff out . . . Lambing usually started on 17th April and there were often snow showers and some snow still lying that late in the spring. Sometimes snow lay in the hollows until May . . . The weather wis different then tae. I mind o the pipes freezin an burstin. We had pipes runnin through fae the house tae the steadin an they had be thawin oot tae get the water through tae water the beasts. The beasts were needin a drink so that pipe had tae be thawed oot. The big thing, improvement wi electricity wis safety. It wis aw safer, because in the aulden days ye were carryin lamps aboot, paraffin lamps an yer workin wi hay an straw an ye had tae be very, very careful or ye could have a fire.

David Findlay remembered the weather in the 1950s/1960s.

. . . we used to get better summers but harder winters. Winters wis really hard, eh, eh, heavy frost, deep snow, an we used to get it more often, an it wis constant, you could actually,

Table 2: Contributed Meteorological Data
[Comparisons with Eskdalemuir (Dumfries & Galloway) and Prestwick (Ayrshire) given if available]

Location of Meteorological Stations

	Altitude (m)	Distance to Firth of Clyde (km)
Eskdalemuir	242m	102
Prestwick	20m	Adjoining
Drumclog	225m	30.5
Saughall	221m	29
Croilburn	235m	23
Whitelee Plateau	230-376m	20-36

Air Temperature, annual average (°C)

Saughall 1988-2005, Drumclog 1983-2005
Eskdalemuir & Prestwick 1961-1990

Site	Av. Maximum	Av. Minimum
Drumclog	11.3	3.4
Saughall	11.5	4.2
Eskdalemuir	10.8	3.8
Prestwick	12.2	5.3

Annual Rainfall, average (mm)

Saughall, Drumclog, Croilburn 1975-2005
Eskdalemuir & Prestwick 1961-1990

Drumclog	1501
Saughall	1342
Croilburn	1727
Eskdalemuir	1538
Prestwick	942

Soil temperature, monthly mean (°C at 30cm depth)

Saughall 1989-2005

Jan	Feb	Mar	Apr	May	Jun	Jul	Aug	Sep	Oct	Nov	Dec
2.43	2.27	3.64	5.95	9.42	12.57	14.09	13.96	11.91	9.09	5.43	3.36

Actual Sunshine, mean (hours/day)
1961-1990

Saughall	3.61
Eskdalemuir	3.06
Prestwick	3.89

Days of Air Frost, mean (per annum)
Saughall 1988-2005

72.75

Number of Gales, mean (per annum)
Saughall 1988-1997

Mean 9.4, maximum 17 gales (1988)

[Data courtesy of Michael Chalton, Saughall Meteorological Station, Darvel and Jim Watson, The Meteorological Office, Edinburgh]

very near guarantee that November, December, January, where now everythin's more wetter. To me the winters are wetter, the summers are wetter, definitely. Ah mean, our river used to freeze up, we [used to] skate on the river.

Farm names are reminders of the unhelpful weather: High and Laigh Unthank, Coldwakning, Windy Hill, East and West Windyedge and Windshields are very descriptive.

Weather information recorded by local residents at their official meteorological stations supplements the direct oral knowledge. **Michael Chalton** runs a met station at Saughall 3km south of Whitelee Plateau and there is another nearby at Drumclog. For some years there was a rain gauge at Croilburn on the Whitelee Plateau. **Jim Watson** of the Meteorological Office in Edinburgh made available this data. Selected features of the past half-century's weather are shown in Table 2. Comparisons with a high inland and coastal met station (Eskdalemuir and Prestwick respectively) are shown if available.

Average annual rainfall is very high. At Croilburn, actually on the Whitelee Plateau, it is higher than the notorious Eskdalemuir: 1727mm is 68 inches of rain a year. Air temperatures can be low, and show a bigger range compared with the coast. The high rainfall and low temperatures contribute to conditions for peat growth. Daily sunshine is comparable with other parts of western Scotland. There are many frosts each year. Soil temperatures give good growing conditions only from June to September.

The picture from all sources is of excessive rainfall, generally low but variable temperatures with many frosts and extremes of visibility. Hard, snowy winters in the 1940s to 1960s have recently given way to wetter winters.

Scenery and Vegetation

Ninety-four year old **Mrs Elizabeth Watson** (mother of Jim the meteorologist) described the landscape of Whiteleehill farm about 1930 when she was courting a son of the family.

Nothing but grass and moss, ditches and sheep, no trees. Open. A most wonderful view from the farmhouse. And on a clear night you could count the three lighthouses on Arran, as well as other lighthouses up and down the Clyde . . . The toilet at Whiteleehill was a dry closet away out at the end of the byre. It had spaces for two adults and one young person. There was a beautiful view from the closet if you sat with the door open . . .

John and Margaret Struthers loved the views between Craigends and Whitelee Hill.

But if ye go up tae Whitelee Hill the views roond aboot wis fantastic, absolutely fantastic. Ye could see right away tae the Firth o Clyde, Arran, Ailsa Craig, Ben Lomond. Whitelee Hill, that's a right watershed ye can look in every direction fae there. Aye, it's nice.

The Isle of Arran from Whitelee Plateau
Photo: Ruth Tittensor

John Telfer of Carrot farm recalled the views of the whole of Glasgow with its lights at night, Arran Island, and the Pentland Hills.

From 1941 onwards, **Hugh Hendry** spent his spare time in the Whitelee hills. He was very observant of the landscape and vegetation.

> *Whitelee area and its landscape was very diverse in the likes o… vegetation. Within the area itself on the moorland there was the agricultural ground which mainly surrounded the steadings, occasionally there was some green patches within the moor itself which seems strange, ye had areas, which in actual fact, were all heather, predominantly heather, good strong-grown heather, other areas, in actual fact, it wis like blocks, ye had other areas it wis like a mixture o heather an white grass. In other areas ye had heather and it wis like red grass, noo Ah'm no up on the likes o plants an shrubs an stuff like that oan grasses but it wis the colours that always kinda amazed me between white and this type o red grass and occasionally there wir like blue grass a kinna sheen o blue. Then, of coorse, ye had other areas where it was grass and typical rushes but mainly it wis relatively flat, Whitelee until ye got tae the north edge of it, coming between, High Overmuir an High Allerstocks, that wis really hill, it wisnae mountainous, a hill, that in actual fact, ye can walk up it withoot losing any breath. There is one or two very steep ravines in the area, one in particular wis the Glen Waters that's between the Pugaven and Low Overmoor that wis like a rocky faced glen – Ah think wi the drawins oan the maps ye'll see there's also two water falls in that area. Other areas in the moorland, there wis like big deep peat gullies, now within they gullies no heather grew, there nothing grew in they peaty gullies, it wis just peat, it wis a great area for the likes o the grouse, ken, baskin in the sun an bathin thirsels.*

And **David Findlay** remembered the heather well.

> *Mm. Looking at it before the Forest, if ye looked over, as ah can remember, it were just like a massive carpet o heather. When you startit walkin throu it, the heather – you could actually see the heather in patches, an in between the patches there wis like bright green, like, ah*

Darvel Moss: unimproveable sheep pasture on Brocklees
Photo: Ruth Tittensor

suppose a moss, an that's where the water is, eh, an you've really got to be very, very careful where you're standin, Eh, because ye can actually disappear in it, it's so deep. Ah mean they've actually lost caterpillar tractors up there in the, the haggs.

In 1959, the Grant farming family came to live on the Whitelee Plateau. **Thomas Grant** remembers the wet, almost treeless landscape of his childhood and the plants which provided such poor grazing for sheep.

Well here there wir hardly any trees at all that wis all open moor right, as far as the eye could see there there wis an odd tree planted for shelter belts aboot the hoose here and the same at Burnfoot Farmhouse. Sayin that there wis a bit o the hill planted maybe an acre but otherwise it wis treeless hardly any trees grow about here ye don't a hedge, ye don't get a tree o any description . . .

It's too acidic, it's too wet. So nuhin grew aw it did wis carry a ewe tae 3 an a half tae 4 acre is what it carried on the hill that 1100 acre carried 320 ewes so it did. That's aw it carried that's aw it could carry. The year that we came in '59 that's what it carried and if it had been there

today it wid still carry the same. The type o grass it is, that wet, that peat, ye can't improve it the wild grass that grows [on] it it's toggles*, up the tap it's heather, it's draw-moass* (aside) d'ye ken whit that is? That dark green moass that grows in wet bits, it's dark green [to JG**] ye yaise it fur yer fruit baskets…Sphagnum moass'll be its right name. [indistinct] ken, bits that ye can hardly walk across go gently ye can walk across it try jumping in an ye'll sink (chuckles) an that's whit the sheep used tae eat in the spring.

[* See Appendix 3 for Glossary of Scots words; ** Mrs Janet Grant was also participating in the discussion]

A view of the landscape was given by **James Mair** who was born and brought up in a nearby town.

Yes, it was a, it was mostly flat. It was like a plateau. Once … My approach from Newmilns came to Heads Farm, and once you came in, out of Heads Farm, up onto the moorland, you were immediately able to see this wide expanse, right across the Whitelee Hill and west and east to Hapton and High Overmuir and places like that. You could see the farms on the landscape mostly once you got on the moorland from Heads . . .

Only to my view of the matter, on a moorland you have different kinds of land, you have what we call peat hags with the heather growing on them, mostly dry and built up above the surface, overhanging, pools of water in between. And then there were places like moss which was mostly rushes, water under the surface, moss growing there in fact, moss which was collected in the First World War. And, and then there were drier bits with just what you call heath and, turf and heath, and rushes, which sheep would probably have quite a good time on. But the sheep, as far as I could see the Blackface sheep eat heather too, and you could see them, always find them in among the heather.

Flora and Fauna

An enthusiastic naturalist, **Bryan Simpson** visited the Whitelee Plateau first in 1960 and has walked there ever since. He wrote his observations from each visit in field-notebooks. His earliest entries for the Whitelee Plateau are presented here without any changes. Latin names for plants and animals are listed in Appendix 2.

1960

Nov. 26th Ellrig Moor *(1215' asl)*

This moor was much wetter than many I have traversed. Consequently the Heather was thinner and the moss/rush association was thicker (possibly muir-burning in the past played its part in this. There was a scattering of wind-stunted Birch and Pine...

Fieldfares were quite abundant out on the moor. As I tramped away the darkness hummed with Lapwings* crying and Grouse* crackling.

* [Later note by Bryan: *very few left in 1992*]

On the road up to the moor a familiar whistling caught my attention and on looking thro' the 'glasses' to my surprise a large flock of birds whirling about became apparent. This was composed of, mainly, one of the smaller waders (prob' Dunlin or Redshank) and Peewits – the

The lapwing, in local Scots peeweep or peezer   Photo: Michael Cruise

swish from such a multitude of whirring wings and wildly gyrating birds was as wind thro' trees and a most exhilarating experience. (Prob' never to be again!).

On reaching the moor came across a 'netwire' Crow-trap with a lovely Kestrel in it. So I did no less than yanked up the netting from the bottom, edged it toward the gap, and away it flew. It was a most satisfying sight to see the bird soar up, free, and circle over my head as if in a gesture of gratitude (!).

1961

March 5th Ellrig Moor

Travelled up to the moors in the afternoon. Came upon 22 dead moles impaled on a barbed wire fence. Disturbed a flock of Fieldfares from trees where nest-building Rooks were all cawing about – (Cleughearn). Peewits and Whaups very active on moor periphery. Collected specimens of Mayfly larvae, etc., from stream. Released a Hoodie (!) from Crow-trap (damaged wing.) Quite a lot of Red Grouse knocking about with the odd Pipit singing away good-style. Flushed a Woodcock and a Snipe up. Tore up snares from animal track through the heather. Startled a pair of Roe deer in 'Eerie-wood'.

May Ellrig Moor

Cool and cloudy but quite pleasant afternoon. Took 'the boys' up to the moor. Visited the chewed ferns and found most of them growing, but sparsely, others were quite dead. Saw the loveliest display of Claytonia in the grounds of 'Cleughearn Lodge' with a great amount down the road and stream sides. Found some magnificent specimens of Primroses by a wood pool. Blackberry, Ajuga reptans, Viola palustris and tricolor (on grassy path), Alchemilla, Bluebell, Anthriscus, and Ran' * aquatilis spp all in flower.
* [Bryan's abbreviation for *Ranunculus*]

Released a pair of C. Crows from trap, catching one (1 legged/footed) to show it to the boys – gave one a good nip. Collected Barn (!) Owl pellets from wood and put the bird up from a Spruce.

Watched a pair of Moor Owls sailing about and occasionally being harried by Whaups. Saw the awful effects of Myxomatosis for the first time – 4 or 5 dead Rabbits in lower woodland and one poor critter hopping about the road stone-blind! The number of dead moles hanging on the fence had increased to 87!

Spotted a solitary Roe deer. Saw the quite unusual sight of a Rabbit leaping up at a Crow to keep it away from the corpse of a baby Rabbit which had been killed by a vehicle! (It's own?).

A short-eared owl and nestlings on the moors near Whitelee Plateau
Photo: Michael Cruise

Iain Hamilton described the variety of animals he saw before the time of Whitelee Forest.

But there again the likes o animals as Ah said earlier on ye'd get the occasional deer, foax ye get stoats an weasels. Bird life? Well, the normal craws, kestrels, sparrowhawks ye wid get snipe, grouse, black coack, nae mony phaisants ye get moass cheepers*, sky larks they used tae abound plenty. In the burn ye had broon troot, normal paddocks* an snakes, ye got adders, used tae get plenty o thaim.

* [See Appendix 3 for Glossary of Scots words]

Pauline Cairns asked **Jim Leitch** whether he had ever seen a rats' flitting.

No. But I've seen a weasels' flitting an Ah suppose it would be much the same, but. One day Ah wis goin home for ma lunch from Gateside tae High Haptone (High Hapton), ma father had a load o drain tiles at the end o a field an when Ah come in at the other end o this field, Ah wis walkin along this road and there was a fence, and Ah could always hear this cheep as if it wis somebody hittin the wire wi a stick but when Ah got tat these drain tiles, there were a big load o them, and there wis a weasel looking out about every second tile, there wis masses o them. Ah got oot the road in quite a hurry.

Naw, the main pests were crows, herring gulls, rabbits, rats, foxes, blue flies and the odd time we were bother with a stray dog. Noo if a sheep wis in trouble, maybe cowped, a crow would pick out its eyes, a herring gull would pou the navel out a lamb – a newborn lamb, foxes, well they would take the odd lamb but no a lot.

Elizabeth Watson spoke about the animals regarded as pests, which included adders.

Rabbits were common and were bad pests; they were shot and used for food. Mr Watson Senior shot them. Hares were taken for hare soup, but not often. Adders were another important pest, not so much at Whiteleehill as at Croilburn, the steading just to the north. Here the Young family kept goats to kill the adders (the goats trod on the adders and killed them).

35

Adders were and are common
Photo: Forestry Commission Picture Library

from August on, later on, the end o August* ye could get salmon up as far as the Mucks Burn which runs up into and through Brocklees and Burnfoot Loch which is within the Whitelee Forest. Yes, I have seen salmon taken at the Mucks Burn. Ah have seen salmon bein caught in that burn. I have seen also sea trout, but funnily enough sea trout was mainly very early in the season than aw the rest.

* [Hugh Hendry later insert: *September mostly*]

Which was where?

Right up into Brocklees Loch. Now that creates arguments/discussion because a lot of my colleagues and friends will turn roond an say that they have never seen sea trout up as far as that, but Ah'll assure ye Ah've seen them.

And **Jim Kennedy** said how common adders were in the heather on a hot day. His wife was once surprised by an adder when turning the hay.

> *If ye got a real dry kinnae bit, or part o it wis sittin high – kinnae hagg bit sittin high – eh, ye'd tae be careful where ye put your foot on it on a really hot day because there were, there were, there were adders on it as well. An it's not the first time a've almost stepped-, stepped on one. Ye get them lying curled up in the sunshine. Ah don't know where they went in the cold weather, but i the sunshine ye got them lyin out baskin in the sun. An even – ah remember ma wife – she got quite a fright one day when she wis workin in the – up near the moss, eh, uh, eh, she wis shaikin up hay for me, an eh, there wis a-, quite a s-, fair size o adder slupped oot frae below the-, the hay, and she got-, so, so, so she wis quite concern't aboot this snake goin around.*

Fishing the burns was one of **Hugh Hendry's** passions.

Ruth: Were there any other fish in the burns? Apart from salmon and trout?

Hugh: *Yes, yes there was, at what we called the back end, probably in the month of… well it depends on spates, dependin on how much rain ye had tae bring the level up so's salmon could run up. Generally, in actual fact, it wis*

Shoaling minnows were common [and often used as bait by fishermen or eaten with fried birds' eggs by the lads]   Photo: Ayrshire Rivers Trust

Ah have seen, in actual fact, a Forestry man catchin sea trout in Brocklees Loch and that wis the individual that Ah mentioned tae you, it wis George Caird. So yes, it wisnae just… ye had trout, brown trout, ye had salmon, ye had a few salmon and a few sea trout, not that many, but ye also had an awfie lot o wee fish, ye had actually minnows and bairdies and ye also had an awfie lot o eels.

I was going to ask about eels.

The Mucks Burn, once more running into Brocklees Loch

it seem tae have more eels than what we had brown trout. We used to hate when we were guddlin, ye ken, an yer hands came against an eel [recoils]... but no there was always quite a lot o eels in that burn.

So you didn't catch them and eat them?

No. Some o them took them tae some o the Italians, they took them. Even in Darvel some o the Italians the chippy at Central... at what's no Central Café, they, in actual fact, well that wis the original proprietors in there they used tae eat eels and some o the boys used tae take eels – Ah didnae like eels, Ah didnae like tae catch them so Ah just ignored the eels but there wir quite a lot o eels.

His observations of other wildlife by **Hugh Hendry** were written down.

Before the coming of Whitelee Forest, there were many White Hares on the Whitelee hills, and many Curlews. White Hares were a big nuisance to shepherds. This was because, at lambing time, the shepherds out on the hills would see white animals the size of lambs in the distance, trudge over to them to check them, and then find that they were white hares not lambs!! Hares were very common.

Badgers were quite common in the Whiteleehill (farm) area before it was afforested. Mr Hendry used to go and watch badgers come out of their setts where the Loch Burn meets the Glen Water. The badgers would go down the valley of the Glen Water, across to Gateside Farm and north-west into what is now Whitelee Forest.

In the 1950s, in the area of ground behind Hapton, the heather was being naturally replaced by grass. There were only patches of heather. This area still held grouse, but many less.

Before Whitelee Forest, Lapwings nested on the arable and rough areas of Low Overmoor and High Overmuir Farms. The rough areas they nested on were peaty-grassy areas with lumps of peat on the surface. There were not many Moorhens – occasionally some passed through Hugh's Pond. In late summer, when the small birds came in to feed on heather seed, there were also lots of caterpillars around.

A mountain hare in winter coat, Glas Maol   Photo: Richard Marriott

The wildlife of the Brocklees and Burnfoot areas was observed for many years by **Jim Currie**.

Jim: *. . . But oan Broacklees Hill there wis a loat a, there wis grouse, an they hid a, a lochan at, Burn Fit Loch they cawed it. Eh, there wis trout in the loch. I used tae feed it in the bad wea*- an we got ducks, geese, various waders an what hiv ye . . .*

* [weather]

Curlew, common on the Whitelee moors before afforestation
Photo: Michael Cruise

Got quite a lot ae greylag. Ye got mallard an teal. I once got one at a golden eye, I didn't know whit it wis a wee golden eye duck. I thought it wis a teal, but when I, after I shot it I realised that it wis different. An I once got a, a duck…, now, I sent it away – I hink it wis a mallard – an I sent the ring away it had been rung in Russiya. An I shot it at Burn Fit. Where it came fae I've no idea. Ken, I sent it, there wis a thing oan it, a ring oan it, an I sent it away tae, wherever I wis to send it tae. Well, when I wis up there there wis a lot a grouse, curlew, snipe, blackcock, varius owels . . . there wis, eh – curlew, various waders, an some o them, an some o the-, some o the places wis quite wet . . .

Ruth: Things like, um, golden plovers?

Oh yes, golden plovers.

Redshanks,

Aye, an, eh, there wis a lot a snipe at one time. Golden plover, peeweet, eh, these were aw, these were aw juist bir-, we used t' collect (the) eggs o the peeweets, but ever the years once they started t' get scarce an thats-, ma – I used t' train the dog, I got. A mean, put it in a field an a dog wid've fun* every peeweeps nest in the field. Ken. But. I had t' watch, cos once I, I got it, I made the mistake o showin it, I brought the egg an gave it it. An it ett it. An then it realised that they weren't. So after that a'd ti keep ma eye on the dug, * [found]

Yes,

Ken? But it wid go aboot pickin up wee grouse. An it kinna. But a've seen it wi half a dozen wee grouse in its mooth. An it juist, Come on you, C'mere. An I'd take them [(a)t] an it stood an watched them runnin awa. Ken. An, eh. Like I say. There wis. There wis blackcock – well a, ah built a place at Burnfoot. I had ma pheasant-, ma, pheasant pens. The biggest attractio(n) when I went there to start wi wis rabbits . . . An then, the big attra-, anither attraction was wis partridges.

Right, and were they wild ones?

They were all wild, no, nihhin wis… nihhin wis

artificial. It wis aw juist wild.

And what sort of ground were the partridges living on?

The gru-, the ground in the partri(dge) wis – mostly arable. Ken. No croppin. [But], ye dinnae get croppin tae ye drop further down tae, eh, High Carlincraig, Barn or, eh, Dyke an aw thae farms. There wis the Moirs.

Ken, I mebbe had, two or three coveys in a season, an each covey mebbe fifteen or twenty pa-, partridges, but out i that ye could tek at least half i them away an ye left enough for the follaein year. Ken. There wis always enough le-. But. But over the years as. Wi change. Wi 'The Forestry' comin, different things at they done – took out dykes – juist various things they done, the partridges gra-, gradually died out. They said it wis because, i thir, chemicals. Ken, they wur sprayin wi. But, I don't believe that, I juist believe that, they drew oot aw the hedges an. To me the. Aw it, a lot i the places (at) wis wet wi rushes an everyhin, they drained it aw. An aw that land, aw, a mean, a hare, brown hares, wis – a mean ye could ae shot brown hares aw year long. An white hares. There wis white hares too.

Professor Sir Alexander Fleming of penicillin fame was brought up on Lochfield farm in the late nineteenth century. It is interesting to see what a biographer (Malkin 1981) said of his childhood on the Whitelee Plateau.

> *Lochfield was the making of the Fleming children. To the boys, it was an adventure playground on a ground scale, their own private country park. Because Hugh and Tom were much older, John, Alec and Robert tended to get together to explore the delightful world of Lochfield. They had no money to spend, but this was no obstacle to enjoyment. Barefoot in summer they roamed over field and moor, keeping company with a great variety of bird life – grouse, partridge, golden plover, peewit, whaup, skylark, mosscheeper, snipe, wild duck, hawk, sand-piper, ringouzel, heron, sand martin and corncrake. Sometimes, they would gather a few peewit eggs, and sell them to local grocers at 4d each for shipment to London where they were considered a delicacy of haute cuisine.*

Glen Water, Burn Loch, and the Pogiven provided trout for rod and line or the lesser sport of guddling. The rocky flanks of the rivers were scaled by the boys to get at the blackberries which grew there in luxurious abundance. Here, in the pools, the boys learned to swim and dive . . . Close and sympathetic awareness of the natural world of Lochfield bred a keen power of observation and a disciplined patience in the Fleming boys – qualities which were to be applied by Alec with spectacular success in his work as a research scientist.

Comment

Contributors talked at length about the environment and ecology of the Whitelee Plateau from 1930 to the 1950s. This selection of their knowledge and memories gives a picture of the extreme environmental conditions, the wonderful scenery and colours, the varied flora and fauna. Bryan Simpson carried on his observations up to the present day,

Contributors had their own particular interests or slant on flora and fauna. However, taken as a whole, an abundance of ecological information about the Whitelee Plateau moorlands in three decades of the twentieth century, has been left by them for us.

The next two chapters describe the many resources provided by this environment before Whitelee Forest was ever heard of.

CHAPTER 4

Natural Resources: Gulls, Game and Gentian

The Gulls' Hags

A superficial glance at the Whitelee Plateau revealed bleak moorland with some sheep, a few cattle and lots of rain. But it was also a place of busy activity and an important reserve of natural resources.

A highlight of the social calendar for communities all around Whitelee took place in May each year. The object was to collect the eggs – by the basketful – of Black-headed Gulls (*Larus ridibundus*) which nested in their thousands on the peat hags. The eggs were eaten by the collectors, sold in nearby towns or to bakers in London: there were still busy railway stations nearby.

Black-headed gull in summer plumage
Photo: Michael Cruise

James Loudoun, who was 80 years old in 2005, remembered it well.

Every May, people from Darvel went with their buckets up to the gulls' nests on the moors. The nests were only a foot apart and there were hundreds of them. You could pick up dozens of gulls' eggs, which you collected in a bucket or wicker basket. Most people used the gulls' eggs for baking.

Hugh Hendry gave a vivid description of the gulls' hags on watery peat which went up and down in waves as you stood on it!

Hugh: *There wis only one area it wis dangerous, in actual fact, and that wis where the gulls nestit and that wis whit wis termed by aw the Valley people, that wis what they called the 'gulls' hags' that wis just marsh moorland, wattery areas and one would always say it wis unsafe, there wir a few carcases o sheep where they had went in and they couldnae get back out an they just rottit away. It wis always said that if ye broke the surface, that's the kinna turf surface, then there wis no sayin how far ye would go down, but actually ye could just stand oan it and just like shudder yer boady an ye could actually see the ground going in waves in front o ye, but yes, that wis an exceptionally bad area, aye, a dangerous area.*

Ruth: But even so people went to these gulls hags? Can you explain what happened, why people went to the gulls' hags.

Nesting colony of black-headed gulls (North Esk Reservoir, Midlothian) like those on Whitelee moorlands   Photo: John MacKinnon

Artist's impression of black-headed gull's nest on Whitelee moorland
Graphic: John Mackie

Ah suppose the attraction, the devilment or the enjoyment or perhaps, in actual fact, it wis hunger, Ah don't know. That wis the area that black headed gulls did nest quite a lot. It wisnae just in the hagg – the wattery area that they nested there were that many gulls in that area that they nested in the heather, dry heather, a place tae run about. Now, their nest in actual fact, wisnae really a nest it wis two or three bits o dry heather just laid on the ground wi a couple o eggs laid on it. Generally speaking there wis plenty o eggs if anybody wis wanting tae lift the eggs there wis plenty gaun aboot, ye didnae need tae go intae the marshy bit, although ye always get some daredevils, ye know they auld sayin, the grass is always greener over the fence, well Ah don't know if they thought they were better eggs in these marshy areas, Ah don't know but ye could go in so far an be very, very careful and ye did work wi a rod an a spoon tied at the end o the rod an pushed aboot an got yer spoon oan tae an egg. Of coorse, there wir other areas ye just couldnae go intae it and that's where ye got faimlies o mallard duck, they nested in a clump o rushes, ye couldnae get out tae the clump o rushes because it wis aw like water an swampy roond aboot it.

So people collected the duck eggs as well as other birds' eggs or was it just these?

Well, Ah daresay if they could have went out the distance they would have lifted the ducks' eggs too but they mainly lifted the gulls' eggs because they were easier tae get. As they walked across the moorland toward the hags there were some curlew nests where some individuals lifted the curlews' eggs. That wisnae all because usually the majority were Darvel people… in actual fact, if they were gaun for gulls' egss they went for gulls' eggs.

And was this a particular time of year?

The first Sunday in May.

[Laughs] Right. Was it a social occasion? Did everybody go up and enjoy themselves or was it just hard work because they wanted the eggs?

During the war and immediately after the war, the last war, there were groups mainly from Darvel, mainly Darvel men, they used tae go up the road really in the dark, early morning and sit in the road an wait for it getting a wee bit light and then they went across tae the gulls' eggs or the gulls' hags an pick up the eggs. That wis very early in the morning an then they would come back doon…but we're no talkin here aboot a pocket o eggs or a hat fu o eggs, yer talkin aboot a clothes basket, ken, the auld fashioned woven basket made wi yer reeds that wid be filled. So Ah'm no talkin aboot a dozen eggs or half a dozen eggs.

So you'd need a couple of people to carry it down again.

That's right.

And what did they do with them? These basketfuls of eggs.

Sometimes, in actual fact, they started fighting between wan anither on the road doon an throwin eggs at wan anither. But usually, in actual fact, they were mainly used for baking, that wis the main purpose, was baking. Whether they used the eggs themselves for their own households – they would distribute them tae aw their friends or relatives local bakers etc, they would all get their supply of eggs. Because remember… there was a friend o mine who's now dead and she, in actual fact, loved gulls' eggs and peewip eggs, she loved them.

Just to eat as they were? Fried or boiled or…?

Naw, ye could do that wi the peewip eggs the gulls' eggs, in actual fact, wis better for the baking, if ye were baking a sponge it made the sponge a wee bit pinkier, ken, a bit o colour. Because remember, a gull's egg it wis a kinna very red yolk that wis in that. It's maybe aw changed noo. It wis maybe in their diet. Ah don't know what the gulls eat nooadays but at the time that's how it wis. But it wis mainly used in baking. I've never o anybody… it's what they did wi the peewip eggs… I've never heard o onybody crackin a gull's egg an just swallowin it, but that wis quite common as far as peewip eggs were concerned.

In his 94 years, **Mr William Barr** has lived on two farms adjoining the Whitelee Plateau. He talked with **Jim Leitch** about the gulls' hags they knew of when they were young men.

Willie: *. . . The' yist tae be a lote a seagulls tae, but the' waur an island up oan the Binner Loch*, but eh, thay took the island away, och, years ago because the' waur that mony seagulls nestin oan it, an thay'd be thinkin thay waur foylin the watter, ken, so thay took it away. But there yist tae be a lote a seagulls nest aboot Loch Goinloch*, but the'r nae seagulls thair nou aither. Ah don-know quhy.*

Jim: *The seagulls seem to hae disappeared awthegither but the' were three different nestin places in oor area, in Gateside, in Lochfield, an High Overmuir. And they're aw away, an there were masses an masses o seagulls then. The black-headed gull.*

* [the nearby Bennan Loch and Lochgoin]

An old countryman showed **Jim Currie** and his mate Froggie how to make 'peat-shoes' from tea-chest lids, to reach eggs in the wettest parts!

Jim: *. . . An, whait they used to say they used to get eggs es put 'em on a basket. Yes you could pu' 'em in a basket (Pause) but you had to pack them all, you could'na just put all th'eggs in a basket b'cause once you, the top just broke all the ones in the bo'om, ken, you had te, you could'na just full soming fu' o' eggs, you had to put it in you fill't it wi moss or some'ing . . .*

Ruth: There were that many eggs?

Oh Aye ken, and you ge' a wee say a basket and what you do you lay your bottle and then you get Spagnum moss, pu'

all the moss it grew everywhere and you packed it all and then you pu' ye next layer-o'eggs on and then ye pu mair moss there put ye next layer right 'n so-on. Well, all they eggs tha' was all aroon the ootside o'it they were'd usually first to go, ken . . .

An Eh, so coming up by, the Co-operative used t'buy their tea in in tea chests an what they done there's the cut an the tap oot, it t' c'oor the tea oot and a' the taps were jus' fallen at the side out the back o' the shop, so Gordie y'sed to gae in and he used to lift fowr o' them and was foor'o'yus . . .

An eh, he used te get their things, an we went a walk t'Burnfoot and Gordie woul' ay 'is wee pipe an eh 'e broucht an aipple or somin for us, an we g'u'there a'th' sunrise an we sat doon an' Gordie was na' he never hurried Gordie. He was so calm and colleted **"Sit doon richt sit doon boy sit here right well we'er goin'e de this we'er goin'e de that. Right you de this bu' you de that bu' ahll si'here and we'll [unknown word] are all richt".** *So there 'e was si'in an then the firs' o' my si' ass [questions]* **"Whas the plywood for?"** *He said* **"Wai' an' I'll just show ye".** *Wi' th' an he coot i' oot an he put foor holes in it. An 'e put a bi' o' string s'roogh. An then 'e tell me tae load up my foot an' 'e tied it tae my fut, one in each fut and he tol' me tae stan' up, he says* **"Right. Walk"** *well of coorse when Ah walked Ah tripped, so 'e cut them doon to th' I could walk, he says* **"Right walk across tha' bit"** *an I walk across it. Ti' Ah was walkin' stuff that had nay way Ah could'ave walked before. 'E says* **"Right goo'oot there an get they eggs".** *So Ah went oot an I discover't Ah could get th'eggs that naebody else could.*

Dr John Morton Boyd an eminent international conservationist, was born and brought up in Darvel. In his book *The Song of the Sandpiper**, he described an outing in the early 1930s.

My first wildlife expedition was with school friends, to a colony of black-headed gulls, high on the moors near Lochfield Farm, the birthplace of Sir Alexander Fleming who had recently discovered penicillin. I was about ten years old. The townspeople harvested the gulls' eggs for food and that was the objective of our expedition.

The whole experience gripped me. The perilous hags sank beneath my every step, and the empty orbits of drowned sheep gaped at me from the mire. In reaching for a nest, one of the lads sank to the waist and had to be hauled out'.

* [See the Bibliography for book details]

Iain Hamilton's Uncle Bob was still collecting gulls' eggs in the mid-1950s.

Pauline: Did ye ever go tae the gulls hags and collect eggs?

Iain: *Naw, Ah didnae. Ma uncle Boab did. He went oot an gaithert them by the basket load an sellt them . . . They sellt them wherever and would tak them tae the local market. Kilmarnock market. He's the only yin Ah can remember that used tae gether them in great quantities. But Goad Ah wis just a boay then, Ah wid just be seeven, echt year auld. So yer roond aboot the mid 50s.*

Other Wild Foods

Jim Loudoun described some other wild foods he collected.

Most people went out and collected wild food of many sorts. Rabbits were so easy to shoot as they were all over the place. Mr Loudoun's family ate rabbit maybe twice every week. His mother made super rabbit stews with 2 rabbits, ham and any other meat left-overs. He loved coming in from school to be given a plateful of rabbit stew; it was luck what you got from in the stew, and which bit of the rabbit.

Peewits nested on open ground, so you could find their nests quite easily. If there were four eggs you did not touch the nest, as the clutch was complete and ready to be brooded. If there were only two or three eggs in the nest you could take two or one, as the clutch was not complete. In that case, the hen peewit would then lay more . . . He would sometimes walk out from home and pick up 4–6 lapwing eggs from their nests quite easily. Then he took them home and his mother would make a very big omelette for her large family. Local people were keen to

collect extra, free food, as times were hard in Mr Loudoun's young days. On the first Monday of every April, there was an outing to collect peewits' eggs.

James Mair summarised the wild plants which he remembers were collected and eaten in his young days.

Brambles*, earth nuts*, gentian*, raspberries*, you mention it, wild plums*, crab apples*, the lot. Everything that was growing in the countryside at that time was collected, either to eat at the time, or to lay up as home-made wine or jams and so on . . . And there was wild plum*, or, a kind of damson, near Heads Farm. There was a whole row of hedges, in a hedge there with masses of wild, wild crab apples, and what I call plums but, it's a kind of plum. And sloes*. Sloes were excellent for making, with wine and sloe gin and things like that.

* [Appendices 2 and 3 for English, Latin & Scots names of flora and fauna]

David Findlay told Ruth Tittensor his memories of picking wild garlic as well as rose-hips in the 1950s and 1960s.

David: *We actually uise wild garlic. Cos we actually have had it in salad, we've had it in cookin, we used that.*

Ruth: This is the thing with the biggish green leaf that comes up in the spring?

Ay, that's it, ye only use the leaf. Eh, ye juist cut it up an use it as a, in the food or on salad, don't ye. Eh, blackberries, eh, a lot o people pick blackberries, eh, raspberries, eh, things lik that for jelly an jam, eh, also, when ah wis a kid at school, we used to go out, ah think it wis sixpence a pound, for rosehips. An that went to rosehip syrup.

An that was, that's interesting, cos I thought that was just in the War and you're after the War.

No, no, when we wis, when we wis at s-, ah wis at schuil an [that] wis, whit, in the fifties an the sixties, an we used to get a – ay, a'm sure it wis sixpence a pound, for every pound ye pick.

The young **Jim Currie** also picked wild green plants for food.

Crab Apples
Photo: Ruth Tittensor

Rosehips
Photo: Ruth Tittensor

Damsons (Wild Plum)
Photo: Ruth Tittensor

Sourocks (Sorrel) Leaves
Photo: Ruth Tittensor

Wild Raspberry
Photo: Ruth Tittensor

Brambles (Blackberries)
Photo: Ruth Tittensor

No there wis... In fact. When I wis a boy, these folk, kenned where sourocks an aw that stuff wis. An gentian an grundnuts. Pignuts sumbodie told me wis their right name. But eh. You ask the young, they wouldnae ken what you were talkin about. In fact, ah don't know. Ah don't ken where ye get sourocks nou . . .

In adulthood, **Jim Currie** brought home many items of wild food for his wife **Anna Currie** to cook, but wildfowling on Brocklees Loch was his favourite.

Jim: *Well funnily enough. Yist ti go in the winter. Yist ti go duck shootin. Ken. Well ma. To me the cream o shootin wis shootin ducks in the munelight . . . Ye'd shoot them as they crossed the moon. So ye uist ti go an huv a cauld wat sleety nicht, rain gaun horizontal, no vertical, ken. Howlin a gale. An me an the dug. On a Friday night, away an get waashed an cheinged. Dug in the motor. Away up. Ye get him oot an. Walk acroass ti e loach. He cooried doun in, inti the hide o the butt. Bring the dog in, he got put in... A hud on mebbe, ma pajamas, long drawers, (Laughs) Troosers. An. Yist ti caw me the Michelin man. Cos, a'd aw that mony claes. Ken. An, eh. Aw thir claes ye yist ti huv oan. An, eh. Ye'd sit an huv a cauld wat sleety nicht. An the dug wid be sittin, then ye'd get a couple a ducks then ye wannered back an come doun, ach, a'll go fur a pint. So. Ye aye went in one pint, but ye wantit hame, cos ye'd the dug [ti sort]. So ye juist went in wan pint an then doun the road. So ah went in an got a pint an the folk, go, in the pub an aw that, whaur wis ye, aw ah wis shootin n – Ye're aff yir bloody heid! Ken. Lyin there oot in that (Breaks in tae hoast). Whaur wis ye? Oh, ah wis up at the loach at Burn Fit. It must be a howlin gale! It's impa-, ah says, ay right, but, bye! the ducks wur comin in. Ken.*

[Ruth starts a sceptical question, but Anna comes in.]

Anna: *An then yir mother once said to me one night. She said, Anna, how dae you know our Jim's away shootin or fishin or whitiver. Ah said, excuse me, huv you ever taken a look at your son when he goes out like that! She says, Why? Ah says, his face is no waashed, he's needin a shave.*

Ah says, an nine times oot o ten, [?], the douk o his erse is hingin oot his troosers*. So ah says, if the'r another woman lookin for him, she wid need tae huv a blin een afore she would take him. Ah don't think she wid want him.

* [Transcriber: his bum was showing]

Jim: *But ye're sayin. There again. Ah aye said ah never shot, unless ah knew exactly whit ah wis shootin at. Well there wis one-. Ah got caught out once. An whit it wis, ah wis sittin there. It wis a. Night. One ae the nights ah could describe – wild, cold, wat nicht. An ah wis coorit in. An a heard them. Chyuh-chyuh-chyuh-chyuh-chyuh-chyuh-chyuh-chyuh-chyuh. An a'm sittin, wha-, ah says, that's geese. An ah seen them croassin richt doun the bottom o the mune. They wur richt doun the loach. Dunk. An they come back up, an ah seen them drappin doun. An ah got the gun. Broke it. Two nummer threes in the barrel. An as they drapped doun onti the [stertit? loach an a, bang! Down their leader went the other yin(s) flew awa. Ah says, wha, a've got yin onyway. So e dug's sittin, right, gid on! An away oot, an it, gets a haud ae this thing. An he's comin back an ah said, bye Christ it – ah dout it's a greylag. An a'm watchin it comin in. Bye christ, it's a licht yin! Ken. So it come in an brocht it in. It wis a swan! (Laughs) So anyway. Whit the hell dae ah dae nou!*

Ruth: (Laughing) Yes!

Jim: *Ah don't know whether ye want ti pit this in or no!*

Jim: [In medias res]... *if a full mune, an it's hard hard frost. Why? An ye can sit an hear shyuh-shyuh-shyuh-shwh-shwh-shwh-shwh-shw-shw-shw. Then ye hear the splash. Ken. Same tae, on a summer's night when ye're fishin. Ye're fishin awa an ye – ah like a, a [snipe drummin], ye look up an ye hear, brrrchrrrrrrrr, an it's a snipe drummin. An a love the sound ae a curlew. Ah hink a curlew. A curlew keekin in the wide open spaces. Ken. Keekin min[d]. Anither time ah remember wis lyin up on the hill. Ah wis sittin. Sittin wi the dug. The dug was ' gude companion. But he wis sittin. It wis a lovely night. An a'm juist lyin on. Juist lyin on the grass an ye could* *hear the win. Ken. Juist the soft win. An the curlew. Ken. Ah says. Ken. That's smashin. Ah wish ah could ha recorded it. Ken.*

Many other species of fowl and fish ended up on Mr and Mrs Currie's table, but normally they were legal quarry!

Other contributors talked of collecting mallard eggs, of catching eels, salmon, brown or 'hill' trout and sea trout from burns. 'Baggie meenies' and 'bairdies' – they are minnows and sticklebacks – were caught and cooked with wild birds' eggs by the lads when up on the hills.

Game and Pests

Ninety-one year old **Mr Gavin Ross**, who, with his two brothers, farmed for over 70 years on the Whitelee Plateau, suffered from competition with hares for his growing crops.

On East Browncastle Farm there were 2,000 acres of moorland, about 500 acres being heather moor. Here there were grouse, black cock and brown hares. Strangely, there were white hares on adjoining farms, but not on East Browncastle. Cartloads of hares used to be shot as pests, because they would go along the drills and eat all the turnip tops off.

The lads went out with a gun and learned how to shoot on rabbits, giving them a bit of rough-shooting sport. A part-time farmer/builder friend came on Saturday afternoons and they all went ferreting, shooting and netting for rabbits.

Two younger residents (in their 50s) were involved in country activities like fishing and pest control.

David Findlay said,

I wis just brought up wi that, I mean basically, weh, we lived in a small country town, we were involved in country sports, country p-, eh, pursuits. Eh, we actually, since as long as ah can remember, we actually fished an shot, chased rabbits, chased deer, ah mean as long as ah can remember. Ma mum always cooked things, we always ate it, eh, an that wis the way ah wis brought up, eh, not to waste anythin; if you shot it ye ate it, if ye trapped it ye

ate it, eh, sae ye never wasted it, eh, so ah wis brought up shootin, fishin, wi ma dad, eh, so, as ah say, ah wis brought up in a long, long generation of fishin an shootin . . . Eh, ah used tae go up to Whitelees Forest before it wis a forest, eh, the Brocklees Farm . . . an we used to run about the moors an the burns, eh, wi Young Tom who's now Father Tom.

And he described the animals considered to be pests, but many were actually a resource too.

David: *Yep. People like myself an farmers wis involved wi pest-control. Specially round March, because that's when the lambin an lambs wis very very dangerous towards the, the foxes, they wes dangerous towards the lambs because o the very insecure, the lamb's just born in March, an they're no very stable.*

Ruth: Okay, and the fox would just come along, what, and just pick it up and eat it?

Mm, yeh, the fox would kill it, well, they'd kill three or four.

Yes. So how were they controlled in the old days and now?

Well, the old days they'd be shot, they'd be snared, they'd be trapped, they'd be, just dogs, eh, but as ah say, there wisnae as many as there are now, now they're just out o control.

Yeh. Pity you can't eat them; it's one of the things we can't eat . . .

We used to actually sell foxes, we used to get ten pounds a fox.

What, the complete body or just the fur?

The complete fox, the complete fox, An it wis sold for fur. Eh, an we sold it to the game-dealer an ah don't know where they went, but he sold them on for the fur . . .

Apart form the foxes, what other vermin was there?

Oh, ther weasels, stoats, eh, mink. Mink is a big thing now, eh, cos it, it used to be [a long time, or], mink is an incomer, mink's American, an it wis actually brought into this country for the fur, an there used to be a mink farm [in] Whitelees . . . an then, a lot ae these mink escaped out ae that farm an they actually settled up-, an now they're

Atlantic Salmon
Photo: Ayrshire Rivers Trust

Mallard
Photo: Michael Cruise

Eels
Photo: Sean Tibbetts

Blackcock
Photo: Michael Cruise

Brown Trout
Photo: Franz Grimley

Red Grouse
Photo: Michael Cruise

all over the valley, an they are really, really hard tae get rid of, again we shoot them, we trap them – in the fishin industry we actually set traps for the mink, eh, an we catch quite a few mink, eh, because they're detrimental tae the, what, birds, fish, mostly nice wildlife if ye like, eh, cos they will steal, a mink's a very, very, eh, it's a very successful predator, ah mean he can, he can, he's got claws, he's got teeth, he's, he, he's quite thin, he can get intae a lot o wee holes, he can fish, he can swim, he can climb trees, so, ah mean he's, he's one ae the ultimate killers, eh, there's no a lot stops them . . .

What about, um, birds of prey and crows an things, were they ever considered vermin?

Oh yeh, [b-] all birds o prey wis considered vermin, oh they wes shot on sight, but again that wis the auld way o thinkin, now ye widnae do that, ah mean birds o prey's a beautiful thing, but birds o prey are actually comin back now; we've actually got, around here now we've got peregrines, we've got sparra hawks, we've got kestrels, we've got buzzards, we've quite a lot o birds now, birds o prey. Crows and the, the actual rook is no so much vermin, he's alright, the, the ones that's the vermin is the actual carrion crow, or hooded crow,

Brown hare, a popular food on and around Whitelee until afforestation
Photo: Michael Cruise

an magpies – magpies are a big nuisance. . .

Yeh, um, now what about hares, were they considered vermin or game, or... ?

*Hares were game . . . Hares were classed as game. But we al-, always shot game s-, eh, hares. Again, hares are, as ah wis brought up an taught, ye don't shoot anythin unless ye're gonnae use it. Ah never ever shot hares unless-, a mean, a, a strong lesson that ah learned wis ah wis out shootin one day an ah wis about at nine or ten an ah shot six hares, and, ah wis made to carry the six, an when ah got back tae the farm ah wis actually shattert at-, ma dad said **"What have ye learnt?"** an ah said **"Don't shoot so many bloody hares,"** an he says **"Exactly! If ye don't cannae carry'm, ye don't shoot them, if ye cannae eat them, ye don't shoot them"**. So hares wis-, ah only shot hares if somebody wanted it. An ma grannie used tae have hares, she wid make hare soup, an also we used tae sell them to The Turf, an o-, old Miss Young used tae buy them an she used tae have hare soup on the menu.*

D'you know how they made the hare soup?

Yeh, it wes what they called jugged hare, it's, they made it from the blood o the hare so ye had to be careful when ye shot it an how-, ye had to be careful when ye carried it, because if ye carried it wi the feet up the blude rin oot it's nose, so ye had tae carry it bi its ears tae keep the blude in the diaphragm.

Ah havnae heard that before. Goodness me . . .

That's, ma grannie taught me that.

And the meat, did the meat, was the meat in the soup as well?

Oh yeh, ay, ay, - What happen[ed]-, when ye, when ye, s-, had the rabbit or the hare cleaned an skinned, ye diced the meat an the meat went intae a pot wi the vegetables an everythin, an ye made like a stew an then it be, it became like a bit o soup wi more water – it wis only at the last second that ye put the blude in, an ye mixed the blude in at the very last.

Right. Very wholesome. Not to today's taste.

Hare soup was described by almost every local contributor, some with delight at the memory, but some with horror!

Lord Weir had many shooting days on the north side of the Whitelee Plateau which **Robin Chambers** remembered with affection because he was a lad earning some money as a beater.

Robin Chambers and his brothers were born and brought up on a working farm in Eaglesham parish on the Eaglesham Estate, just below the steep, north-east slope of the Whitelee Plateau . . . As part of his education, he was sent as a lad (initially of under 11) as a 'Beater' on the shoots of Lord Weir and Mr Russell Laing which covered Carrot, Cleughearn and Threepland Farms and right across the high Whitelee Plateau westwards to Flow Moss and Rough Hill . . .

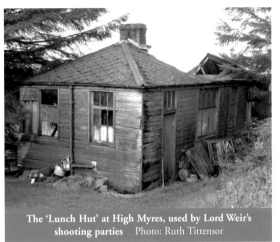

The 'Lunch Hut' at High Myres, used by Lord Weir's shooting parties Photo: Ruth Tittensor

Lord Weir had a full-time gamekeeper in the 1960s and 1970s, whose name was Iain Stewart. The Keeper paid his young beaters 10 shillings for a day's work, and gave them tea afterwards in his cottage at Cleughearn . . .

In order to produce good grouse numbers for shooting, the moors were well-managed by the keeper. The heather was regularly burned, often with help from the Estate farmers. The moors were also drained to keep the peat dry enough for good heather, which is 'choked' by wet soils. The drainage ditches could be up to 6 feet deep. On Drumduff Hill, the drainage was carried out by machine. Bridges made of railway sleepers were erected over the big drains, so that the shooting parties could move across the moors easily. These sleeper bridges were also used by the tracked vehicle which accompanied the shoots to carry the shot game back to headquarters. The keeper's work also included repairing the butts and the lunch hut. Mr Willie McWhirter was the Farm manager on Carrot and he drove the 'Snow-Trac'. His kids Dougie and Christine helped with the beating.

The highest 'Bag' Mr Chambers remembers from his young days was 140 brace (ie 280 grouse in total) of which some were Black Game, but most were Red Grouse. The normal bag of the Carrot / Cleughearn / Threepland shoot was, however, about 100 brace a day . . .

The heather moorland of Drumduff Hill, once the famous grouse moor of Lord Weir
Photo: Ruth Tittensor

Fluffy leaves of 'Gentian', East Browncastle
Photo: Ruth Tittensor

On grouse-shooting days, one 'used to trip over white hares, there were loads of them'. Mr Chambers reckons the large numbers of hares, rabbits and grouse was due to the good keepering, so that predators of these animals were scarce. Predators included raptors and vermin like foxes, stoats and weasels. The keeper killed about 100 foxes a year on the grouse moor.

The difficulty of being a farm tenant at Shieldhill, where the laird kept the shooting in-hand, was described by **Willie Barr** in his old Scots speech.

Ruth: Did you let the shooting or did you do the shooting?

Willie Barr: *Well, ye see, Sheilhill didnae belong tae ma faither. So. Thay hud the shootin. But ye'd be alou'd tae catch a rabbit or a hare, but ye wurnae allowed tae catch the grouse or the black cocks. Thay wid pit ye oot the fairm nearly if thay caught you catchin thaim, but thay did it oan the sly, but ye'd tae watch ye didnae leave nae feathers lyin aboot.* [Ruth, Jean and Jim laugh] *Ye yist tae snare thum tae, cause the – sum o the, the – oor… Sheilhull belonged tae Eaglesham Estate an Gilmour hud the – eh – the big hoose doun thair, so he hud a gemm-keeper, so – ma faither must ha been settin snares an, he stook't the corn an then ye could pit [it intae] bigger stuff intae huts if it wisnae awready dry enough tae come in, so he must hae had the snares in the huts. An did the gemm keeper no come up an get the bliddy – coorse he come tae the door an, but ma faither wisnae in an – coorse, ah kent he wis the gemm keeper an, coorse, whan ah seen him ah started tae greet.* [Ruth, Jean and Jim laugh] *Ah wis feared fur hum. He spoke, eh. But eh, ah hink ma faither hud tae go an apoalogise tae the, tae the – the Laird, for catchin the gemm.*

Willie Barr learnt from his father's mishap and he went out to shoot grouse from amongst the oats stooks very early in the morning!

Another formal shoot on the Whitelee Plateau covered several south-east farms, and was run by the 'Manufacturers' or owners of textile mills in the Irvine Valley. However, local people were also able to access wildfowling, game shooting

50

and pest control because many of the owner-occupier farmers preferred ad hoc game and pest management by locals they knew well, rather than letting the shoots to paying syndicates.

The 'Gentian' Plant

There is a tradition of collecting a plant with pharmaceutical properties from several localities. The plant's local name 'Gentian' is a surviving Scots language name now lost elsewhere in Scotland.

Mrs Morag Gillett (née **Loudon**), who lived at Low Overmoor Farm until 1948, when she was in her early 20s, wrote a letter about the 'gentian'.

One of the snaps I sent you has the Gentian Hill on it. If you drive through the meadow gate and park by the mound, which I believe is an old Bronze Age burial site, and walk towards the Glen Burn you will come to the Gentian Hill which doesn't look much of a hill but is steeper on the other side where the gentian was dug from. There used to be a fence running down the side of it between it and the primrose Rock right down to the burn. I'm not sure what time of year the gentian grew but I think Spring.

It is a small plant, leaf similar to a carrot leaf and the root colour of a parsnip the root itself no bigger than a pinkie.

As children, we used to dig or scrape a bit out to chew, more out of bravado than liking as it tasted horrible and yes, very pungent.

We had a postman, Davie Wilson, who suffered from boils and each year when the gentian was through he dug a little root to chew the juice out of it and swore by it as a cure for his boils. He said it cleared the head. A small penkife or sharp stone was all that was needed to unearth it. Lots of local people also came to get some gentian.

Gavin Ross knew of the gentian flowering on his land.

The 'Gentian' plant grew on East Browncastle farm. One place it grew was adjoining a layby on the East Browncastle to Little Calder Bridge road, about one mile east of the Farm steading. Before the gentian flowered each

year, while the leaves were still young, fluffy and 6 inches to 9 inches high, people used to come and dig for the root.

Local resident and historian **James Mair** gave yet more interesting information.

Well it's gentian, it's the root of gentian which has pharmaceutical benefits. If you… I don't, I don't know too well, but I've seen gentian, and I have collected gentian. What we colloquially call gentian. And various people in the town think they've got all their own little secret plots where they can go and pick gentian, and find out that (laughs) most people know about it. Anyway, these are, every certain… every so often local fellows, mostly the poachers, they know where the gentian is. And they can go to that place, dig up some gentian, dry it out, hand it to people for, if you like the taste of it, and think it's beneficial for, I don't know, digestive problems. So, there it is, the gentian flower, which you see growing on the verges of the moor . . . You have to dig it up, dig up the root. But they try to avoid spoiling the, the whole plant.

Jim Loudoun is still very familiar with the gentian and knows where it grows. He explained that workers in the Valley lace factories and miners from the Valley who worked down the Auchinleck and Mauchline mines (a few miles away to the south) used to chew the Gentian. Lace workers were not allowed to smoke in the factories, so this was an alternative for them. A plant grew outside one of the factories, and workers popped outside every now and again for a chew. Miners used it to moisten their mouths in the hot conditions down the mines.

With help from several contributors, some gentian was collected and was identified. It turned out to be *Meum athamanticum*, a white-flowered 'umbellifer' related to herbs like fennel, angelica and parsley. It is known in English as 'spignel', 'meu' or 'bawdmonie', where it was used by women more as an abortifacient, than a pungent stimulant.

The old Scots name 'Gentian' is just about extant in the Whitelee Plateau vicinity, as the plant is still used. The true gentians (*Gentiana* and *Gentianella* species) are different, unrelated plant species, so the reason for the Scots vernacular name 'Gentian' can be only surmised.

Table 3: Social Activities on the Whitelee Plateau in the Mid 20th Century*

Barytes Mine: in sporadic use
Birdwatching: ornithologists known
Burial: local people in the moorland
Catching song birds: for domestic pets and breeding
Collecting 'Bog Moss': for medical purposes
Collecting eggs of curlews, gulls, mallard and peewit: for food
Controlling pests: to enhance game numbers
Digging 'Gentian' root: as a stimulant
Cycling: by locals for work and visiting
Digging stone: for farm roads
Draining peat: by hand and machinery
Erecting utility poles: electricity
Exercising dogs: especially greyhounds
Fishing: in many burns for trout (stickleback and minnows by lads)
Gamekeeping: by 2 employed keepers
Meteorological recording: 3 rain-gauges known
Military training: during 2nd World War
Mowdie-man: to control moles
Muir-burning: widespread on farms and grouse moors
'Old Peat Roads' to public peat-digging sites: use declining
Ordnance Survey mapping: at least once known

Peat-digging: frequent on farms for fuel
Picking green plants and berries: for food
Poaching: widespread
Raising pheasants: by local people and keepers
Reservoir: one, others nearby
Rough shooting: by local people
Scout and Boys' Brigade meetings: held in several places
Sheep-dog trials: regularly at several locations
Shooting game: for sport
Meeting friends: frequent
Swimming: in pools on several burns
Tree-planting: a few farm shelterbelts
Trig Points and Bench Marks: used by O.S.
Walking: by locals between farms and towns; by rambling club from Renfrewshire
Water supply to homes and farms: from burns or wells, using wind or electric pumps
Wildfowling: by local people

* Before Whitelee Forest got under way.
Source of data: contributors

Looking over Bowhill Mount
Photo: Ruth Tittensor

Families swimming in the Black Calder Water 1970s Photo: Jim Currie

Comment

The Whitelee Plateau and its environs was a very busy place in the decades leading up to the initiation of Whitelee Forest. Many men and boys worked or enjoyed themselves at raising game; rough shooting; game shooting; organising shoots; pest control; beating; wildfowling; ferreting; poaching; and collecting birds' eggs and green plants of several kinds. Women went picking brambles and other berries, but they mainly cooked wild foods.

Apart from raptors and perhaps foxes, it seems that game and pest species were common, and sources of wild plant and animal foods were prolific. But the Whitelee Plateau was used for much more than country sports or obtaining food. The many other activities described by contributors are listed in Table 3.

In the next chapter, the predominant use of the Whitelee Plateau (farming) in the decades leading up to its afforestation is discussed.

CHAPTER 5

Farming the Whitelee Moors Before the Forest

Types of Farm and Farming

At the start of the twentieth century, the farmers were tenants of estates such as Avondale, Eglinton, Hareshawmuir and Loudoun. By the 1960s these estates had sold many farms to their own tenants, who were now owner-occupiers. Map 4 shows the farms.

Two main types, *'Moorland'* and *'Hill'* farms characterised the Whitelee Plateau, dependent on the type of ground. *Moorland farms* tended to be much larger: they needed to be. Predominantly peaty ground precluded almost anything but hill-sheep grazing at low density. Groups of ewes, their

mothers and daughters, had a home-range or 'heft' on the moorland. A lamb learned the best grazing ground on its heft from its mother, so making the most of what was seasonally available. Ewes lambed alone on the moors, giving the shepherds heavy work in spring.

Moorland farms also had small acreages of 'inbye', consisting of a few enclosed fields around the steading, at least part used as a 'Hay Park'. Hay was needed to feed the cattle and house-cow in winter. But often, the cattle spent all the year out on the moorland, maybe with some hay provided out on site when necessary. They were hardy hill-breeds for producing calves and heifers to sell, not milk for human

Map 4: Farms

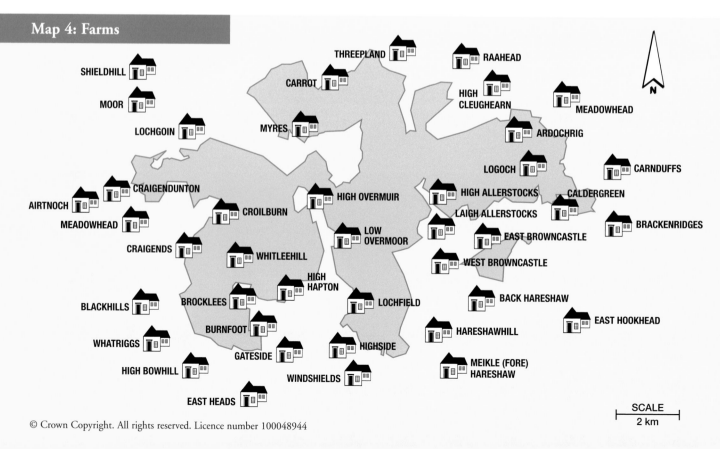

Air photo of Logoch 1946. The rectangular inbye is marked by the public road (right) and Logie Little burn (bottom). Ardochrig inbye is at the top of the picture. All else is moorland or bog
Photo: Courtesy RCAHMS (RAF Air Photographs Collection)

consumption. **Jim Leitch** wrote,

> *The dairy farmers always liked the heifers off the hill, they did much better than the ones from lower ground.*

Hill farms were smaller than the moorland farms. Although also predominantly peat, they were lucky enough to have areas of glacial till, alluvium or volcanic outcrops too. So there was more inbye with mineral soil suitable for cultivating crops such as oats, turnips or cabbages, as well as to grow hay. More stock could be fed in winter, so they could either keep more hill cattle or have a milking herd of Ayrshire cattle which produced rich, creamy milk. There might be an 'outbye park' or 'lambing park' where some of the ewes lambed instead of on the moors.

55

The old inbye and distant moorland of Meikle Hareshaw
Photo: Ruth Tittensor

Hill Farms

John Struthers spoke about life on the hill farm of Craigends in the 1930s to 1950s.

Aye. Well ma father wis in farming all his life 42 year he farmed at Craigends Ah wis born on the farm and Ah worked there for ma father until Ah left. It says here aboot employin other help, we always men come in doin drainin an the likes o that Irish boys come over you know an dae the job o ditchin an drainin . . .

Noo the landscape before the Forest well it wis all sheep an cattle and the sheep really kept the grass and everything well down, specially in the spring it wis right doon tae the root.

At Craigends we were six hunder and forty acres and there wis a hill farm wi inby ground. The inby land wis used for, eh, hay, oats and we grew cabbages for the sheep and then we had a wee plot a wee half acre o vegetables tae keep the house going an things like that. Then ony particular sheep we wanted tae keep an eye on they were broat doon into the kinda lower groond too.

Number o worker employed in the place there wis juist the family. Ah had a school friend come up and he helped us wi the hay and things like that. There wis basically sheep we had eh hill cattle we hadnae the facilities for fatternin them off we hadnae any dairy. We done aw the work wirsels . . .

John and Robert Struthers planting cabbages on Craigends inbye 1950s
Photo: John Struthers

Breeds o sheep wis Blackface and ours were Cross-Bred Leesters.* The numbers o sheep in thae days wis aboot twelve or thirteen score. The Blackfaced sheep wis a very hardy breed o sheep that could pit up wi a lot o rough weather an as long as they could get a bite tae eat that kept them gaun. Ah've seen them buried in drifts o snow an they could lie in there for a day or two tae we… until they were dug oot.

* [Leicesters]

Dogs. We had generally aboot four dogs an they were aw boarder collies and faither trained them an whit not an we kinda trained them tae because it wis juist a wey o life in these days and they worked wi sheep and cattle nearly every day. There wir certain dugs ye were particularly fond o some dugs were juist lik an extra person aboot the place. One dog in particular wis Vic he was a great, a great show dog tae he wis a nice collie but he worked the sheep and the cattle and he wid go tae the burn at night tae bring the ducks oot, bring the ducks in, bring the hens in an he liked a game o fitba tae. Aye, he wis quite a character, Vic . . .

Other farm animals wis the horses, pigs, hens, ducks the odd goose now and again and the pheasants but they were wild. We hadnae any goats. Pigs, we had twelve brood soos at one time.

The horse, it went away when we got the tractor we were doon tae one horse by this time when we got the tractor and well ye've a lot o fond memories o the horses and he but we were quite pleased tae see the tractor because it helped tae kinda ease the work that we done. Farmin in these days it wis eh it wis all liftin and carryin there wisnae the machinery that we've got today it wis… ye had a dung midden wi aboot fifty ton o dung on it that wis all shovelled, forked and carted tae the field it wis all done by men there were no loaders nor nothin then it had tae be spread after it wis out there wi a fork again – the auld word for that is a graip – but we sterted aff wi a Ferguson tractor but this wis a tractor that wis inventit by Harry Ferguson he wis brought up in Northern Ireland and it wis the same there it wis all hard work and Harry

Ayrshire cow on West Mossgiel: Ayrshires were producers of creamy milk (but they kept their horns in the 1950s) Photo: Ruth Tittensor

Blue-gray cow on a Borders moorland: they are naturally hornless Photo: Ruth Tittensor

reckoned there must be an easier way tae life than this so he inventit the Ferguson tractor . . .

Well, we had Ayrshires and then the Galloways – black Galloways – we had what we called Blue-grays – we had roondabout forty or fifty o these on the hill, they were a hardy breed o cattle. The Ayrshires they come in in the winter but a lot o these hardy cattle wi a bit o shelter we fed them outside an kept them gaun.

At the age of 13, in 1940, **Jim Leitch** left school to work on the hill farm of Gateside.

> **Jim:** *Well, Ah left school when Ah wis thirteen, it wis just at the beginning of the war and Mr Churchill at that time that we should grow all our food. Now ma father was in the habit of ploughin about thirty five acres and he ploughed seventy acres now that wis wi two pairs o horses and when it came oan tae seed time in 1940 he wis*

Blackface ewe and lamb on Burnhead farm adjoining the Whitelee Plateau
Photo: Keith Hobley

needin hands and he decided that Ah wis more needed at home that Ah was at the school. Ah wis still thirteen at that point but fae then on Ah had a pair o Clydesdale horses fae Ah wis thirteen. Even during the… later on we got up in the morning the rest o the people went tae the milkin an Ah went tae the stable tae the horses, fed, groomed and mucked out and had them ready tae go oot by half past eight.

Pauline: What time did ye have tae get up in the morning?

Six. Breakfast aboot eight an Ah've seen me comin home fae a dance possibly between two and three in the mornin an no getting very long in bed an Ah would go tae the stables and Ah would say tae maself, 'Ah must get these horses done in a hurry'. an sit down in the hay in the corner, there were always loose hay piled up in the corner for the horses, and Ah would sit down among that hay, supposed tae be for ten minutes, fall fast asleep. Ah knew nothing else until somebody wis sliding the door open, an said, 'Are ye no comin for yer breakfast the day?'

Ah really enjoyed ma horses. By the middle 1940s the tractors had taken over and the horses were juist out the game mair or less. We tried in 1950 tae bring the horses back but there wisnae much… the tractor won in the end. That wis it. Since then Ah've always had ma horses. Kept

Jimmy Struthers working the hay-rake 1940s; moorland beyond
Photo: John Struthers

a thoroughbred stallion, kept four brood mares, bred foals every year, now Ah've cut down a lot an Ah've just goat ma driving hoarse.

Wis it no easier wi tractors rather than wi horses?

Naw, naw. It was a lot more pleasant wi horses. Ye had company. Yer horses wis yer company . . .

Have any names for sheep – I mean things like 'yowes' and stuff?

Well certainly yowes an hoggs an wethers.

Wethers?

Wethers is a castrated lamb. Do you know what a heft is?

Nope.

No. Well a heft is a group o sheep that stay in the same area where they were born, now it's usually made up o mothers, daughters, grandmothers. The number o sheep in a heft can very a lot and the number o hefts on a farm depends on the size o the farm.

At the end o the year when ewe lambs maybe go away, the ewe lambs that's kept for stock go away tae better grass tae mature them during the winter, when they come back oantae the hill they just work their way back tae that heft where they were born . . .

You have a note here about yer faither.

Ma father attended tae his sheep and wis very fond o his dogs, usually he had aboot four Border collies, all sheep dog trial dogs. Sheep dog trials wis his hobby they dogs were workin everyday on the hill an he trained them hisself. They were kept in the byre an their beds wis the cows' trochs filled wi straw. Their food, mainly porridge an milk an some cod liver oil . . . an this wee bit o cod liver oil among it put a shine on their coats. When ma father had a litter o pups he put down a plate o fish meal an the pups had a wee lick at this fish meal as they fancied and their coats wis shinin like a shillin'.

How long did it take tae train a sheep dug. Ah mean did ye pick the best one oot the litter…?

Three collies (sheep dogs) herding Blackface sheep on Gateside inbye 1930s
Photo: Jim Leitch

Naw, naw. At that stage they didnae know which was the best one, it had tae be that wee bit older before they could see if it wis gaunnae be worth while, usually when they were aboot eighteen month they were working. Although it might take that bit longer tae get them, ye know, tae the perfect stage, if ever they were perfect. There were a lot more that never were perfect than the ones that were.

Border Collies were the common sheep-dogs in the area, several on every farm, living outdoors or in the steading. Jim Leitch's father Jimmy, had a friend **Willie Barr** of Shieldhill, who was also an avid trainer and handler of collies and went to his first sheep-dog trial at the age of 12 in the early 1920s. **Gavin Ross** worked and trialled sheep dogs all his life too. The Whitelee area still produces champion sheep-dogs and handlers.

Moorland Farms

Whiteleehill, at 282 m altitude and exposed to wind and weather from all directions, was a moorland farm of 1522 acres. Mr James and Mrs Margaret Watson took its tenancy from the Hareshawmuir Estate in 1911. **Elizabeth Watson** (she married their son James) remembered farming at Whiteleehill in about 1930.

At that time, Whiteleehill ran Blackface Sheep as the main enterprise. The sheep were bound to the land, so were bought along with the farm; it was the custom not to move hefted sheep away from a farm, except to sell for meat. One or two house cows were kept for milk, and some hens were also kept. There was no arable land, though potatoes and vegetables for the family would have been grown in the garden. Hens' eggs were eaten, and sold to help pay for groceries. Mr and Mrs Watson went to Kilmarnock Market once a week, when the shopping was done, as well as the buying of stock . . .

Every year the family dug peats from the hills for the fire. They cut enough to last a whole year. It was cut from the mossy part of the moors and was carted in a sledge with runners pulled by a pony called 'Obscurity' (the name came with the pony!). The pony was also used to take the family to town in a buggy or trap. As there was no arable land at Whiteleehill, there were no big working horses. The family ate their own mutton, as well as wild rabbits which had been killed . . .

Mr and Mrs Watson of Whiteleehill owned High Allerstocks farm before they came to the area from Tigh na

Bruaich. It was also just a sheep farm with a shepherd. The shooting rights belonged to the Watsons, as shooting rights go with a farm. However, they are often let out to Shooting Tenants, as this produces an annual income. Mr and Mrs Watson Senior are buried at High Allerstocks, where the gravestone can still be seen, just near the edge of what is now Whitelee Forest.

In 1922, at the age of seven, **Gavin Ross** moved with his family to East Browncastle on the south-east slope of the Whitelee plateau. It was also a moorland farm, of about 2000 acres of which only 45 acres were arable. After the death of his parents, Mr Ross and his two brothers ran East Browncastle for over half a century. Sheep were the main enterprise, with 500 hefted onto the 2000 acres demonstrating the low productivity of the land. The sheep were out on the moors all year except for about two weeks at lambing. The Ross brothers bought some hardy beef suckler cattle, which grazed the tough vegetation on the summer moors, making it more suitable for sheep. The cattle were brought off the hill in the winter, so hay was needed to feed them. The 45 acres of arable land at East Browncastle grew turnips which were winter food for stock, and seed potatoes. The Ross brothers eventually bought the Moorland farms of Muirhead and Logoch, to extend their land onto the smooth south-facing slopes and high moorland of the Plateau.

Thomas Grant moved with his parents to the Whitelee Plateau from south Ayrshire in 1959. **Tom** and his wife **Janet Grant** discussed the farming system then.

> **Pauline:** Your farming system before Whitelee Forest how yer father ran the farm.

> **Tom:** *Sheep, the sheep, out there were self-sufficient they never got anythin they leeved out there 12 month a year never got anything, never got fed at all. There's a wee drap grass in the low bits here that kep them gaun in the summer time an the winter (hesitates) there wir plenty o roughage there wir heather kep them goin in the spring they had Sphagnum moss had tae grow before the grass that kep them goin an later oan the grass started that kep them goin and that wis what kep the ewes aw the time . . .*

Brocklees steading in 1974; the farm had over 1000 acres of moorland in the 1960s Photo: Courtesy Janet Grant

Aye… [indistinct] we come in here wi 25 cows we started tae farm an at the finish up it was carrying 60 cows [indistinct] we started tae plough the inby ground more. Plough it, feed it lime it, slang it an eh sow better grasses wi seedin it grew better if ye farmed it more an there wir also grants then tae encourage ye tae dae that. So ye fenced a bit aff… fenced they fields aff ploughed it, sowed it out so's it drains… that gied ye more grass for keep tae carry more sheep more cows. So it did…

What's the question? (Laughing) I know nothing aboot this! Breeds!

Janet: *Well at that time on the hill it wis Blackfaces, all Blackface ewes pure went tae a Blackfaced tup… the fields wis Blackface ewes an went tae at least a tup there ye are.*

A cross lamb, a bigger frame lamb which grew more it wis worth more oan the hill there it only could keep a black… a pure Blackface yowe an lamb it wisnae good enough tae carry anyhin else there wisnae enough grass but out in the fields whaur ye had improved the grass an that ye could cross them wi at least a [indistinct] tup. Whit ye would call now a Mule lamb, ken whit that is?

So two different breeds…?

Tom: *Aye. But in turns a Mule ewe an eh it goes down tae a laigher farm an ye book a tuip where ye stand better grass it does better an inside noo but that's whit ye keep noo an on the fields noo it's aw Mules Black faces…[indistinct]…Cows d'ye ken, Blue-grays Galloway cows because ye kep them outside they're all kep outside wintered outside ye ken two dairy cows for the house and ye milked a cow ye used tae be able tae… the cow warm at night at the house ye made yer own butter. Eventually ye got lazy an ye juist put the cat oot at night (laughter & general noise)… nooadays yer able tae buy milk so naebody keeps a dairy coo now . . .*

So when ye did keep cows… dairy…

Blue-faced Leicester tups, a common breed on Whitelee before the Forest Photo: Ruth Tittensor

Tom: (interrupting) *yes we did keep cows*

Dairy or beef?

Janet & Tom together: *Beef*

Tom: *Beef. Always beef. It's too high up for dairy. It wis beef cows, suckle cows these Blue-gray cows, Galloway cows put them tae a Hereford bull an ye got a calf wi a white head.*

Do you know a Hereford calf? D'ye 'ken whit that wis. Well, aye… At that time it wis aw Hereford calves, Hereford bulls an ye croassed them that wey and that's what ye'd get… ye kep them they calved March or April and ye sold them in October [unclear] an eh… an the cows ran out on the hill wee bit hay and some cake in the winter time and they stayed oot there aw the time no expense wi it. We kep hens, as Ah say, we sold the eggs on a Friday night, we went round an sold the eggs we got regular customers on a Friday night. Whiles ken we kep an odd pig tae drink the excess skimmed milk an then ye killed it an made it intae bacon . . .

Wis this farm typical o the other farms in the area

Tom: *Yes, basically. They were all the same, if ye went up tae Overmoor further up there, or Whitely [Whitelee] Hill ye kep a milk coo — two milk cows — he kep at Whiteley Hill Mr [indistinct] kep pedigree Galloway cows. They were never inside and it wis all roughly the same. If ye were needin some mutton or lamb ye killed a sheep. Cut it up pit it in the freezer, that's whit ye done. Mair or less self sufficient.*

Was the farming system affected by the presence of peat land on the farm?

Ye only could farm according tae the ground ye had so… Ah'll no say affected… Ah've known nothin else… but it's bound tae… if you wis down at Darvel ye wis never used wi peat ye wid need tae adapt yer system tae suit peat ye cannae go oot wi a big tractor or ye'll juist sink it cannae cairry the weight ye cannae… wi the beasts at the same bit oot there on the peat they wid juist disappear . . .

**Carrot steading in 1970 before it was demolished and rebuilt.
Carrot had over 4,000 acres of moorland but only 25 acres of inbye**
Photo: Christine McWhirter

John and Edith Telfer bought the 4,300 acre moorland farm of Carrot from Lord Weir in the1970s. They found little of the inbye was ploughable and the summer was too short to grow sufficient oats and hay for winter feed for stock. They took over the 1400 hefted sheep and 44 long-haired, hardy Luing cattle which lived out on the moors all year (except for female calves which overwintered indoors). The Luing had to be confined to an area of firmer peat at the Threepland end of the moors. They were beef cattle: there was not even a choice of having or not having dairy cows, *the soft Ayrshires would never survive* John Telfer said.

**The first Luing heifers home-bred by the McWhirter family,
April 1970, on the Carrot moors** Photo: Christine McWhirter

It was a different style of farming from their Scottish Borders origins, so they set about learning from Lord Weir's farm manager and shepherd Mr Willie McWhirter before he moved on. In earlier times there had been three shepherds, and of necessity, three homes for them (shepherds were usually homed because of their importance to the farm, while other farm workers lived in a bothy or room in the farmhouse). In their written contribution, **John and Edith Telfer** listed the ten hefts and described farming on the Whitelee Plateau at Carrot.

> *Threepland, Munzie, Fallside, Drumduff, Forest, Meadow, Loch Hill, Crook, Myres House, and Fence, the furthest from the steading. Ardoch was a non-hefted area. Sheep on the different hefts were marked with different colours, so that the shepherd could recognise instantly if one was in the wrong place . . .*

> *When out riding [his] horse to check the mineral blocks for the sheep, Mr Telfer's horse would refuse to go off the track onto ground that was soft. But the sheep were not so lucky. Many were lost each year: the very boggy ground was covered with bright, pale green vegetation, which seemed to entice the sheep onto it to feed. But they sunk down into the very soft bog and were lost forever – there were never even any bones left to find. Annually, about one-and-a-half-score (30) sheep were lost in this way.*

> *This is why the soft, green, boggy ground was called '**The Black Death**' . . .*

> *The game species on Carrot Farm were mostly grouse and blackcock. It was very difficult going for a day's shooting up on the hills, because of the soggy ground, into which one could sink almost to the waist with one's gun! One year in the late 70s there was a snowstorm at the beginning of June! The young grouse were decimated. We don't know whether they ever recovered fully.*

The moorland farm of Low Overmoor, run together with another family farm from 1948 to 1969, was described by **Iain Hamilton**.

> **Pauline:** How much dae ye remember o the hill farmin landscape before 1960? Specially the muirs an…

Low Overmoor steading in 1948, home to a moorland farm of 1,400 acres   Photo: Morag Gillett

Iain: *O the moors were juist like a typical West Coast moorland farms, they kinna varied fae what they cawed inby parks… well at Low Overmuir we had hayfields and then ye had the ootby parks which ye brought the multiple births tae at lambin times so that they could graze there and you could keep an eye oan them and there's areas where there's auld bomb holes where the bombers come ower before the end o the war – well they miss cued Clydebank – how the hell they missed Darvel for Clydebank God only knows – they dropped a bomb there just between Low Field and Low Overmuir.*

On the other side facin Whitelee Hill ye had the Moss Hags – they'll leave Moss Hags Ah don't think they'll be planted tae this day because they're an absolute nuisance these things, they're aboot twenty feet deep. Ah mean they were worthless as far as even trees were concerned. It wis a typical hill ye had the peat cuttin faces – ah think they're still there, ye also had the kinna high knowes, ye wid say, it wis dry but oan the whole it wis Sphagnum moss, blaeberries, bog cotton an various heathers, sprit grass juist the kinna usual an nice, clear runnin water.

What was the sheep grazing, moors, and vegetation you've told us about. What did the sheep and cattle eat?

They ate various things, ye kept the heather shoart because they nipped the heather, sprit grass the normal moorland grazin that ye would get that any o them would eat. If ye're wantin some evidence o it there's a photograph here o some belted Galloway cattle on Low Overmuir . . .

What wis the breed of whatever stock ye had? And what were the numbers?

Well, in Low Overmuir it wis Blackfaced yowes, there would be, oh Ah don't know, nine hunder yowes, nine hunder tae a thoosan plus a dairy coo, the coo would be a traditional Ayrshire for mulk an any excess milk ye dindae yaise in the hoose ye fed the calves wi it. Durin the summertime there would be – well ye can see there by the picture – whiles ken there would be Aberdeen Angus croasses, an Hereford croasses, doon in the hame ferm ma grandfaither pit the dairy away in 1923 and it wis juist a mixed stoack oan it, ye ken, there'd be. For a while there ma faither used tae rear black an white calfin heifers sell them at calfin, again there wid be croass yowes, fattened lambs. Did a bit o croppin an ken, the usual, a pig or two, twa / three hens for eggs and a dairy milk cow. Mother used tae make butter many years ago, she used tae make a lot o butter usually kinna fairly self-sufficient.

63

What markets did you use? Did you sell… well ye juist said that ye selt…

Stock oaf Low Overmuir were kept, then the draw o the lambs were brocht doon tae the other ferm, ken the wethers an the excess yowe lambs we sometimes kept a yowe but it wisnae kep for stoack but it would be broaght oan doon there an then dressed an sold at Lanark at the yowe lamb sale. Wethers were the same they either went away or goat selt for stores at Lanark market. Ken, the fermer never yaised Aye* because the kinna folk, well the buyers ye got lookin tae buy your produce didnae go tae Aye they went tae Lanark or whiles there wis Stirling. Ma faither used tae travel quite widely as well, he'd buy likes o store, store cattle and store sheep at Dalmally, Oban whiles it wis Fort William…

* [Ayr]

That's far afield. Ken.

Aye, but ye wir buyin them oaf the hills then yer gettin them… ma faither wis a bit o a dealer in his day, he wid buy them up there an bring them doon, they'd fatten quite quick an then sell them fattened. Comin oaf the kinda high hills they thrived a guid bit better an pit a lot on on the low pasture.

What other animals did ye have? Pigs for example? Did ye kill pigs?

Naw we didnae kill pigs. The last pig Ah remember at, that killt pigs wis ma Uncle Boab Smith that wis in Feoch which is on the road tae Overmuir. An Ah'd been a gey wee boy but he used tae kill a pig an saut it an cure it an cut it. He wis a richt character but he's deid noo tae he wis the only fella Ah ever kent cooked parritch* an pit it in a drawer . . .

* [porridge, often made weekly, stored in a drawer and eaten cold]

Family Help

The family was an integral part of the team. Women's work on the farm of the 1930s was described by **Elizabeth Watson**.

The women of Whiteleehill made their own butter and cheese from the milk of their house cow. Janet Watson went to 'Dough School' in Glasgow, a college for young women to learn domestic skills. The women did all the housework. Janet helped lift the peats too. The women cooked meals for all the neighbours who came to help with the sheep-clipping in the summer. Clipping was a big social occasion on every farm. The women baked every day, usually making pancakes and scones. They also made their own bread. Flour and oatmeal were each kept in big sacks, made of a linen-like textile.

It was similar in the 1940s as **Jim Leitch** wrote.

At sheep shearing time a farmer would decide what day he wanted to clip, he would spread the news, possibly asking the postman to tell other farmers. A reply would come next day from the postman. That morning all the farmers and shepherds would arrive. If the sheep were dry clipping would commence, if not, they would wait till the sheep were dry then start. One man catching, five or six men clipping, one man rolling fleeces and one man packing fleeces, stopping only for lunch and tea. When we were first married Emmie was flabbergasted when she realised she would have to feed approximately 12 men that day, but all went well.

On Low Overmoor in the 1950s and 1960s, **Iain Hamilton's** mother brought up three kids and could turn her hand to all the farm work too.

Oh aye, ma mither she had a full an active part in the farm as well apairt fae rearing the three weans, ye ken, she fed hens, pigs and a coo, she wuid turn hye or drive a tractor juist the same as everybody else did. It wis wan o these things whaur ye juist mucked in. Ma mither could turn her haund tae maist things she wis kinna a resilient buddie.

Tom Grant spoke about some of his mother's activities on the farm in the 1960s.

Pauline: *Wis yer mother… did she have any involvement?*

Tom: *She did at times but mostly…Well she kep eggs tae start wi yaised tae be in that office there used tae be battery cages an they kep hens an they wid deal the eggs take eggs down the miners rows . . . Prestwick. Used tae go there on a Friday night when the miners had the money – took yer eggs an ye goat yer money then. That wis every Friday night fur years that wis whit we always done. So it wis.*

And **Archie Mitchell** explained the need for farmers to rely on their families.

Margaret Mitchell and Land Army Girl Madge Bell in the yard of Whatriggs (a hill farm of 160 acres) 1948; the vehicle behind them took PoW to the farms daily
Photo: John R Speirs

Archie: *. . . In the spring o the year when ye were needin tae be ploughin or sawing manure an wan thing an anither an aw thir byres were tae muck an that wis the worst thing aboot byres wis muckin out they byres. As the time went oan in the moarnin an you couldnae get oot tae the fields ye were still mucking byres and then ye began tae think, Ken,* **"Ah think some slats would be a good thing".**

Pauline: Presumably ye were on yer own?

Aye. Ah wis on ma own because Matthew wis away at university and ma other son wisnae interestit in farmin. Ah wis actually better oaf when Matthew wis at the school at Galston an Jimmy wis there tae an when they come hame at night that wis great and at the weekend they were a great help. They actually spent their time workin for me for a while – an they were at the school, an Ah ken yer no supposed tae have child labour an aw that but Ah don't think it did them one bit o harm.

Comment

Farming on the Whitelee Plateau was carried on under conditions which stretched people's resourcefulness. There was a short growing season not conducive to cultivating cereals, the inbye soil lacked plant nutrients and needed constant fertilising; areas of moorland were too wet for horses, tractors, cattle, people or even sheep to go on for much of the time. One contributor remembered watching Wimbledon on television in June because the grass for hay had not even started growing!

The small size of the inbye compared with the rest of the farm was frequently emphasised. So, producing sufficient winter food to increase stock numbers was difficult, while buying feed bit into profits. Anyway, if more stock were kept during winter, the summer moorland could not support them nor could the inbye, which was needed to grow hay. One sheep to 3 to 4 acres of land was the norm, a very low stocking density especially for smaller sheep like Blackface.

It was a hard life physically: the whole 500, 1000 or 4000 acres of moorland had to be walked daily with the dogs to check the flock (more frequently at lambing time) and the inbye had to be worked as well. Fat lambs had to be sold in October because all the ewes needed sufficient winter grazing without competition from the growing store lambs. So farmers could neither be choosy over autumn sale prices nor wait to sell till later.

Cold, wet, misty and often windy weather, moorland which could not be improved for agriculture despite regular draining, tree-trunks buried in the soil, extremely poor grazing ground and too small an inbye were features of farming described by farmers of the Whitelee Plateau from the 1930s to 1950s.

So what changed in the early 1960s that had not pertained previously? Farmers of the Whitelee Plateau were now mainly owner-occupiers. And farmers are not normally keen to sell off part or all of their land, because they have such a strong attachment to the way of life, whatever the conditions.

Why did so many owner-occupier farmers on and around the Whitelee Plateau sell land for afforestation when that option came along? This very important point will be discussed by contributors in Chapter 7.

CHAPTER 6

The Background to Forestry in Scotland

Why a National Forestry Agency was Needed in 1919

Landowners and politicians of the later 19th century certainly understood that the woodland and timber resources of the country had reached a parlous state after several centuries of unsustainable use. Most British woodlands were owned by private landowners, but a few remnants of medieval Royal Forests such as the New Forest still survived.

The First World War (1914–1918) caused further enormous devastation of Britain's woodlands. Pit props, particularly, were needed for the coal mines and timbers were required for building and maintaining the trench network from which many battles were fought in Europe.

So in 1919 the British Government inaugurated its forestry agency, the Forestry Commission. The intention was that the Forestry Commission would ensure a strategic supply of two years' timber in case of another war. This necessitated both afforesting land which had not borne trees for many centuries and restocking existing, but devastated woodlands. The booklet *Gwydyr Forest in Snowdonia: a History* by D. L. Shaw (see Bibliography) shows just how difficult this was. Very few professional foresters, skilled woodsmen and suitable homes were available in the early 1920s to prepare ground and plant trees on thousands of acres (and later hundreds of thousands of acres) of Britain's remote and derelict uplands.

The Forestry Commission has gone through many tribulations since 1919, but has had much success in both growing the nation's forests and in promoting forestry amongst private landowners. The tasks of the Forestry Commission have varied throughout the twentieth century according to the whims of politicians. But the results of its endeavours can be seen in many, often conifer forests, now an ongoing feature of Britain's upland scenery.

Young plantation in Traquair Forest, Scottish Borders
Photo: Forestry Commission Picture Library

Instigation of the Forestry Commission

Four men who have been deeply involved with the Forestry Commission and Scottish forestry, contributed their accounts of the development of the Forestry Commission in Britain. They explained how Scotland fitted into the national forestry programme, how staff were affected by expectations of both government and public, and how they, personally fitted into the overall picture.

Gordon Cowie
Photo: Courtesy Gordon Cowie

Gordon Cowie (retired acting chief executive of the Forestry Commission) spoke about the changes he saw and experienced in Scottish forestry and started by explaining why the Forestry Commission came into being and how its remit has changed.

Gordon: *Now the state forestry is, the land is owned by the Government in the name of, it used to be the Secretary of State, I presume now it's the, in Scotland, the First Minister. And managed by the Forestry Commission for the benefit of the State. And these benefits can include non-market as well as market benefits. And the balance can change, depending on the nature of the* Government. *The private forestry, really, there have been private forests for centuries of course... but private forestry was seen as a, an equal partner after the First World War, the Forestry Commission was set up because the private forests were pillaged, there's no other word... for the First World War needs. And the first aim of the Forestry Commission was to achieve a two-year reserve of standing timber for the next war.*

Unfortunately it came rather soon. But the need for strategic reserves was restated after the Second, or during Second World War, in 1945 Forest Policy. And, it was recognised that there was a role for the private sector, and they were encouraged by grants to replant the forests that had been cut in the Second World War, because most of the Forestry Commission forests were not ready.

These grants were simply to replant.

Until later, in the late Fifties into the Sixties, they were for new planting. And to encourage the private sector, tax relief was given. And that led to a long story where some individuals really misused the system to obtain tax relief on their investment, and there was no thought to anything other than just sticking trees in, painting the map green.

And that led to the backlash in public opinion of the late Sixties, Seventies... and, a total review of where forestry was going and what it was for. Until today, we have multi-purpose forestry, for both the state and the private sector.

Ruth: Gordon, you talked about how things might change under different governments, when you were working in the Forestry Commission, that's the state forestry, how things might change according to different governments. Can you explain to listeners how this affected what you did in your work and your career?

Yes, surely. I started in the Forestry Commission in 1966, and at that time there were really two primary objectives, as there seemed to me at the time.

The one was creating a reserve of timber for industry; the war objective which I referred to a moment ago had more or less disappeared, not quite but more or less, because of nuclear war, the expectation was that the next war would not last two years. So that became less important, although it was still hovering in the background.

The other was job creation, both directly and indirectly. Indirectly, through the creation of a reserve [of] timber for industry, industrial development. And that was seen as very important in the Sixties; while I was working in Fort Augustus in the early Seventies, the paper mill of Fort William was opened, and that was, there were great hopes for that, and big sawmills were opening.

So that was the, one objective, was economic development. And the other was providing employment in areas of no employment opportunities . . .

I was involved with the economics section. And in considering whether or not to expand in certain areas, we were allowed to use shadow costing. Shadow costing took account of the cost to the State of unemployment benefits. That is totally heresy nowadays. (Laughs) But at that time, it was felt that it was better to employ... It was job creation. And, so, what... we were encouraged to buy land in some parts of the north-west Highlands, which would never have met any of our economic criteria without shadow costing. And they were called Special Planting Areas, where we were allowed to apply these concepts.

Yes. Right. So you could decide to buy a particular area of land because you, your costings suggested that it would be useful to the local community... in providing employment...

Yes. And that had been the case since the Second World War, when the Forestry Commission established forest villages. And, job creation was seen as a, a very important topic, right up to the late Seventies. And, it changed in the late Seventies because of the political circumstance changing, when Mrs Thatcher came into power.

OK. Yes. And, so what, how did that affect this strategy?

Well there was no shadow costing. Everything was looked at very commercially. We were certainly encouraged in the objective of industrial development. And my career followed that. I was involved with finding a, getting a paper mill for North Wales, and this was from the Finns. The Finns were making a lot of money at that time, but they were very much under Soviet domination. And they were concerned as to what they could do with the money. So we, my task, along with others, many others, including European Investment Bank, was to get them to come over to Britain and invest in paper mills. Which they did . . .

And during the Seventies and Eighties, industrial development was the most important aspect. I remember in the early Eighties when the pound strengthened against every other currency because of oil, we lost eighty-five per cent of our industrial base in paper, and wood-using industries. And we, yet we were able to make that up. We got new investment in during the Eighties. We got over a billion pounds at the time, which was a huge investment, of overseas investment into a new industry. So that, the industrial development side pushed the situation in the Seventies and Eighties. But as the Eighties developed, and we moved into the Nineties, the other aspects of conservation, which were always there, we all, under the Forestry Act we had a duty of balance, but conservation became more important. Recreation, which had been important since the end of the Second World War, in some areas became the most important aspect. And in the south of England for example, timber production ceased to be a primary concern.

So, even in the days, the halcyon days of economic imperatives, conservation was always important. And the public in my whole career were welcomed into the forests, there were forest walks, this was seen as most important. And landscaping was important in the early Seventies, became vitally important later on. There was always conflicting objectives, and the job of a forest manager was to try to balance these. You couldn't satisfy everyone... most of the time.

Scottish Afforestation in the Mid-20ᵗʰ Century

Bill Sutherland
Photo: Isobel Cameron

Bill Sutherland, who started for the Forestry Commission in Scotland in 1942, wrote vividly about its philosophy then. *The Forestry Commission was formed in the aftermath of the First World War when timber became a scarce commodity and the Government decided it had to increase forestry in Scotland to 10% of the land surface. This was to prepare for future wars by creating a reserve of growing timber, should we ever again become isolated as an Island.* **In my days afforestation was the**

Glentress Forest, Scottish Borders: Afforestation was the primary goal
Photo: : Forestry Commission Picture Library

primary goal*, and to produce pitprops for mining and other timber as quickly as possible.* **Absolutely Nothing Else Mattered***.*

Sitka spruce, in its blue-green foliage, is the main species used for Scottish forests
Photo: : Forestry Commission Picture Library

So we embarked on huge scale planting of fast growing conifers. Native Scots Pine (Pinus sylvestris ssp. Scotica*) was marginally acceptable in North Scotland and in low rainfall areas, but for high rainfall areas, only Sitka Spruce (Picea sitchensis*) or Lodgepole Pine (Pinus contorta*) served the purpose. There was also some planting of Norway Spruce (Picea abies), especially in frost hollows, and Japanese Larch (Larix kaempferi) or Hybrid Larch (Larix marschlinsii – Larix eurolepis in my time) and a little Douglas Fir (Pseudotsuga menziesii – Pseudotsuga douglasii in my time) and Western Hemlock (Tsuga heterophylla).

Norway spruce, in its bright-green foliage, is of less importance in Scotland
Photo: : Ruth Tittensor / Forestry Commission Picture Library

The notion of growing oak (Quercus spp.), birch (Betula spp.) and ash (Fraxinus excelsior) etc was seen as ridiculous.

My first inkling that there just might be something more to Forestry than just planting fast-growing conifers was when I showed Sir Frank Fraser Darling and his wife round the Forest of Ae. After an hour's walk they compared notes of the birds they had seen or heard. I was amazed. I think it was 30 species.

Professor Mark Anderson wrote **"the choice of species"** pleading for the Forestry Commission and other tree planters to use a wider range of species, but he was viewed as a quaint, loveable character with his head in the clouds. So we continued to plant Sitka Spruce (with a little Japanese or Hybrid Larch for **"amenity purposes"**), but anything more than a chain wide round perimeters was unacceptable!

Next came Sylvia Crowe (later Dame Sylvia Crowe) our first Landscape Architect. She had a big impact, encouraging planting of native species on forest edges, demonstrating forest design to improve the unnatural appearance of plantations and so on.

Lodgepole pine, in its dark-green foliage, is prone to wind-blow and snow-snap   Photo: : Ruth Tittensor

Larches, whose colours vary with the seasons, are often grown to improve amenity   Photo: : Ruth Tittensor

70

The new breed of conservationists followed, stressing the importance of the landscaping of forests and the encouragement of wildlife, public enjoyment, preservation of peat and preservation of rare habitats. But I think all this stemmed from the teachings of Fraser Darling in the book he published.

The year before I moved to Edinburgh, my financial estimates showed that we had advanced from being an annual drain on the national purse to a situation where our income from timber sales exceeded our total expenditure. We were making a profit! I retired from the FC feeling satisfied!'

* [It is usual for Latin names to be italicized; some of Bill's Latin names are now outdated]

Expansion of Scottish Forestry After 1960

Christopher Smout
Photo: Courtesy Christopher Smout

Chris Smout has spent a lifetime studying Scottish social history including woodlands and forestry, and also advises the Forestry Commission. In his written contribution, he explained the political background to Scottish forestry in the second half of the twentieth century.

So the Forestry Commission was set up with the expectation that it would provide a strategic timber reserve against another war, and that by dong so it would provide significant economic and social benefits, including increased rural employment. Its first chairman was Lord Lovat, and the influence of the grandees of the Royal Scottish Forestry Society was evident from the start.

At one level, the first 40 years of the Forestry Commission ended in almost complete failure. Set up to afforest the country, by 1960 it had succeeded in raising the level of Scotland's woodland cover (in the official statistics) only from five per cent to six per cent since the start of the century. Dependence on imports had not been reduced and no strategic reserve had been grown. The Zuckerman Report of 1957 concluded that in a nuclear age there was no point in growing a strategic reserve of timber anyway, since the next war would be over in a flash . . .

In 1939 the Second World War fell upon it when the timber planted since 1920 was still too immature to be of much use, and private woodlands were devastated for a second time to meet the emergency.

On the other hand, the Commission had survived many changes of government and much hostility from the Treasury. It had devised a scheme in 1945 for private landowners to dedicate their woods to permanent timber production in return for tax concessions, and by 1956 it had planted a million acres of its own land with trees. It had established admirable training schemes and created a cadre of professional foresters. At the very least it could say that it had repaired the deforestation caused by two world wars. Further, it had set up a series of Forest Parks where people could enjoy themselves – in Argyll in 1935, Glentrool in 1947, Glenmore in 1948 and the Queen Elizabeth Forest Park in the Trossachs in 1953. It also admitted the public to all its woods, truly a bonus in Scotland where there were no national parks and only a rudimentary network of public rights of way. It had created jobs, some 5000 in its own employment by 1954, many associated with forest workers' holdings and forest villages.

Most important of all, the Zuckerman Report did not conclude that the nuclear threat made the Commission irrelevant, but rather that forestry should be encouraged for its social and economic benefits, especially to marginal upland areas, and because of a perceived need at the time for import substitution. The Scottish ecologist Frank Fraser Darling also persuaded Zuckerman that afforestation even by non-native conifers could have ecological benefits, as growing trees was in his view the 'natural' use of uplands that had been turned into 'wet deserts' by sheep grazing. The Treasury argued that, on the contrary, there was no real economic justification either for forestry or agriculture on marginal land: **"it would be better for the national economy if the land were left bare and people moved"**. But they accepted that for social and political reasons this was impracticable. Forestry was again given the green light for expansion.

Chris Smout then explained that despite the green light for forest expansion, which included Whitelee Forest, the outcomes in the longer term were not what had been hoped for or expected.

By 2000, the proportion of Scotland under wood had grown from six per cent to seventeen per cent, most of that being Sitka spruce, and almost all of it taking place in the uplands. It was an extraordinary transformation of the face of the countryside, not all of it directly due to the efforts of the Forestry Commission as an increasing proportion of the trees came to be planted by private estates

and forestry companies encouraged by tax breaks.

Employment, however, did not grow in proportion. By the start of the new millennium, about the same number were employed in the forests as had worked for the Forestry Commission fifty years before, though the area under wood was nearly three times as great. An additional 5000 or so worked in wood-processing, which had been given a shot in the arm when a new pulp mill was opened with a large subsidy from government at Fort William in 1963, the minister proclaiming it a first step towards the repopulation of the Highlands. It did not achieve that, and closed after seventeen years, but apparently more sustainable was the great Caledonian Paper plant built by Kymmene of Finland at Irvine in 1987. Only a small number of additional jobs were to show for the vast amount of public money that had been poured into the trees in the previous four decades; the total forestry sector came to employ about 10,700 people, but many of those were in fragile rural communities where they were doubly welcome.

The Caledonian Paper Mill, near Irvine, Ayrshire
Photo: Forestry Commission Picture Library

Chris Smout also explained why Scotland received such a high proportion of the 'factory-farmed' Sitka spruce plantations described by Gordon Cowie.

The answer is that Scotland especially wanted it. In 1965 and again in 1967, for example, the Secretary of State for Scotland, Willie Ross, fought tooth and nail in Cabinet committee to increase the acreage targets for planting in Scotland per year from 25,000, where it had stood in 1962 towards 50,000, which he hoped would be reached in 1976. Civil servants in London described the manoeuvres of the Scottish Office as **"the result of political enthusiasms and pressures"**, *explaining 'there was no economic case for increasing the national planting programme', and rightly describing the amount of employment provided by both forestry and the wood-using industries as* **"pretty small, and fantastically costly per job"**.

If the Scots were to get their targets, London was determined that the planting should be done as cheaply and economically as possible, to limit this effusion of funds.

Public Pressure

High-profile afforestation by celebrities of the valuable conservation region called the 'Flow Country' in Caithness and Sutherland, made the public and politicians very aware of the 'farm-forestry' production phase of the Forestry Commission. **Gordon Cowie** described to Ruth Tittensor what it was like to be at the receiving end of increasingly negative attitudes to forestry.

Gordon: *My first awareness of anything other than isolated opposition to forestry was when the planting was taking place in the so-called Flow Country in Sutherland. Now we were encouraged initially by the Nature Conservancy people, back in the Sixties. This was seen as something that would add to the diversity of the area. And then of course there was the realisation of what was happening to the site. I'm not apologising for it, but, we went into it without any negative connotations... It was seen as a good thing.*

And when there was the opposition, the initial reaction was, **"Oh they don't know what they're talking about. These people from cities"**. *But, over a few years, we began to realise, no, we've got to be careful. But that was when the damage was done. And, there was a general perception that big, large-scale planting wasn't a good thing. But that would have been in the late Seventies, early Eighties.*

Ruth: So that is when you feel that the public's attitude generally became negative towards forests?

It, it was more of an urban public attitude, and a media public attitude, than an attitude that we met actually out in the countryside. But... But generally, if you said you worked in forestry, **"Oh that's good"**, *you know. This was seen as a very positive thing.*

Until that period, it switched in the early Eighties.

Right. And, how did that affect your work, and the work of staff on the ground?

[hesitation] *We began to develop a feeling of being under attack obviously. And, there was this, I suppose anybody in this situation, feeling from, the attitude that we were well-respected and what we were doing was appreciated, to suddenly a negative attitude, took some getting used to. And some, some... we got over it, I believe the industry has got over it now. But it's taken a lot of adaptation. And a lot of necessary changes, changes that might not have come about if it hadn't been for these pressures.*

Forestry Commission managerial staff like Gordon Cowie, had to respond to political and public demands. Forestry Commission workers in places like Whitelee Forest were also affected by changing policies and demands, resulting in changing work practices: their accounts will be given in later chapters.

Where Whitelee Fitted In

Forestry Commission managers were moved regularly between jobs and did not always have a choice as to where they went. In 1969, Welsh forester **Alister Jones** was posted away from the Welsh forests, firstly to Peebles. After a break back in Wales in the 1970s, he returned to Scotland, this time to Ayrshire.

Yes, there was quite a lot of forestry in Wales, but there was even more in Scotland. And I was offered the job of district, District Officer, in South Ayrshire, the office in those days was in Girvan. That was 1981. In 1984 there was a, a small reorganisation, and the office... There was a new office, in Straiton, which was about fourteen miles south-east of Ayr, and that became my base. And the boundaries of my district changed a little over the next few years, and by 1986 I think it was Whitelee Forest became part of my area of responsibility, and shortly afterwards Arran Forest, the Forest of Arran became as well. So at that time I was known as the Forest District Manager for Ayrshire and Arran.

And Whitelee was, just under twenty per cent of the whole of the forest area that I had to deal with.

Alister Jones then reiterated what Gordon Cowie had said about the early Forestry Commission, in order to place Whitelee Forest in context.

But I think it might be interesting just eh to cover an aspect which, or certainly technical aspect, which eh affects, prompted really by questions I have heard asked about Whitelee, namely, why did anybody ever plant any trees there? (Laughter). And I think, it might be worth saying something very quickly that... The Forestry Commission was set up in 1919, and it had a strategic objective of increasing the forest area in Britain, with the ultimate aim of some sort of self-sufficiency of timber supply. And that was a sort of two-pronged attack, it was a start of state-owned forests as we now know them.

And there was the revitalisation of private forests, which had been the main source of timber during the First World War, when our lack of timber supplies had been sorely understood. And this broad direction for the expansion of the forestry estate in the country was reinforced by the, by the Second World War, where we were a bit short of timber once more. And, there was also some, I was going to say support for it, I mean, during all of this time there was research work going on to some of the technical development work on cultivation techniques and forest nutrition, and this gained pace after the Second World War. And subsequent forest policies have endorsed this whole idea of forestry expansion, but with increasing integration with other forestry objectives. Now, Whitelee was not in the first phase of all of this work, it didn't start between the wars, and it wasn't you might say in the second phase, which was the immediate post-World War II forestry expansion. It...

You could say, looking back on it, it was part of a third phase.

The first few phases concentrated on areas where there was a certain amount of forestry tradition, and where conditions were more appropriate for early afforestation.

And I think what kept Whitelee out of the picture was the relative or marginal attractiveness of the farming enterprises, and possibly also of the grouse moors, because Whitelee had quite a lot of heather on it . . .

And so, I... Obviously I can't say exactly when the first Forestry Commission person would have started to talk to anybody in the Whitelee area about buying land, but, the type of land which we now know as Whitelee Forest was of marginal agricultural value, and possibly became even more marginal as time went on, and quite good prices were paid to landowners who were prepared to sell their land for forestry development, and one thing led to another, and once one sort of property had changed hands and been planted, the neighbours saw the benefit of this sort of move, and that's why Whitelee grew.

Comment

The Forestry Commission was formed when the nation's dwindling timber resources had become reduced below crisis point. It experienced political stops-and-starts, changing remits and varying levels of support from the public. People working in the forestry sector coped with these external factors and their efforts produced an increasing (but long-time-growing) crop for the nation, which spawned an associated processing industry.

The sudden change from moorland to forest on the Whitelee Plateau came in the last phase or push for afforestation in the twentieth century. In the next chapter, the farmers and landowners who sold land for the new Whitelee Forest from the 1960s to 1980s describe their part in it. And the Forestry Commission staff who went about acquiring land on the Whitelee Plateau, describe how they approached their work and how they felt about it.

Pit Props, vital products of 20th century forestry
Photo: Forestry Commission Picture Library

CHAPTER 7

Why Whitelee? Buying Land for the New Forest

Coincidence of Timing

The difficulties of farming on the Whitelee Plateau before 1960 have already been vividly described by contributors.

Mechanisation came late to the Whitelee Plateau. **John and Margaret Struthers** explained that the lower (hill) farms had Ayrshire dairy cattle, more arable land and therefore more money in the family 'pooch' than upland (moorland) farms, where mechanisation was later.

> **John:** *The tools before the tractors wis the horse. The main tools Ah kin mind o wis a shovel an a fork – the word we yaised for a fork in they days wis a dung graip and it'd four prongs quite a heavy fork and that wis what it was used, ye shovelled and ye shovelled and ye shovelled that wis…*

> **Margaret:** *And ye'd scythe oot tae.*

> **John:** *Hyeuk. That wis another auld thing tae.*

> **Margaret:** *They were things that we yaised.*

> **John:** *But ye see in thae days it wis aw hard graft there were nae mechanization.*

> **Margaret:** *In yer hull ferm it wis later comin intae mechanization than whit the likes o a dairy ferm wis.*

> **John:** *The dairy farms were more arable an maybe better oaf an they got the tractors an the machinery first whereas the hill farmer he worked his wey more gradually.*

> **Margaret:** *It took that bit longer.*

> **John:** *It aw depends on hoo mechanically mindit ye da wis.*

> **Margaret:** *Or hoo much money he had in his pooch.*

Jim Kennedy and his wife bought East Hookhead in 1958. He explained that it was then that he changed from horses to tractors.

> *Although ah, ah worked wi horses until ah came here. But, eh. A'd-, ah changed over tae tractor wark, eh, when ah came here. In nineteen fifty-eight . . . The horses were still, were still on wur, wur home farm. Mean ma, ma young brother an ma father were still left there. When ah come here. With horses. For four years. But, eh. The labour si'uation tae work horses when we weren't workin them wursels became impossible. An they changed over tae tractors. In sixty-two or sixty-three.*

The intractability of the moorland may have prevented Whitelee farmers benefiting from the greater profits to farming enjoyed by the rest of the industry in the three decades after the Second World War. This could be a reason that they were happy to sell their land for forestry.

A nearby resident, **Robert Miller**, wrote about it.

> *Farmers would not have been unhappy to sell land for forestry, as it was the worst land – the moors – high up on the hills. These were the only areas that had sheep at that time. (There were cattle everywhere else, on the lower slopes, they were dairy herds of Ayrshires and Friesians).*

Tom and Janet Grant agreed.

> *In the late 60s sheep farmin wis in depression the Forestry Commission come in an probably done good… for it… for the sheep wisnae payin if they hadnae've bought it probably naebody would. So they probably did the farmer a good turn. If ye goat rid o that grund an ye could go an buy better grund.*

Mathew Mitchell suggested that the money offered for the poor land was attractive.

Well, a'm quite sure there was, a mean everybody, everybody, ye make decisions every day an, eh, everybody assesses their situation, or their bank manager assesses their situation for them no doubt at times, an it wid aw depend on everybody's personal situation, em, a'm sure they were given a gude price for their farms, and, eh, if the, if the money's there people follow the money and, eh, for relatively poor

Farmers Tom Grant (left) and Jim Kennedy
Photo: Isobel Cameron

land it would be, y'know, above its value and you could change tae a better farm so I imagine the younger people did as you said, eh, they went to better farms elsewhere, uh, especially if ye had enough acres, a mean that wis the thing abute the hill farms, they would have a gude number a acres so it would come tae a wee pot o money.

Richard Roberts, a Waterside resident, described what he and his wife noticed when they explored the Whitelee Plateau in 1970.

I think, in some ways the Commission may be seen as an early form of agricultural diversification, because there's no doubt about it, that, at the time we moved into Waterside, there were a lot of farms on the periphery of, of the plateau, and in fact the whole of Whitelee area, that were marginal, and that... You could tell that in fact. I mean the, the dilapidated buildings you know . . . Oh, just one of those things. The land, they couldn't afford to till the land. To do very much at all. They were fighting on, you know, the edges of peat bogs, a lot of things like that. And, and agriculture is a terribly fickle industry, business, call it what you will.

And, quite often, there were people in fact, I can give one example . . . who struggled on almost to the bitter end.

Now the farm had been in the . . . family, I think it was third generation. But in fact, at the end of the day, didn't do anything with it, and they did in fact sell to the Commission. They did retain the house, but, but... and maybe a couple of paddocks. But they sold. And, I think there must have been a lot of, of great sadness, as any normal family person would feel, that, we've been here for three generations, and, you know, we're the ones that have let the family down, or some such. But in fact, I think, it really was a godsend. I mean, they certainly weren't paying terribly high prices. But then, this was what . . . I mean it wasn't even B grade of agricultural land, you know, it was pretty well unprofitable . . .

So I mean that, that certainly happened there, and that was the nearest farm of which I was directly aware. Although it was obvious from the regular treks and trips we made around the area to see that this was happening over towards Eaglesham and, also towards Strathaven.

There were other possible reasons why Whitelee farmers took the opportunity to sell their land for forestry.

Many had been tenants of the Loudoun Estate up to 1921, when the estate was disbanded. Perhaps the new owner-occupiers had worked so very hard for a lifetime and hoped to pass on the inheritance to their family. But after the Second World War times had changed and the young people may not all have found the hard, poorly-rewarded life of their parents attractive. And in the post-War period there were alternatives. Some sons of Whitelee Plateau farms had already started a new life away from the family farm when their parents decided to sell in the 1960s.

Heather and moorland grasses dominated the drier parts of the Whitelee Plateau, but several contributors suggested that the grass had expanded at the expense of the heather within their memory (this ecological change is usually caused by exceeding the stock 'carrying-capacity' of the land). But grouse and blackcock need young heather to feed on. It is possible these birds gradually declined with the change in vegetation. Reduced shooting bags and incomes may have been the result and this would affect both individual farmers and big estates like that of Lord Weir's Carrot Estate.

The Push For Suitable Afforestation Land

It seems that a number of factors had produced a situation where financially rewarding farming was extremely difficult at the same time as a potential buyer of large areas of land came on the scene. But the Forestry Commission had its own difficulties.

As a result of the 1957 Zuckerman report (discussed in Chapter 6) the Forestry Commission was into a period of huge expansion of new planting. It was now needy of large areas of the right sort of land for afforestation to meet the annual targets set for new planting on bare ground. But it could not be any 'bare' ground: agricultural quality land was out of bounds so the Forestry Commission was restricted to buying land in upland Britain, land with the worst soils!

Gordon Cowie explained that land had to be 'cleared' as unfit for agriculture first. This very poor land, often on peat, was certainly not a forester's first choice for growing trees!

Ruth: What sort of land would you have chosen, and what species would you have grown?

Gordon: *Well you're quite right in what you said at the beginning of that, that question, because, the first thing we had to do if we were interested in land was to get clearance from the Department of Agriculture. And if they said the land could not be cleared, was the expression, that was the end . . .*

The, the best forests are actually on slopes, in mineral soils. By choice, we would not have wished to go into the peaty areas. The mineral soils give you far more flexibility in practising the type of forestry that professional foresters want to practise, thinning the plantations, diversity of species, wildlife, so on. And the forests that I enjoyed managing best were those forests. I had, as a district officer in the Great Glen, I had the slopes of the Great Glen, big Douglas fir areas as they were, but, very productive. Lots of oak woods, lots of broadleaf within it. I love that.

I also had vast areas of bog. And, that was what I called earlier basically farming.

Yes. Tree farming.

Tree farming. We had to do it, because, we had to provide the combination, and the primary objective for most of my career was industrial development, providing a base for industrial development. And we were proud of that. And we were particularly proud when the sawmills and the factories came along.

From 1966 onwards **Bill Sutherland** worked within the Forestry Commission 'acquisitions team' and he wrote about the process of finding and acquiring suitable land for afforestation.

As Acquisitions Forester I became part of a very efficient team based at 25, Drumsheugh Gardens, Edinburgh, under the charge of the Chief Land Agent (Geoff Forrest, later to become Senior Officer for Scotland). He was an astute Land Agent serviced by two civil servants (Higher Executive Officers: Jimmy Bissett and Douglas Pringle).

My job was to inspect properties, which they had found through adverts in papers and local knowledge. I would meet the owner (seller or tenant) and survey the property assessing its value for tree planting and prepare a report on my findings. My Acquisition Report would be examined by the Lands Staff of the Department of Agriculture and Fisheries for Scotland. These were qualified agriculture degree personnel (such as George Robertson who until very recently was Secretary of the European Union). They decided if the land or how much of it could be transferred from Agricultural use to Forestry. And the Forestry Commission had to abide by their decision or we held mutual site meetings to negotiate the final outcome.

If DAFS* approval was granted, I or Geoff Forrest or both, would meet the owners and seek to agree a purchase. Not infrequently this would result in a compromise whereby only part of the land could be planted, and the remainder had to stay under agriculture. This could result in the total purchase by the FC on condition that only the agreed acres could be planted, the balance becoming a 'surplus asset'. My job in such a case became a matter of disposing of the surplus asset, ideally by selling it to another farmer in exchange for other plantable land. One of the really intriguing land use situations thus created was to find a *farmer who was attracted to the idea of selling part of his farm in order to buy some better land.*

* [Department of Agriculture and Fisheries for Scotland]

If there were 'surplus assets' the Forestry Commission could let them to a farmer or find its own tenant from among the ranks of its own workers. In this last case, a 'Forest Workers' Holding' was set up, where a Forest Worker and family lived and ran the farmland as a smallholding, with the husband working concurrently in the surrounding forest.

'A Stab in the Dark'

This is how **Peter Innes**, boss of Bill Sutherland, described buying the farmland which became the very first block of Whitelee Forest. It was Whiteleehill farm, with the steading perched near the top of Whitelee Hill, a high point of the Whitelee Plateau.

I was Chief Acquisition Officer from 1958-1978 and negotiated the purchase of the first block and also the subsequent additional blocks. From memory the first acquisition was from a farmer called Pyper and I think the price settled was about £7 per plantable acre, certainly less than £10.

At that time the Commission was desperate to acquire land to meet the large planting programme and it was not a question of what will we take, but what can we lay our hands on.

Whitelee at high elevation on deep peat was in many ways a stab in the dark and a lot of people in the FC doubted if it would be successful. However J.A.B. MacDonald, Conservator, South Scotland at the time was a forward looking man and decided to take it up.

The Forestry Commission distinguished between the 'plantable' land and other land which could not be planted with trees, being buildings, land suitable for agriculture or too poor for either. Thus the Forestry Commission reckoned a total price for property, and a price per plantable acre.

Why were staff of the Forestry Commission uncertain about taking on the land of Whiteleehill farm, when they were quite used to having to buy and afforest the poorest land? Why was the new Whitelee Forest 'A Stab in the Dark' and if so, why and how was it expanded to nearly 6,000 hectares in the next two decades?

The remote steading of Whiteleehill, the first farmland sold for afforestation 1961   Photo: Holly Saunders

High Hapton, once hirsel of Whiteleehill, sold in 1961 for afforestation
Photo: Ruth Tittensor

Whiteleehill farm, its 463 hectares of moorland, its farmhouse and steading was sold to the Forestry Commission by Mr John Gair in June 1961. At the same time, Mr Gair also sold the moorland of Gateside and the hirsel of High Hapton which consisted of 126 ha, so the total land sold was 589 ha or 1,196 acres. This was a sizeable chunk of farmland and a good start for a forest which became 'Whitelee Forest' after the farm and the nearby high point of Whitelee Hill. It seems Mr Gair wished to leave Whiteleehill farm because of its isolation and the difficulty of educating his children. **Tom Grant**, a nearby farmer, suggested an additional reason when he wrote:

Mr John Gair was the farmer who sold Whiteleehill Farm land to the Forestry Commission. He had bought High Hapton land from the Leitch family about 1954. When he sold the land, Mr John Gair went to Shankend Farm in the Peebles/Hawick area, where the land is much better. In the Whitelee area, the stocking rate was 3.5 or 4 acres for one sheep, whereas in the Peebles area it would be 1 sheep per acre.

This sale seems to have been a one-off, with no thought at that time that Whitelee Forest would expand beyond its original size. Isolated blocks of state forest were not uncommon at that time, when almost any land was better than no land for the Forestry Commission. But whatever the reason that Mr John Gair sold Whiteleehil for forestry, eight farmers in the locality followed suit later in the 1960s, 12 in the 1970s and two in the 1980s (some of these are the same farmer selling several units). Including sales by non-farmers, 26 units of land were sold for Whitelee Forest, while several other farmers sold to private forestry firms in the same period.

It is unclear why Mr Gair sold his land to the Forestry Commission and not to another farmer. There were no recent private or state plantations in the locality. Did he read of the land requirements for forestry? Did he know someone in the Forestry Commission? Did someone suggest it to him? We shall never know.

Tom Grant described how the buildings, with sheep, of Whiteleehill farm were re-let for five years, with a dwindling area of moorland, as the initial plantings took place.

Well, when Whiteley Hill wis sold there wir two or three o us went tae the valuation . . . an ma father wis at it an he went tae the valuation the Forestry taen all the stock all the sheep stock at Whiteley Hill it wid be valued at the market value in a lot o cases they wid loass money… they'd rent it back oot again tae a farmer or a butcher they'd rent it back oot – they'd probably loass money oan it but it wis the only wey ye could buy at the time. When we sold that bit [indistinct sentence]. But a loat o times the Forestry wid prefer that they didnae need tae take the sheep but in a loat o cases they either taen the sheep or [emphasized] they bought the sheep an then sold them. But in the case or Whiteley Hill when they bought it an then they pit a shepherd in, a shepherd in, a temporary shepherd tae let it back oot so they let it oot for five year Ah think it was an then they started the next year plantin maybe a hunder acre a year Ah think it was… by the time they get a forester there an get things set up it wis five year before it wis all away it wis all planted up.

Bill Sutherland was still District Forest Officer for South Cowal (Argyll) when Whiteleehill farm was sold. He explained how he first heard about Whitelee Forest and how he became involved.

Bill: *Mm. Well, I was, I was at that time District Officer in South Cowal, but that, that district, which was based on Ben More, in the Cowal Peninsula, also included the forests on Arran, Glenrickard Forest on Arran. And then,* *later on, a small forest began at, at Wemyss Bay called Leapmoor. And I had to go by boat to Arran, and I had to cross the Clyde to get to Leapmoor. So when Whitelee was purchased, it, I was the obvious, I was the nearest district officer. So it was added to my, my... patch.*

And I used to have to go by car, across the ferry, and then travel down to Whitelee. Probably stay a night there, and then do something else on the way back. And, I don't remember a lot about it. I can't even remember the forester's name . . .

But anyway, to begin with there was a junior forester there... and he took on, I think four or five workers... to do a small planting programme.

Ruth: The initial... small area.

Initial planting.

So, this was before you became Acquisitions Officer?

Yes, this was while I was still... District Officer South Cowal.

The first bit of Whitelee, you were still a District Officer.

I was still a District Officer. And I saw the first planting there . . .

Buying More Land for Whitelee Forest

Forestry Commission staff were moved from place to place at intervals, so Bill Sutherland was not surprised, in 1966, to be moved from Argyll to Edinburgh to take up the post of Acquisitions Officer.

Bill Sutherland remembered Whitelee Forest and decided to go about enlarging it.

Bill: *And, as I explained, in the course... my investigations as acquisitions officer just by chance really, I saw other areas which were adjacent to Whitelee. So I say, all right, well, we'll, we'll get that. So I then started to concentrate on Whitelee to try and develop it into a forest. It wasn't really, it was just an isolated piece to begin with. And it all depended on how things developed... whether a forest was created or not.*

As it happens, Whitelee proved to be a very good centre. Although, the quality of the land was pretty low. It was pretty marginal. (Laughter)

Ruth: Was it? Yes. But, but your analysis of, of the land, and Mr Roy Harvey's surveys and so on, suggested that, that it was good enough.

It was acceptable. It was acceptable, yes. And indeed, practically all the land that we got subsequently was of similar quality. It was just one of these big areas of open Border type country. And, that's where the Commission was able to buy big areas. I mean I can think of, in north of England, Kielder... became a huge area, and similar land. In the Borders, there are other big forest areas like that. Forest of Ae became quite a big one.

And now, Whitelee was one of the other developing ones.

His knowledge of the area from his days as a district officer came in very useful. During the 1960s and 1970s, he kept a personal card index of how his acquisitions were progressing.

Bill: *I, I was familiar with the territory, I could... it was very obvious. It was a big area there. And so I always kept my eye open for areas of land there. And... the extraordinary thing is that once you start... once you start buying bits of land, then all the other farmers round about say,* **"Oh... Chance of getting some, some cash".**

Ruth: So, you were acquisitions officer, and you must have seen one or two more farms or areas for sale in that part. Can you remember which was the first bit you bought?

... with my, my card index, which was my own personal property.

And it's not very exact, but, this is all the information I have. The old forest, that was up till 1966... had 1900 acres of plantable land. And as at December 1970 there were 1300 acres planted. No. As at '68, there were 1300. At '70 there were 2600.

And then, and the ones that came in after that, as far as my record goes, were, the Overmuirs, High Overmuir and Low Overmuir, Croilburn, Ardochrig. And then, Brocklees and Windshields.

Right. Yes.

Then later on we got Highside, Allerstocks, then Logoch, Lochfield, Caldergreen, Lanphin, Raahead, Glenouther, Hareshaw, Carnduff, Hookhead, West Browncastle, Lairfad, Lambhill, and Titwood. And we lost Threepland... Blackhill and Craigends...

Yes, yes. So this is an awful lot of farms that... that were sold for planting at Whitelee Forest . . .

Well you see, a lot of them, for instance Lairfad was only 180 acres. West Browncastle was only 100. Hookhead,

100. . . Logoch was 1,400 acres. And Brocklees and Overmuir, they were quite big. That was 4,800 acres. . . The total area was growing fast. So that's how it built up.

Yes. Yes. And over what number of years would this have been?

Well, I finished in, when I was... I finished when I was fifty-eight... from the Commission. So that would be, fifty-eight and... That would be '79. I, I finished acquisition for the Commission in '79.

Not all the farms in Mr Sutherland's card index were eventually sold to the Forestry Commission. Map 5, based on his own hand-coloured map, shows the main parcels finally acquired for Whitelee Forest.

Bill Sutherland then said how he contacted landowners who might wish to sell land for afforestation.

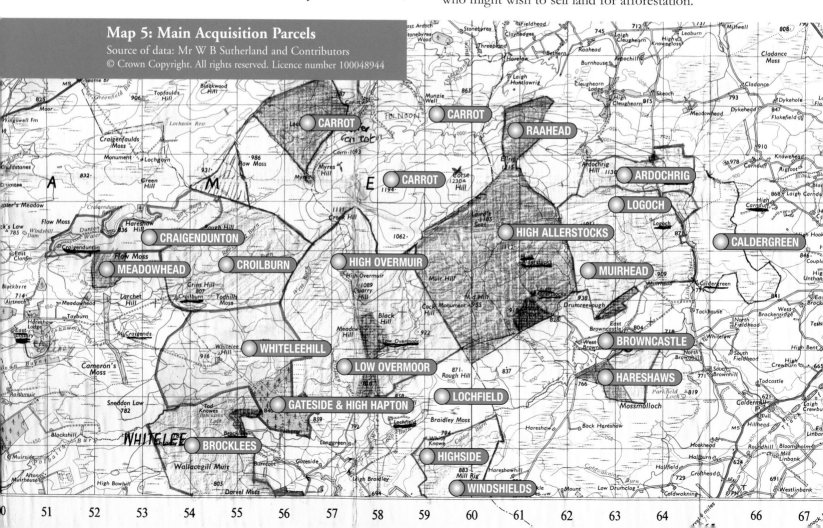

Map 5: Main Acquisition Parcels

Source of data: Mr W B Sutherland and Contributors

Ruth: And to start with, you kept your eye on the newspapers or the sales schedules… as to what became available. Did any of the farmers or landowners actually approach you?

Bill: *Oh yes, yes. Oh quite a number. All these smaller ones were never advertised. They just came… and offered the land to us. When the, when the private forestry really got going, then, that was a competition with, with… At one time we were (practically) the sole purchasers of land for planting. When private forestry came in, there was more competition, and as a result we lost some of the better land, and… and so on.*

Mm. Mm. And did they offer all their farms, or some of the land, or just said, "Would you like some, I've got some I don't need"?

Yes, that, that's really how, how it worked. If a farmer needed money, and he saw that his adjoining neighbours were selling pieces of land to the Commission, then he gave a ring and said, **"Would you be interested in some land?"** *and I would go and have a look and say,* **"I'd be interested in this, but not that bit"**. *And so on.*

So, sometimes we won and sometimes we didn't.

Yes. And so, did they already know you, did you, were you in the area quite often, or, or did they ring the forester on the spot, who then told you?

I think mostly they, they rang the Forestry office, headquarters office where I was.

I see, in Edinburgh. They knew your name, or…? Or the neighbour gave them your name?

Yes. Yes. They normally… I didn't, I didn't know any of the people that I acquired the land from until I actually visited them… to look at it.

Ruth then enquired how long it took for the negotiations.

Ruth: So how long do you suppose it would take you from the time a farmer first telephoned you, or when you first saw an advert for one of the Whitelee farms to

be sold, between that moment and when the legal details were sorted and the land became Forestry Commission, was it weeks, months, years?

Bill: *I would say about three months.*

Well that's quite quick.

Because… We had to, we had to go to the Department of Agriculture for approval… and the Regional Advisory Committee. And that, that took… Especially the Department of Agriculture, because I couldn't really make an offer until I knew how much land they were clearing for planting.

OK. So they had to do a survey as well?

They had to do a survey using the maps provided to show that was plantable. Sometimes we did it together. But their job was, was really just a day's work just to have a look at the place. But… Yes, I would say roughly three months.

Three months? So that's, that's, that's pretty, pretty quick really.

Yes, it's quite quick. I mean some of them, the more complicated ones took, obviously took longer. But they would never take more than six months I would say to get the whole thing done.

Forestry Commission staff like Gordon Cowie and Bill Sutherland, enjoyed their work and felt afforestation was worthwhile for the country, for the farmers and for those farm workers who obtained work in forestry when farms were sold.

Ruth: So you don't feel sad that you caused unemployment or anything like that? Or farmers to give up farming?

Bill: *No, I always felt that… I always felt that, the farm, farming community was gaining at the same time as the forestry. They were getting better land, and more cash to improve their land. And we were getting the poorer land for planting. So no, I, I don't think I feel any regrets at all. I found it an interesting career.*

How did the Families Feel Who Sold Land for Forestry?

Six families have discussed or written about the sale, or lack of a sale, of land to the Forestry Commission.

Tom Grant explained that his father, Mr Tom Grant Senior (now deceased), went to the valuation of Whiteleehill and the Forestry Commission later approached him to see if he would sell. He explained that there was little choice on the price given.

Tom: *It wis the forestry that put the price o the ground tae start wi.*

Pauline: An wis the price for the land OK?

There wir only one price. If they'd have said it wis only worth a fiver an acre they would have goat it just the same for it wis then that Whiteley Hill… Ah wid hae said that Whiteley Hill would be £4.00 an acre, something like that.

An wis that a fair price at that time? Or…

Aye. It wis probably abuit the market value. Ye widnae hae got it for [indistinct] o that.

Right, OK

At the finish up there when they were buying it they were payin seven or eight hunner pound an acre at the finish up, that the price they set.

Tom and Janet Grant said that Father Tom eventually sold some land – the worst, mossy, peaty land they said - and in November 1970 the Forestry Commission started ploughing it. They wrote that the decision to sell was beneficial.

However, selling the land did not affect the farm deleteriously, for two reasons. First, with skill, it was possible to keep the same number of sheep afterwards as before. The sheep were brought down to the nearer, lower, better ground. They did not have to sell the hill sheep. Secondly, the finances gained from selling the land were invested in other farmland. This was some of the better land of the nearby Burnfoot farm.

At East Browncastle farm there was something of a surprise about the land sales by the three Ross brothers. The memories of 92-year old **Gavin Ross** were written for him as he spoke.

At one time, a nephew-in-law* of Mr Ross lived in Whiteleehill farm, where 1500 acres had been sold to the Forestry Commission for tree planting. His nephew worked for Fountain Forestry.

* [Mr Pyper mentioned by Peter Innes]

An Aunt (his mother's sister) and cousins lived at Craigendunton farm at one time. And one of Mr Ross's brothers went off and bought what was left of Croilburn farm from the Forestry Commission (after the Farm and land had been sold for tree planting), stocking and keeping it separate from East Browncastle Farm. Thus, Mr Gavin Ross had many relatives at what was to become the west end of Whitelee Forest.

The three Messrs. Ross themselves were also persuaded to sell 1500 acres to the Forestry Commission in the 1970s. Sheep farming was in a poor way at that time, and they sold the marginal land from three farms of East Browncastle, Muirhead and Logoch, which they now owned. Muirhead Farm had no-one living there at the time.

They did not intend to sell as much as 1,500 acres . . . ! It happened that one of the brothers went off one day with a chap from the Forestry Commission to discuss selling about 500 acres of marginal land for forestry. When he came home, he had sold 1 500 acres . . . ! They did not think they got a very good price, which was £10 - £12 per acre. But they invested the money wisely.

The family of **Iain Hamilton** owned Low Overmoor, but were tenants of Allanton farm, much better land to the south of the Whitelee Plateau. He explained the background to the sale of Low Overmoor to the Forestry Commission.

Pauline: Can ye mind how ye first heard aboot the forestry in the area?

Iain: *Oh my Goad! Aye, aye. Again that wid stert away in* *the mid 60s they stertit planning* at Croilburn an Craigends an it juist spread lik a cancer efter that swallawin up ferm efter ferm Ah think Whitlee Hill went efter that. Ah remember Sandy Middleton, he wis at Whitelee Hill at that time an his place wis slowly planted oot. Again Ah think it wid be great grants given for great swathes o trees. Ah can remember it well.*

* [planting]

Did you sell land tae the Forestry?

Ma faither did. By that time ma faither wis the tenant at Allanton Farm and Low Overmoor wis sacrificed tae purchase it. Just, as Ah say, it wis an opportune moment there. They were offerin mair than ye could make off the bloomin place, break it tae plant trees on it. It's when yer business heid takes ower fae the romance, it whit ye caw the realities o life.

An ye got a good price for it, obviously.

Och aye. He wisnae unhappy aboot it but Ah don't know if land [indistinct] hadnae hae been decided tae sell aff the ferms Ah wid probably still had it, that's somethin Ah don't know, ye cannae answer.

An he used the cash tae buy the…

Well that's right he got a chance tae buy the other ferm.

John and Edith Telfer sold some of Carrot land to the Forestry Commission in the late 1970s.

The Coming of the Forestry Commission

The Telfers sold several large portions of land to the Forestry Commission. On one occasion, they sold land for four times the price they had spent when buying it . . .

Another time, the Forestry Commission was apparently lacking sufficient government funding for acquiring more land. But the Forestry Commission still required planting land. They approached Mr Telfer and suggested to him that the part of Carrot Farm called Threepland was suitable and just what was required for tree planting. So Mr Telfer swapped a portion of Carrot land for Stoneyhill

and South Halls Farms near Dungavel, where he, Mrs Telfer and their adult family currently live and farm, still with some Luing Cattle.

Mr Telfer got on well with Mr Bill Sutherland, the Acquisitions Officer of the Forestry Commission, with whom he negotiated (and Mr Sutherland has fond memories of his time at Carrot Farm).

Hugh Hendry wrote about another, later, swap.

When the Forestry Commission bought land in this area for afforestation, it usually bought the farmhouse, steadings, muir and inbye. However, sometimes there was a swap, as when Mr Brown of Lochfield farm obtained Low Overmuir and its inbye, in exchange for some of the land of Lochfield farm.

John and Margaret Struthers said that their family farm of Craigends was sold to a private forestry firm for several complex reasons.

John: *The Economic Forestry Group. They come on the scene and then the Forestry Commission they were in too. But in these days… by this time Margaret and me we had made up oor mind what we were gonnae do in life and I had went and got a job when this wis aw happenin. There was a lot o that side o the… selling the ground when Ah wis aw… wi ma father an, well it wis his business as faur as Ah wis concerned and Ah wis quite pleased tae see that it worked oot for him, ken.*

Margaret: *For it wisnae big enough tae keep a faimily, ken within a faimly the ferm wisnae big enough for that.*

John: *We made up oor mind that Ah would go oot an get a job an make wir ain way in life. We didnae want tae make life… well, we didnae want father tae worry about it, ken we had tae make wir own way in life. Ma brother he had went tae Australia an then he come back an got a job with the Forestry. It wis helpin ma father at the same time, workin wi the Forestry Ah wis oot in a job workin and Ah wis able tae give ma father a bit hand too, ye ken.*

An by this time, well for father it wis a way for him tae cut things down and move into kinda semi retirement.

He kept a hundred acre which kept him wi sheep.

That wis all the inby ground he kept all the… Economic Forestry bought all the hill ground. An this wis away… he had a pound or two in his fingers an be able tae kinna semi retire and still at the same time keep his hand in wi his sheep an he loved a good deal. He wis aye oot at the markets daein a bit o dealin and this wis his wey o life an we were happy tae see him carryin on like this. It wis a wey he could cut things doon an we were pleased for him and that we could get joabs an carry on an make wir ain wey in life . . . Everybody wis quite happy aboot it we were pleased for Mother and Father because he had done forty two year at that place an we were quite happy tae see him winding it down.

Mathew Mitchell told Ruth Tittensor there were several reasons why his father and grandfather did not sell any land for afforestation.

Matt: *The problem wi Whatriggs were that we wur only a hundred-an-sixty acres at that time and [if] consider-, a mean, eh, at the time, while that wis bein, eh, planted a mean ma father was in his prime, probably still thinks he's in his prime, but, eh, at seventy, but he's, he's, wis definitely in his prime then so he would be thinkin that he could farm it better than anythin else, an it wouldnae be big enough, eh, to really go anywhur, eh, an a can imagine, as a said, there's quite a bit o history here, an, eh, although ma father isnae too interested in it, ma grandfather probably was very aware of it, an, eh, he would be there at that time, eh, a would think it, well certainly in the early sixties, it wis a partnership between ma father an ma grandfather, so a don't think there's any way he would, he would sell up the farm, and eh, as a said, ma father would think he wis well capable – as he was, and as he turned oot to be, a mean, he, he made a very gude, eh, go of the farm as a farming concern, eh, an the farm wis big enough in those days, uh, it's only because o the recent scale o operations you need, eh, a would say since nineteen-ninety, eh, that we've been strugglin, eh, to be, to be viable, y'know, until we got Hyver Hill*, em, so*

ay, everybody would have their reason, a doubt if very many o them really regretted it, uh, there wouldnae be many o them wi, wi huge histories mebbe [?...] an ye've gotta be realistic, no matter how nostalgic ye might get, a mean, farmers are business men at the end o the day and, uh, you get the chance a mean, like they say fae, from the west o Scotland if ye move anywhur, east or south, it's an improvement all the time, uh, an especially fae these, what were really probably poor farms – but who am I tae judge but I imagine they wid be hard – hard life, eh, tryin to make a livin, it wid be a hard life tryin to make a livin fae, fae a lot o these places.

* [High Bowhill]

Ruth: I think so from what other people have said. And some people have commented that farming was in a particularly bad way, or hill farming was at those times, um, which I didn't realise.

Uhu,

Uh, because I thought in most parts of the country in the decades after the Second World War farming was doing particularly well.

Eh. Well, a'm really no, as I say I wis too young (Ruth laughs)*, very, very young at that time, eh, but that, a know there are times that, eh, as a said previously, eh, dairy farmin had a guarantee, so we were in dairy farmin, eh, so we had this guaranteed price an, an, an we were insulated frae that whereas, eh, hill farmers were really very, eh, open tae eh the weather an the markets, eh, so they were quite precarious and, eh, they certainly wouldnae have, eh, security that dairy farmers did at the time and, eh, a lot o them would be – again it's like today when, when, eh, well there's no retirement schemes or anythin on the go at the moment but, . . .*

The Mitchell family has family connections with Whatriggs which go back in a direct line to 1796, and to 1527 indirectly. This was another reason they did not consider selling their land.

Some families or owners decided not to sell to the Forestry Commission, but to private forestry firms at higher prices than the Forestry Commission could offer. **Bill Sutherland** lost out on a number of his negotiations for this reason, and in a couple of cases he wrote on his file cards:-

Sold to EFG at X 2 our offer!

Offered £15 acre for 545 acres (£8,000) on 6/12/68. Sold to EFG £20/ac.

These all now form large areas of private forestry adjoining Whitelee Forest to the north-west and west.

Why Whitelee?

One farmer decided to sell over 1,000 acres for forestry in 1961. The Forestry Commission learned enough from its survey of this land, Whiteleehill farm, for Peter Innes (chief acquisitions officer) to think that it was going to be 'A Stab in the Dark'. Why did it go ahead with buying land so avidly after that?

District officer at the time that Whiteleehill farm came into the fold, Bill Sutherland, saw the type of country it was and noted that certain tree species already grew there as farm shelterbelts.

Bill: *Well . . . it was a very bare countryside. I mean there were the occasional shelter belts. The hill farm, hill sheep farmers could get grants for building very small shelter belts. Two, two chains wide sort of thing – called Hill Farm Shelter Belts. Just to give shelter for the sheep. So there were these little shelter belts around the countryside.*

Ruth: Yes. Of what species?

Oh nearly all Sitka spruce. Or, Sitka spruce or, or larch if it was good enough ground . . . or, or lodge, lodgepole pine... was the other one. Pinus contorta (Lodgepole pine). Which grew on very poor land. And it was very, it, it was very much that sort of open moorland country . . .

The tree species mentioned were known by foresters to thrive on very poor land, and here they were already growing in a few planted shelterbelts.

Pat Armstrong Head Forester from 1975 to1987 wrote about the ecological factors which made afforestation of the Whitelee Plateau very difficult.

The high open moorland of Whitelee Hill and High Hapton, with Brocklees shelterbelt; Franz Grimley poses with gun, mid 1960s
Photo: Jim Currie

Ecological Factors at Whitelee Forest

Wind

Very high winds on all parts of Whitelee Forest. The nearest horizon in any direction is 10 miles away.

In the Highlands, one can plant trees to 1200–1400 feet altitude, particularly on the sheltered sides of mountains.

Exposure and Altitude

But things were different at Whitelee Forest. Even though the altitude at Whitelee does not reach so high as this, it is exposed from all directions, and this affects tree growth deleteriously. Therefore much windblow of trees was both expected and takes place at Whitelee Forest.

Rainfall

There is extremely high rainfall, of at least 60 inches per annum. This gives considerable drainage problems, because Whitelee is all peat ground. Plantings are therefore unstable and this adds to windblow problems.

Ground

The ground is wobbly like blancmange. There is a very high water table.

However, other factors made it the right sort of place for timber production and **Gordon Cowie**, who was involved with Whitelee Forest three times in his forestry career, described them.

Gordon: *And then there were areas where there were no constraints, and Whitelee was one of these.*

Ruth: Right. And it does, it is interesting that many people involved in Whitelee say they wonder why a forest was planted there, because the land seemed so poor, and from what you've said, forestry, a lot of areas were out of bounds of forestry... to start with. So can you explain something about that?

Well they were out of bounds because of their sensitivity. As I say, either landscape or ecology, or archaeology, which was quite common in certain areas. Field bound,* old field patterns.

* [boundaries intended]

Yes.

Things like that. Whitelee, landscape-wise was considered of no great relevance, because it was a plateau, primarily, so you could only see round the edges. There was very little archaeology in Whitelee. The site was considered suitable for growing Sitka spruce, which was seen as the main species for industrial development. Which is what happened of course with the paper mill at Irvine, places like that.

So, Whitelee was attractive. It wasn't a word that we were ever allowed to use nor encouraged to use, but it was basically tree farming. Whereas other more complex areas were more forestry.

In the sense that, there were far more factors had to be taken into account. Whitelee was very much production forestry, and a good site for that. That was how it was envisaged.

That's an interesting view that I, that I haven't heard, because, it's sort of, I suppose, felt in the locality that it was put there perhaps because it couldn't go anywhere else, and the land was available because it was very poor for, for farming, and, because forestry couldn't go to all these other sites, it was allowed to go to Whitelee.

Well there is a, there's a... that is correct of course.

Because we had government-set targets for expansion. So we tended to go to areas that were suitable for that expansion. But we were constrained, as I say, by the site factors, and also the economic factors. But Whitelee was seen as near any possible industrial development. And, straightforward forestry. So it was very much a positive decision to go there.

But these people are right to an extent, that, we went there. And also to other similar areas in the south of Scotland, where there was a rather bland landscape, for the blanket forestry which then became so despised in later years. But when we were starting, it wasn't despised at all.

Yes. Right. Because your remit, the Forestry Commission's remit was to plant up... as much as possible... because the nation needed . . .

That's right. And, and... And there was general public acceptance.

Comment

The lack of political constraints: a plateau landscape where blanket conifer forestry would not be seen from the outside, a site with little known archaeology, a landscape perceived to be lacking in beauty, and a site where 'factory farming' of trees could take place over a wide area, were perhaps the reasons why the Forestry Commission was so proactive in its search for units of farmland on the Whitelee Plateau which could be bought. The fact that there were so many farmers wishing to sell their poor land on the Whitelee Plateau seems to have been a secondary consideration.

How the Forestry Commission set about turning the Whitelee Plateau from a 'Stab in the Dark' into a growing 'Whitelee Forest' of 6,000 hectares is expounded by the people who did it in the next two chapters.

1946 air photo of Whiteleehill steading surrounded by moorland except for a tiny inbye and shelterbelt. Bottom right is Pley Moss with Brocklees Burn rising from it while Whiteleehill Burn rises in the middle of the picture and flows north
Photo: Courtesy of RCAHMS (RAF Air Photographs Collection)

CHAPTER 8

Preparing the Land: Ploughing and Draining the Peat

Machinery, Men and Motivation

Turning moorland into forest is not just a case of planting trees! It is a complex process which in the case of the Whitelee Plateau involved several ingredients.

First, it needed **Machinery and Tools** which could cope with the difficult ground conditions. New versions of machinery, developed by associated industries, were brought in when earlier types could not manage the conditions.

Second, **Men** of many backgrounds with a variety of skills were involved. Few women were involved nationally in practical forestry in the main planting period of Whitelee Forest between 1961 and the 1990s. The known woman members of the Whitelee team were the part-time secretaries in the Forest Office and a Forest District Manager late in the 20th century. Table 4 shows the remembered workers of Whitelee Forest.

Third, the people who took on the task of establishing Whitelee Forest required **Motivation**, which many had in abundance. The forest squad, tractor drivers and other workers were out on site for long hours, in all weathers and with low remuneration. And Forestry Commission managers strongly believed in the long-term success of the Forest.

The first main forestry task was to plough and drain the newly acquired moorland. In earlier times tree seedlings had been directly into the ground by 'hand turfing'. But by 1961 tree seedlings were planted onto upturned ridges of soil produced by ploughing. Before the forestry tractors and ploughs could come in, however, there were several things to see to.

Removal of Sheep and Cattle

The stock – sheep and cattle – were removed from what had been farmland for several centuries. Stock and trees do not go together because these animals nip off and eat the tips and buds of trees, preventing them growing any more.

Ruth Tittensor heard how the Forestry Commission handled it from **Bill Sutherland**, who had negotiated the purchases in the first place.

> *Well, yes, when, once we had bought the property, there were various things that you had to agree. For instance, if it was a farm with a sheep stock, you had to agree whether he was going to sell off the sheep, or sell them off in parcels, and we, as we planted, he would sell off more sheep. Or, he would say, "**I want nothing to do with the sheep**". So then, the date of the sale would be fixed according to that, and we would take over the sheep stock, and the Department of Agriculture would value them, and we would give a price for the sheep, and take over the whole thing . . .*

> *. . . We would then hand the sheep over to, we'd hand the farm with the sheep over to the Department of Agriculture. And if it was a big farm, usually these were quite big areas, the Department would manage the sheep, and gradually remove them. We would put up temporary fences, plant part of it, plant... and then they would say, "**Right, clear the lot**".*

He also said that if there were sheep and cattle to be removed from a tenanted farm, the entry date for the Forestry Commission had to coincide with the agricultural Term Days, usually Whitsun or Martinmas (the anniversary of the tenant's entry to the farm)

Table 4: Some 20th Century Forest Workers			
TRACTOR & DIGGER DRIVERS	**FOREST SQUAD**	**TRAPPERS & RANGERS**	**CONTRACTORS**
Robbie Allan	Alec Baird	Alexander Fenton	1960s: Willy Malone and his workers:
Dan Blair (1st tractor driver)	Stuart Baird	Robin Heaney	Thomas Grant
Iain Cummings	Rex Boland (1st squad member)	Bob Logan	Campbell Templeton
Hughie Davidson	Alan Elder	Jim Newall	George Young
Donald John	Alexander Fenton	Stan Share	
Angus Kennedy	Campbell Hamilton	Iain White	Late 1970s/1980s:
Neil McClelland	Ian Hamilton		Robert Menzies (workers not known)
Archie McIntyre	Lawrence Kennedy Snr		Prisoners (Dungavel Open Prison)
Iain McKellar	Lawrence Kennedy Jnr		
Jake Roberts	Alan Kerr		
Robert Struthers	David Lennon		**SECRETARIES IN FOREST OFFICE**
George Webster	Alan Mealy (Foreman)		Doreen Flett
Ronnie Webster	Hugh McClymont		Edith Gillies
Thompson Wright	John O'Brien		
	Alf Peter		
	Grant Peter		
	Ian Peter (Foreman)		
	Robert Peter		
	Alan Robson		
	Robert Smith		
	Brian Speirs (2nd squad member)		
	Jim Wilson		
	Fenwick Worrell		
	Jim Young		

Source of data: contributors (apologies to those not remembered)

The Forestry Commission bought the farmhouse, steading and all the land of Whiteleehill and High Hapton 'lock, stock and barrel'. Contributors remember the farmhouse, steading and inbye being let temporarily to a tenant as a smallholding. The moorland was used by him too, but it gradually decreased to zero over five years as it was gradually covered with little trees. What was left of Whiteleehill then became a Forest Workers' Holding tenanted in the long-term by the Messrs. Kennedy who also worked in the forest squad.

Some families had been on this land for a long time. How did they feel about having to get rid of all or some of their stock when they sold land? **Gavin Ross**, who with his two brothers had sold 1500 acres of moorland, was sad about it.

When the Forestry Commission bought this marginal land from Messrs. Ross, they, the Forestry Commission, put up new fencing around it. A big plough came in to plough the ridges and furrows. Then the tree-planting men came in. Of course, Messrs. Ross had to take away the sheep before all this could happen: this was quite sad. They took away the sheep and sold them.

The tinge of sadness at removing many sheep was perhaps offset by the incoming finances.

However, **Iain Hamilton** said there was little sentimentality on Low Overmoor. It had been sold so that the family could buy the better, but tenanted, farm of Allanton.

Pauline: Did ye have tae move cattle off the land? Yesterday we were speakin tae Mr Kennedy and the bit of the farm he sold tae The Forestry he didnae have tae take any animals off it because the land he sold wis so poor it wisnae worthwhile puttin the sheep on it. Did you have animals on the land that you sold or yer father sold…

Iain: *Aye there were sheep oan it but aw these sheep were aw heftit - ye ken whit Ah mean by 'heft'? Aye? Ye do? Well the hefts were sellt aff, the stoack wis sellt aff. There wis nae wye the other place could cairry that amount o stoack. Cattle were brought doon, whit little cattle there wis, they were brought doon tae the other ferm but the sheep wis still sold oaf.*

An wis yer family sad aboot that?

Well, again the…

Sentimentality didnae…

No really. Had it been the hame ferm then it would have been [sad], because that had been in oor possession for generations but Low Overmoor wis only in oor possession Ah wid say – nineteenfortyecht he bocht it and sellt it in 1969 so twenty year.

Sheep and cattle were not the only animals which had to leave if a farm was sold. Those unpaid workers, the collie dogs, no longer had a job to do. **John and Margaret Struthers** remembered what happened to the six collies at Craigends.

Well, faither he had eh friends and ma sister she…took two dugs. Aye, Ella* taen a couple for they had a ferm. An a coupla neebours taen a dug, they aw needit a dug.

An faither kept a couple o dugs. But there wir two dugs went tae ma sister's, ken. A loat o work in collie dugs, they're a valuable animal. Ye don't pit a good workin collie doon. Ye'd raither gie it away tae a friend as that, aye. That wis yer best freend at times.

A collie dug wis like two men aboot the place. Especially the auld Blackfaced ewes, if they seen ye oot there withoot a dog they'd say, 'aye, we've goat him the day'. And they could really be difficult . . . * [John's sister]

Fencing

When the stock had been removed, the individual farmland parcels would need new fences if they were in poor condition. By the time the Hamilton family had sold Low Overmoor in 1969, **Iain Hamilton** had left farming to set up a fencing business. When he took on contracting work to fence parts of Whitelee Forest, he found it could be hard, lonely, cold and frightening up on top of the Plateau in winter.

By that time Ah wis in the fencin business an Ah did a loat o fencin on Whitelee Forest, miles o the bloody stuff. Ah don't know whether ye ken it or no but…years ago Ah wis daein a fence oot there [indicating a picture] Ah'm quite shair it's in Allerstokes…there's a ceemetary oot there…it

A forest fence separates farm stock from growing trees
Photo: Ruth Tittensor

neighbouring stock would go onto it. The fence he put up gradually became useless from the effects of wind and snow, and a few sheep then went into the new plantation for shelter. In the end, the Moss Mulloch fence was taken down, because it was cheaper to do that than keep mending it!

Pest Control

There was yet one more thing to do before any new land was ploughed and tree-planted, and that was to reduce what were called 'vermin' or 'pests' which would eat and damage young trees. **Stan Share**, a Forestry Commission trapper at the time, was sent to clear the very first parcel of Whitelee Forest, at High Hapton. He wrote a fascinating and detailed account in his own hand, of what he was required to do.

wis tae a fella fae Newmilns, aye, he'd be a chemist or something it wis his faimily's wish and his wife's that they'd be buried oot oan the moor…must've loved the moors an they built a…ken the graveyaird is surrounded by iron railings an it's got a wee miniature covenanters monument oan it wi their name an they were fae Toonheid in Newmilns this is where they're buried. Noo Ah cannae…but Ah could take ye tae it but it surrounded by trees noo. I could walk oot tae it, in fact Ah walked twa mile tae go an see the bloomin thing, unusual, it is unusual but Ah've seen a loat o things oot there now ye ken, that's unusual. There wis yin fence Ah pit up at Ellrig that run rig back tae the Carrot an away oot the tap o these ridges are buchts* an Ah've sat in they buchts* eatin ma piece oan a snawy January day, fencin. Frichtenin, thon…

Well ye can hardly see onything in yer haun for snaw an it's a long walk back tae whaur yer vehicle wis, by that time ye ken yer maybe two or three kilometres oot. A long walk.

* [he was sitting in a sheep enclosure (buchts) eating his midday meal]

The whole of the infamous Moss Mulloch which was 'spongy and quaking' was fenced by Brian Speirs and his mates in the squad. He thought it did not really need fencing as no

Stan Share with faithful dog, holding a mountain hare 1960
Photo: Courtesy Stan Share

I joined the FC in 1951. I specialised in control of wildlife (rabbits etc) harmfull to forest trees and I was sent over to Whitelee to clear rabbits & hares before it was ever fenced or planted this was 1961/1962/63. The moorland heather parts and peat hags where pretty well populated with rabbits. Brown and white hares. No deer.

My Forester I believe was Bert Mitchell. I advised on rabbit netting stock fences (not deer fences then) with 12 inches or so cl netting dug under, curling to outside to try and stop rabbits digging under fence.

The lower grassland private areas adjoining FC ground were alive with vermin and I got permission from the private land owners to shoot vermin (not snaring) and snaring was the main way of controlling vermin on FC ground mainly on old fences. Being conservation minded I tended the snares pretty regular and released any game birds caught mainly Red grouse.

I used an old Morris 1000 Van and slept in it to be on the ground at dawn & dusk using a FC issue DB 12 bore shotgun hard hitting long barrels fully choked with 3 1/4 inch chambers for high velo cartridge which we used for Roe deer control in the early days. I was presented with this old gun on my retirement in 1996 which I had carried on FC duties for 45 years. The gun was specially made for FC in 1940? and has engraved on top rib, **Forestry Commission Pest Control**.

I mind it was a bleak cold rain sodden areas and I even had snow in May in 62. Perhaps the moisture retaining hag areas etc is why we grew quick healthy trees . . .

I mind the long peat hags between rows of solid land with heather, like long channels. These were later drained. I

Growing tip of young larch nipped off by a hare
Photo: Ruth Tittensor

had to X some of these hags and be very carefull not to get bogged down in treacherous swamp like places especially carrying several heavily bodied hares etc and being on my own all the time (then). I was to shoot and assess the tree damaging wildlife pests before it was fenced and the fence started above Darvel 63. Rabbit net adjoining lower farm areas and sheep netting (I warned FC that hares will come in stock fences high ground [but costly to rab net]) stock on higher heather areas. A huge area fenced off first and I had to concentrate on all vermin pests left inside before planting operations etc.

This job was so large the FC gave me another young trapper To help, Donald Crawford and we both stayed at L Hapton* farm as we could not both sleep in my old Morris Van or food etc. We drove the remaining Hares white & brown to each other for shooting carefully with DB 12 bore shotguns, being safety minded for each other.

* [Laigh Hapton]

We could not use working dogs because of the blasted adders especially on sunny days and we wore wellies and leggings ourself for protection from averse weather and snakes (about 6). Any adders we saw we shot for safety to ourselves and other later planters FC Workers etc also to protect wildlife (young birds etc) which adders preyed on especially pipits & sky larks etc We saw odd foxes on the moor who raided any snares we had on old fences but we left (did not tell local sheep farmers we left Reynard – the Red fellows)) the foxes because they help to keep down young rabs & Hares and ground vermin mice, voles etc that chewed young trees.

We were allowed to keep what we caught and shot as an incentative (no overtime allowed) so we ran some of the kill to Mac Fisheries shops in Gourock, Paisley in my old van and got 1 shilling for Hares (not gutted) for soup makers

Rabbit fencing around plantation
Photo: Andrew Tittensor

and 2/6d per pair rabbits. This was big money to us being on basic pay about £21 in those days. (Happy poor days).

Sorry bad writing and spelling left school at 14 and Ive never looked back . . . my apologice for unruley writing and Bad spelling etc. Was no good at school in Lancs. Cheers.

Bill Sutherland neatly summed up why fencing, pest control and ploughing were needed before tree seedlings were planted.

Well, trees can be planted and will grow in fertile soil, on grass. But if you plant trees on heather and peat, they just, they go into 'check', they say. And as I've explained, they'll just stay the size they were. If you plant them on a ploughed furrow, then the tree gets, it's free-rooting, it's, it's got no competition...for the first year or two. And it will grow, it would grow to, it would grow six inches in the first year, a foot in the second year, and then go on at eighteen inches a year. And then it very quickly becomes established. Provided the rabbits don't eat it, or the deer don't come in and eat it, and that sort of thing. These are the, these are the main hazards. Or sheep. Well we, we have to fence the area pretty carefully against sheep. And add, add netting against rabbits if, if rabbits are there. Also hares can be very troublesome.

Ploughing and Draining

Land for planting trees, like land for planting wheat or potatoes, needs preparation. Wet land, like the Whitelee Plateau was also drained, or the young trees would go into 'check'. Pauline Cairns asked **Iain Hamilton**,

Dae ye remember or did ye hear what the Forestry Commission did wi the land at the start?

'How dae ye mean? Wi the jungle busters? Ploughin and that? Och aye, Ah used tae see it.

Jungle busters: the name given to the Forestry Commission's huge tractors and ploughs used to prepare the moorland for draining and tree-planting.

How were the problems of ploughing and draining the difficult ground approached?

Ploughing produced 'ridges and furrows' like farm ploughing, but over much bigger areas than a farm field. **Fred Cowie**, a head forester at Whitelee Forest, wrote,

Ploughing was generally straight up and down the hill with drains at intervals to prevent scouring and water running on to rides, roads, etc'. He also noted that, 'There was a planting programme of about 400 acres per annum.

95

Drains were ploughed at right-angles to the ridge and furrow, to take away water from a large area. Draining was carried out by hand-digging, by ploughing an extra-big furrow, or with a mechanical digger, such as a 'Backacter'. Wide, deep, open-topped drains were produced, which led water into natural waterways. There were two types of drains, as explained by Brian Speirs, expert hand-drainer. 'Cross-drains' were deeper than the ploughed furrows, but shallower than the main drains, while 'Main-drains' were much bigger: 3 feet deep and 3–4 feet wide at the top, 1 foot wide at the bottom. Vehicles carrying out drainage usually had caterpillar tracks or very large wheels covered by a cage to spread the load: this was necessary to prevent heavy machinery sinking into the peat.

Roy Harvey was Ploughing Forester for the Forestry Commission's West Conservancy when land on the Whitelee Plateau was bought. It was his job to survey newly acquired lands, work out the ploughing pattern, choose the machinery and keep an eye on things. He hand-wrote his contribution, explaining how it was done at Whitelee.

Ploughing

The cultivation programme virtually followed the acquisitions. The drier areas were cultivated by using single-furrow 'Clark' (S 45) ploughs pulled by BTD 8 crawler tractors on standard width tracks. As we progressed we encountered soft ground conditions & moved to double-furrow ploughs (D45) to reduce the chance of breaking through the surface when turning at the end of the furrows & reducing the number of runs across the soft conditions.

In the very, very wet & soft conditions a very light tractor the TD500, which had wooden slatted tracks which moved across the bogs by squeezing the surface of the bog between the slats without breaking it was employed. The plough used was doubled furrowed & the furrows were 18 inches (45 cm) deep.

The straight furrows changed into bendy furrows – this facilitated a gentle turn at the end of each furrow & again to avoid cutting up of the surface.

The furrows for planting were approximately 6ft – 2m. apart, & trees were planted into steps cut into the furrow, or on top of the furrow.

Draining

Because the area was very wet drainage was required. This was carried out by using Bowen 60 tractors. These were tracked machines with longer tracks than the cultivation machines & the tracks were wider (30 inches). The tractors were used in tandem pulling & large single-furrow Clark plough (S90) producing a drain 3 feet deep 12 inches wide in the bottom & 3 feet wide at the top. The drains crossed the cultivation furrows, which ran up & down the slopes if any, at an angle to get a fall. In the very wet areas it meant machines moving one at a time – i.e. the front tractor moving 30-40 yds along the drain line across the cultivation furrows then attaching the hydraulic winch rope to the 2nd tractor & assisting him to move up close to the first machine. The second machine then winched the plough along to meet up with it. This was a very slow & arduous operation to keep the outfit above ground. In places where the ploughs could not operate, a Ford Backacter tractor with 4 flotation tyres i.e. 3 ft wide & inflated to a low 6 lbs per sq. inch. In the very wet area this machine would be $^1/_4$ – $^1/_2$ submerged in water at times &

Table 5: Large Machinery Used

FOR CULTIVATION

Drier Areas BTD8 Crawler Tractor with standard-width tracks	Pulling: Clark Parkgate S45* plough; shallow furrow	Working in twos for safety
Softer Areas BTD8 Crawler Tractor with standard or extended-width tracks	Pulling: Clark Parkgate D45* and D60* plough; deeper furrow	Working in twos for safety
Very Wet And Soft Conditions International TD500 Tractor with wooden, slatted tracks	Pulling: Clark Parkgate D45* and D60* plough; deeper furrow	Working in twos for safety

FOR DRAINING

Bowen 60 Crawler Tractor with long and 30" wide tracks	Pulling: Clark Parkgate Deep-Draining S90* plough (alias 'Humpy')	Working joined in tandem
Ford Backacter Digger with 4 wide Flotation tyres, pressure 6lb per sq. in.	With: Bucket or other scoop attachment	Singly
Priestman Cub Digger working on three wooden mats	With: Bucket on side dragline	Singly (Banksman present)
Balloon-Tyred Marshall	No information given	
Wooden Mats 14ft x 6ft	Each Mat made of several 'railway sleeper' sized pieces of wood bolted together	Used in threes

FOR DEBOGGING

Long and Wide Ferguson County (crawler) Tractor**	With: Mechanical Winch	Winch out ('De-Bog') BTD8 and plough
Atlas Digger working on three Wooden Mats	With: Bucket or Scoop	Dig drain behind sunken BTD8

FOR OTHER FUNCTIONS

Vans, Land Rover	-	Carry personnel, tools and materials
Bombardier or 'Muskeg' with rubber tracks	Fitted with mesh panniers	Transport tree seedlings, fertiliser and fencing
Tarpaulin tent 15x5ft	-	Wet-weather shelter
Quad bike	-	Carry spraying equipment to work site
Big trailer	-	Carry containers of water to work site
Very heavy trailer	-	Permanently loaded with fire-fighting equipment (ready for use)

*   S = Single-Mouldboard Plough (single furrow)   * D = Double-Mouldboard Plough double furrow)   * 45, 60, 90 = depth of furrow in centimetres
**   The only tractor with a mechanical winch: all others had hydraulic winches | Source of data: Roy Harvey, Fred Cowie, Brian Speirs, Robbie Allan

the driver would have to stay put until he reached firmer ground usually at the end of the drain line.

Within a few days of creating the drains either by plough or digger the softness of the ground reduced the depth & width of the drain by half.

As ploughing forester for West Conservancy I was responsible for equipment & techniques of dealing with all sites. This area was particularly difficult because of the very soft conditions of parts of the forest.

What Roy Harvey described was a slow, arduous, difficult, dangerous process out on the moorlands. Table 4 lists some of the men who did this work. Table 5 sets out the machinery described by Roy Harvey and other workers of Whitelee Forest.

Tom Grant remembered only too well the very first ploughing in the new Whitelee Forest, on High Hapton in the very cold winter of 1961–1962.

Well at the start it wis seen… they started a Haptone Ah'm no gaunnae go oot an see a car… tryin tae ploo that… the tract[or] wis taen tae Haptone… the auld… he wis sittin aboot [19]61 mibbe 62 he wis sittin auld Major tractor… ken whit that is? An auld Ford Major tractor [indistinct] Sittin an half frozen wi a great big jaiket oan, sittin plooin away, could hardly get aff the tract[or] it wis that bluidy cauld (laughs) *he wis juist aboot frozen tae the sait* (laughs) *bit he worked awa there.*

The poor tractor driver who was frozen to the seat while ploughing the first patch of ground for Whitelee Forest in the very cold winter of 1961–1962, was Dan Blair.

Robert Allan is a Doric-speaking Aberdonian whose love in the 1970s and 1980s was tractor-driving on the moorlands of Scotland. He started at Whitelee Forest in 1970, a year after starting work with the Forestry Commission. Over the years, he ploughed right across the Plateau, from Croilburn in the west to Ardochrig above East Kilbride and Caldergreen near Strathaven. He spent weekdays in a caravan and went home to Lochgilphead at the weekends, although Mrs Allan and the family sometimes came to Whitelee.

Robbie Allan described in detail the intricacies of ploughing and draining the Whitelee Plateau. At first, a single-furrow plough was used, but then the Forestry Commission bought double-furrow ploughs which had been designed by Scottish firms.

Tractor drivers Robbie Allan (left) and Hugh Davidson on their caterpillar-tracked tractors, Croilburn 1970s   Photo: Robert Allan

Robbie: *And at that time we wis ploughin wi e single furr plough, y'know, it juist-, wis e old fashioned single furr plough, and it wis the, the ones wi the, the wire rope, used ti hiv ti put the winch in an the wire rope hooked up the plough ye see an awye ye went, an then of course later on when we got started there they come oot wi the modren hydraulic plough, an of course it wis, ye juist (short whistle) pulled the lever an the plough went up, an ploughed the . . .*

Ruth: Right, so, for people like me who don't understand tractors very well, to start with you had a plough on a, on a wire, on the end of a wire, pulling it?

A wire rope, ay, an the, the, the plough, an there wis a, a winch on the back o the tractor, an a, an a winch rope come out an went through the plough an then you pulled it t'click it up when ye wis travellin empty an then when ye wint e plough down, ye'd ti release the brake [bumps something] *the, the, the, oh,*

Sorry.

[ti] release the brake o the the the winch an the plough fell down an that wis you off. An then …

And is this plough like, um, an agricultural plough, did it look similar, or,

No, much bigger, much bigger,

No, right,

It wis really quite big, ye know, and, eh… but, nineteen-seventy ah would've said when the hydraulic powereds come oot, that wis the first I seen o't, wis nineteen-seventy…

And what does that mean, how is that different?

Well, it wis, eh, the same as whit the modern tractors is now, all hydraulics, an, eh, ye juist pulled a lever lik that an it juist wis a hose an the hydraulic goes in an there's ram in the plough - "ps" - up it wint, it wis so much easier

So was that easier – easier

Oh! a lot easier, a lot easier, yeh. So that wis, eh, wis – but at didna come in – ay we ploughed the single furr plough fir all o Croilburn an the first at we hid the double-throw plough, whit ye see t-, now,

Yes.

The first that I seen it is, we did it up at High Overmuir, right?

The Forestry Commission had used double-furrow ploughs made by Cuthbertsons of Biggar, but in Mr Allan's time at Whitelee Forest, the ploughs were all made by the firm of Clarks near Dumfries.

Robbie Allan explained that the reason for the change from single-furrow to double-furrow ploughs was to encourage the little trees to grow better roots.

It's, ay, this wis the idea wis to, t' throw it out more becuis, eh, I think probably one o the reasons, there might hae been a few reasons, but, when we did the single p-, furr, y'know, ye can imagine, there wis only a bit o ground, wisna much wider than that, an it sat the top, lik is, right?, so ye'd to walk along an plant e trees. Now I think they were findin at when e trees got up y'know they were blowin down a wee bit more becuis ye know the roots ye know, there wis a ye can imagine this wis, where we furred

oot so it wisna too good so but doin it the ither way ye wis splittin it a lot further so the trees hid a, a much more substantial bit o ground and, eh, I remember the bloke speakin aboot releasin the nutrents in the ground an aa this kin o stuff so it wis quite technical y'know.

Two tractors in tandem pulling a Parkgate 'Arched Beam' or 'Humpy' plough with a 'Single-throw' mouldboard, Whitelee 1976
Photo: Courtesy Norman Davidson, Forestry Commission

The 'Humpy Plough' was used for ploughing the very soft ground of Craigendunton. But it needed two tractors in tandem – and an unbelievable scenario - to pull it through the soft ground.

Robbie: *I remember iss, iss wis a terrible soft bit up here…It wis terrible soft and we* [disturbance] *drained all that wi the Humpy Plough. Whit they call the Humpy Plough.*

Ruth: What's that?

Now, it wis a drainin plough, an honest t' god, you could walk underneath it wis so big, it wis that big, an it took two tractors to work it, ye know, an, eh, I hid it, I hid e plough at e back o me, an en there wis a bloke – no – Iain Kennedy hid e plough at e back o him an I used ti g' away – I could g' away down t' at house an let the winch rope go as far out as at an I would juist give him a wee wave…

Ay, an then I could winch him straight inti me so he could come straight throu the soft bits an then I would let her…, eh, let the, the, winch off again an I'd gae away out again an sit there an then look [unclear words] oh it wis very difficult…

So you had two tractors one behind the other an the second one had the plough?

E second one hid e plough. I hiv seen it so soft thit the secont tractor hid to un-hitch off the plough an we 'id to move everyhin separate, it wis so soft, t'know, so, an that wis one o, the, the worst places r wis.

Accidents happened sometimes. There were no radios used in Whitelee Forest at that time (and no mobile phones!). If forest workers had an accident, there was no help at hand and injured men had to walk, or to drive their colleague in a tractor cab, several miles from the Plateau top to the nearest house in order to get an ambulance.

But there were good times too. One day, Robbie Allan was ploughing high up at 330m on Crook Hill, on the boundary between Ayrshire and Renfrewshire. He remembered with amusement that the forester came along to check things out.

Robbie: *An I could never plough, eh, a duck's nest. I juist could'na do it. An I, I got t' the stage where I could, you know if a bird lifted, y'know, it depends what kinna bird, I could normally git him-, I would git out an hiv a look, ye see, an I wid pit a pin in wi a, a wee flag in it an I would lift the plough an go roun aboot wi't raised, [tickled] an Bill Meadows come up one day an he says,* **"Whit's aa this bloody flags aa ower the (place)",** *there must've been aboot twenty y' know, it wis birds' nests, an I juist couldnae do it, ye know.*

An it, that wis e first time that a'd seen a peeweep buildin a nest on in ma ploughin, right? becuis e peeweeps always built e nest on the, in the, in the fields. Now a horse wid never stand on a peeweep's nest, right? An, the, the, the farmer or ploughman wid go round about it, e same as I did y'see? But when the old tractor come in it juist kept gaun over it an of course wi the peeweep, he wis gettin a wee bit pushed (a)side . . .

A peewit nest and eggs like the many saved from ploughing by Robbie Allan who marked them with flags
Photo: : Jim Loudoun 2004

Eh. So that wis Bill Meadows there aboot the, that . . .

Ruth: Criticising your care for wildlife. (Laughs)

Tractor drivers were on the look out for remains in the peat, but Robbie Allan found only one thing. He was on Croilburn land, high up on Rough Hill, when he ploughed up what he thought was the plane of Rudolf Hess.

Robbie: *This where, I wid say juist in here, where I picked up, e, eh, a plane.*

Ruth: A plane?

A plane, ay. And, eh, there's a wee story to that too becuis juist two 'r three month after we hid, eh, a'd din that, ah wis speakin ti a bloke in Newtonmore and, eh, he could tell me who the pilot wis, when the date o that plane went down an everythin, y'know. [An] a've still got a bit o that plane in the house here somewhere, ay.

I mean you ploughed and a chunk of plane came out of the ground?

Well it wis peat, it wis peat, ye see, an it, an, an, an, the plough caught suming an it come up, an ah thought, Whit's that? an ah went out t' hiv a look, ye see, at'-, bluidy hell, it must be a bit of a plane, so a started ti kinna dig

100

aboot an ah got quite a lot o the plane, so that where hit wis, wis there – becuis I thought that, when I ploughed it up, I thought I'd got Adolf Hess's plane, ye see, an when I come back to the farmer at night I says, Hey, I've ploughed up Adolf Hess's plane, an he says, No, he says, ye hivnae ploughed hit up, he says, He, eh, landed away across – it wid a been away across this area somewhere.

Right. And, eh, he landed intact. Hess's plane landed at Netherton which is the next one down. That's where his plane landed.

The… so anyway, we got this story later on when ah met this bloke an he wis a trainee pilot, and, eh, he'd gone down, and, eh, he wis killed there, so that wis it. So anyway, we ploughed that, now that's in…

But, e, funnily enough we never found the ingine o the plane or onyhin, so that's where it is, is in there.

Robbie Allan really enjoyed his time ploughing the moorlands of the Whitelee Plateau and is very proud of the quality of his work.

I like t' think that, ye know, ye made a beautiful job becuis when you looked back an it wis nice an tidy, ye know, t' me I got great satisfaction o that. But, if it wisna right it wis like racin e motor cycles, y'know, when ye come off, I know I hivna done a good race, ye know, an I don't hiv t' be told at a, a, a hivna been very good cos I know, an it wis e same wi ploughin, there wis, I felt I wis very fussy wi ma ploughin, it hid t' look nice, it hid been nice . . .

An, eh (pause) if I hid my life ti live owre again, I wid go back ti plough it. That's e, that's e thing I loved. I wid. Ay. And, eh, becuis of, I got a lot a satisfaction out o that. Mhm.

The Ploughed Landscape

Frank Jackson was training to be a forester when, in the mid-1970s he spent a day at Whitelee Forest with a fellow student to study ploughing. He vividly remembers that day.

Frank: *And, I've got to say at that stage Whitelee looked extraordinarily different to what it is today, and, the*

ploughing furrows were enormous, stretching for miles, or it seemed like at that stage anyway, so…

It was a nice day when we were down there, it was nice and sunny (laughter) so I might have got the wrong impression. But, it was flat moorland basically, it seemed to stretch for miles and miles. With odd grouse flying over et cetera. So it was featureless almost.

And I think people who live in that area will probably agree, certainly if they're living there on a wet day and it's featureless and the winds blasting in from the west with nothing to stop it, then yes. And so, it was a flat landscape, it was moorland, and as I said, the ploughing furrows like, seemed to stretch like ribbons for one black mile after one black mile. So, it was quite it was inspiring it was quite awe-inspiring in the amount of ploughing that was going on and what they were doing, and, the previous exercises where the trees had been established and they were growing, et cetera et cetera. But, it wasn't terribly awe-inspiring I must admit as landscape goes.

A landscape of double-furrow ploughing in Kielder Forest 1950s
Photo: : Courtesy Roy Harvey, Forestry Commission

Ruth: From a technical point of view, or from a landscape point of view?

From a landscape point of view.

Yes. And what about from a technical point of view?

Technical point of view, it was, it was very good. The techniques they were adopting and the people that were doing it were first class.

And, and the drains, you learnt a lot about ploughing and the drains, the drainage needed on the site?

We, we certainly did. It was... On reflection it was pretty straightforward, because there wasn't an awful lot of impediments like sort of, heavy boulders et cetera et cetera, because it was ribbons of peat that were being dug out, in the main. You did get your crops of mineral soil et cetera et cetera, but, they were more in the west than what there were in the areas of the east where we were looking at, at that stage, because the west areas had all been ploughed and planted previously to that. And so, yes we, we learnt quite a bit.

Bogging and Debogging

Tractor drivers had great difficulty ploughing the wetter 'sinks' or 'hags' of peat and the drivers had to be adept at jumping out of their cabs when they started disappearing beneath the peat surface! There were several instances, on both Whitelee Forest and adjoining private afforestation land, of tractors and ploughs becoming bogged down out of sight. Getting the machinery out was a long and expensive task. They were occasions of hard work for the men brought in to 'debog' the tractors. And they were probably occasions of money-loss for the Forestry Commission: trained men and special machinery were brought from Aberfoyle on these occasions and debogging could take weeks or months.

But these boggings and deboggings were occasions of great interest and hilarity in the locality, which are etched into the memories of many people.

Janet Grant remembered three sinking incidents, the first because she had only recently got married and moved to Brocklees. She read out what she and **Tom Grant** had written about it.

BDT8 tractor and Clark's Parkgate plough half-submerged in Darvel Moss 1970; 24 hours later they had completely disappeared
Photo: Courtesy Roy Harvey, Forestry Commission

Janet: *. . . three tractors were stuck in one place in Darvel Moss on the first of December 1970. Now, two tractors pulled one plough Tom called it 'shadowing' where there was one tractor hooked on to the second tractor with the plough behind. He called it shadowing. Now another tractor was brought in to rescue the three tractors and before it reached the three tractors that tractor got stuck. A tractor from Economic Forestry was brought in now the Forestry Commission must have go a loan of a tractor from Economic Forestry to pull out number four. Rescued number four then number three went to rescue number [hesitates] then number four went to rescue number three but it couldn't move the other two. The drivers could not move these two either and the head of Contracting Division a Mr Low came down. He was brought in to try and pull out the two tractors. The two original tractors went down out of sight because they didn't unhook the plough. Tom said that the plough was still hooked to the second tractor. A drag line and a slurry pump was to be brought in and a trench was dug six hundred yards from the gully but they found they were still on the moss. Then, emm, the workers dug all round the tractors to connect wires to winch the tractors out and they winched the tractors about six hundred yards till the tractors reached* the hard ground and then they reappeared to the surface. Tom stated that if they had cut the plough off the tractors would probably have got out on their own. He stated that this took about three months, ahh, the two tractors approximately seven thousand pounds worth were three months old when they came to work at the Forestry at Whitelee. Ahhh, Tom said that it probably cost more to bring them out than the tractors were worth.

Never heard of the final cost of recovery. The following year two International tractors were brought in from Canada supposedly these tractors were unsinkable but one sunk in the same hole and this took approximately ten days – a week to ten days – to recover.

Hugh Hendry's memories of another incident were written down.

The Day the Tractor got Stuck in the Moss

. . . But on one particular occasion, the tractor went right down until the roof of the cab was level with the ground surface! The tractors were not linked that day. The other tractor driver helped out the driver of the sinking tractor from his cab. The Forestry Commission almost decided to leave it there. But in the end, it brought in a digger, and made two platforms of railway sleepers on the ground. The digger was placed on the platform and a second platform of sleepers was placed on the ground in front of it. The digger then moved forward onto the second platform. The first platform was then moved in front of the second one and the process was repeated until the digger reached the sunken tractor.

On its journey across the Moss towards the sunken tractor, the digger dug a very wide ditch, maybe several metres wide, and of unknown depth in an attempt to drain the area of the sunken tractor.

The sunken tractor was pulled out along this ditch and then to the edge of the Forest, through a narrow unplanted FC area. The sunken tractor arrived at the edge of the Forest, opposite the entrance to Low Carlingcraig farm, on the 'Five Mile Road'. A Low Loader was waiting on the track leading to Low Carlingcraig Farm. Metal cables were

taken from the Low Loader and back across the Five Mile Road, where they were attached to the tractor that had been sunk. While the metal cables were stretched across the road, Margaret Russell came along, driving from Long Green farm. She did not see the cables and hit them . . . ! Her car was thrown up into the air. She was OK!!!

Fred Cowie remembered it too, as he had a phone call from an irate husband that evening.

A tractor got bogged down on Wallacegill Muir, and when they got it out, they took it to the roadside. The low-loader carrier was parked down a track opposite, and they stretched the cables from the carrier across the road and onto the tractor, in order to haul it onto the carrier. That was done and the sunken tractor was taken away to be cleaned. But that evening, [I] had a phone call from Tom Russell at Long Green Farm, "Hey, you've lifted the roof off my wife's car".

Margaret Russell had been driving along that road and not seen the hawsers, which had sliced through her car just under the roof, horizontally. She was OK, luckily. The Forestry Commission paid for the repairs.

It took two tractors to get that one tractor out of the moss.

Looking south-west to Meadowhead from Flow Moss where a tractor and plough have completely sunk while attempting to drain the peat 1976
Photo: Courtesy Norman Davidson, Forestry Commission

From his farm at East Hookhead, **Jim Kennedy** saw and experienced several sinkings on Moss Mulloch, on both Forestry Commission and private forest land. First, a digger, making forestry drains, became sunk, even though it was working from large wooden 'mats' made from four tree-trunks bolted together. He told how the land was going up and down in waves.

When these, these. Particularly the diggers that wis workin. It wis unbelievable. An it takes a bit o believin. But ah can assure you it wis right. The land wis gaun up an down anyhing tae twelve tae fifteen inches. It wis gaun up an down, an also goin that way. The machine wis rockin lik that when it wis, when it wis workin. When it [went] doun lik that, a mean. Mean, like the, the ground kept … movin lik this.

The one that ah wis tellin ye about got stuck for a long time [puttin a]…after a. Anither one that come back in after that one. Tae do a, a job sumthin the same. He wis workin with what they cau'd mats. D- dae ye know what ah mean? Where they hud. They hud about, eh. Oa-gh, five or six set of four trees wi long bolts out through them. Y'know, the rowe o four trees. And eh. He got ontae the. He put these down an got ontae the top o them. An as he moved forward, he liftit the one wi his machine an brought it round and reversed ontae it. He kept movin them round lik that. Now the ground got so soft where he wis diggin that if he really stretched his arm* as far out as possible to dump the stuff that he wis diggin out well away because if he juist done lik that, put it near the side, it would push it back in. So he wis puttin it right as far out lik that, and wuth him huvin his arm away out lik this, [Jim demonstrates digger cowping] it went, it went lik that and ye see, these'll – these machines. Ye'll never move-, they're, the'rs – absolutely solid, if they're sittin goin straight forward. But they slide sideways. * [digger arm]

An that slid off… When he pit his arm lik that, wi the weight an that, it went down lik that an slid off the side, an that wis when he got stuck. He slid off the mat. Slid off sideways.

One of the sunken machines, despite several attempts to rescue it, lay in the peat for nearly two years before someone came along to finally debog it. That someone was none other than Robbie Allan, who had by now left the Forestry Commission and was working for a private contractor.

Bryan Simpson, an experienced naturalist, took regular forays onto the Whitelee Plateau. In early 1970, he noticed that some of the northern moors had been ploughed and wrote a brief comment in his field-notes.

Headed, finally, for the be-cairned Drumduff Hill and noted ploughing in the area below. Probably forestry . . . On the way over a Golden Plover piped plaintively from a tussock, this being one of several I disturbed on the heights.

The green of the Sphagnum pods fair glowed in the sunlight making a vivid and arresting sight in the general somberness of these muirs. Heading back towards Cleughearn by Corse Hill I had the most extraordinary luck, almost plonking a foot on the nest of a Whaup, 4 lovely eggs nestling in a depression on a tussock – the second in donkey's ages (!) A little further on a Pipit shot out of a ditch and lo' there on the face tucked away as neat as ninepence was its eggfull nest made with, primarily, dry bent* leaves'.

* ['bent' is a type of grass, see Appendix 2]

Comment

Removing the stock, fencing, ploughing and draining took place on every parcel of land on the Whitelee Plateau as it was bought. These were labour-intensive, time-consuming and needed many skills, as their operators have described.

These processes produced huge changes on the Whitelee Plateau in a short space of time. There were physical changes, to the land surface, hydrology, and peat or mineral soil caused by ploughing and draining. The same factors, as well as pest control, produced immediate ecological changes. The result of all the pre-planting processes was immediately visible (as Frank Jackson noted) as landscape change to the Whitelee Plateau. In later chapters, the people who saw and experienced these massive changes will describe what they observed.

CHAPTER 9

Planting Millions of Trees

High Hapton: the First Block of Forest

The first forester, George Caird, had his lodgings and office in the farmhouse of Laigh Hapton. **Tom Grant** remembers him and the first two Forestry Commission squad workers starting work at High Hapton in winter of 1961 to 1962.

Young Sitka Spruce on Moss Mulloch
Photo: Ruth Tittensor

Noo! it didnae boather us it didnae make onie difference tae us…they employed two youths Ah wid say at New Mills*, they walked up started tae do the work walked up tae Haptone there for half past seven the finished at half past four at night they had tae walk back tae New Mills*. They wouldnae do that noo, the widnae be able tae dae it, three mile that wis juist the, the, the way they did it.

* [the town of Newmilns]

But that [indistinct name] he worked right up tae the finish up there… he wis workin tae he wis 60 maybe mair. But he started when he left the school, ken. He wis the longest servin employee so he wis.

O we wid yes, George Cairns. Did ye ever get intae contact wi him? He wis the forester then.

Aye but he wis at the forestry at Haptone. He stayed there an it wis him that started it he got the ball rolling that wis their agent here. But no! The Forestry never actually boathered us when they started at Haptone they fenced it off and then we hid two days shooting either side …we got two days shootin (laughs) an then they planted it …but naw! It never boathered us as such.

The two youths were Rex Boland, the very first squad member, and Brian Speirs, who was the longest-serving squad worker mentioned by Tom Grant.

This is how **Brian Speirs** remembers starting work for the Forestry Commission in the new Whitelee Forest, opening up the drain ends to connect the ploughed cross-drains to the main-drain.

Ruth: Mr Speirs, you've said that you moved from working in the Lanfine Estate to working with the

Forestry Commission at Whitelee Forest. Can you remember your first day of work in Whitelee Forest?

Brian: *It wes e beginnin o January and the first job we got wes draining and it really was cold. It really was cold. It was that cold we asked the forester if it wes aw right ti wear gloves because wur hands were numb. But that was the first job we had to do.*

Right and um working on a – on a cold day without gloves in January, did you wonder whether you'd made the right decision to change jobs?

No. No no. It wes just uncomfortable. That wes all.

Right yes and can you explain um what tools or machinery you were using and what sort of drains, why you had to carry out draining.

The drains – the forestry tractors were ploughing. And they would plough a drain or – every six feet up and down hill. And the idea o this wes to plant the trees on the furra that were throughout. But every so often they pulled a deeper drain across the way. An this wes to take the water – rather than having it comin all the way down hill – this was tae take the water away from it. An the job o draining at the time wes to go along thur deep drains. An make sure that thur other drains were free of turf an that kind o thing to make sure the water did run in ti them an hit wes clear as well, that was the idea.

Right so this was before the trees were planted, or...

This was before they were planted. Yes. Yes.

107

And the – the tractors were ploughing up what had been the – the moors that you used to visit birdwatching?

Yes yes.

Right, how – how did you feel about – about that, uh that big change from moor to ploughed land?

Well at the time I didn't truly think too much about it. Because we started – the first operation wes aboot a hundred an twenty acres. Done. But there was plenty more acres. That hadn't been touched. So it didnae really bother me at the time.

Yeh, right, and you worked – when you worked for the Forestry Commission um, and you started off with this draining work on the newly ploughed land, um, how many of you were there working?

Two.

Oh just two . . . Were there other people – was this all that Forestry Commission employed at the time, or were there others doing other things?

That wes all employed at the time.

Oh I see right right, um and how far away was your work from your home at that time, did you have far to go?

'Bout five miles.

So how did you get there?

Pushbike.

Some Whitelee Squad's tools, from left to right, Howk, Brashing Saw, Rutter, Bottoming Shovel
Photo: Ruth Tittensor

Right (laughs). Right um and once you reached the forest, did you have to go further then, or, or, that was it was it, the five miles?

Initially it wes only yards further. But as years went on it got further. And further but initially it wes only yards. It wes only yards

Yes (laughing). And can you remember whereabouts in Whitelee Forest it was that you started work?

Yes it was High Haptone. Which was, at that time wes a ruin.

The First Tree Planted

Rex Boland and Brian Speirs went on hand draining for two months, and then – **the first tree of Whitelee Forest was planted!**

Ruth: Right, um, and how soon after – of clearing the drains from the ploughed land – how soon after that did the Forestry Commission start actually planting the trees?

Brian: *Roughly 'bout March. Early Spring.*

So did you plant the first tree?

No, the second tree.

The second (amused) oh right so who planted the first tree?

The forester at the time. George Caird.

Right were you um would you have liked to have planted the first tree?

No it didn't really bother me. No, no I was quite happy to be involved. In the first planting, but no necessarily the first tree.

Was there a little ceremony of any kind, or...

No.

108

You just came out and planted it?

Yes.

Right so at that time your main tasks were um draining and planting the young trees, is that right?

Yes that's right.

Mhm was it, er, a hard – hard work and a long day?

It was reasonably hard work. Mean we started at half past seven in the morning. Til half past four in the afternoon. But wi all the rest o the industries includin factories they went roughly the same hours so. It wasnae too bad. Exceptin (a small laugh, remembering)...

Except in the winter (laughs).

Except in the winter. A lot o the time.

The first plantings which the two young men carried out at High Hapton extended to about 300 acres and were shown as woodland on the next, 1963 edition of the Ordnance Survey one-inch map.

A Young Worker's Account of Life in the Squad

In 1977, at the age of seventeen, **Alexander Fenton** joined the Forestry Commission at Whitelee Forest. He explained how on his first day, he too did hand-draining, just like Brian Speirs.

Alec: *Well, it was ideal, because, all my brothers, my Father was a foreman in the woollen mill in Galston, and all my brothers went from school straight into the mill. (laughter) Which wasn't, well, I mean, that just wasn't for me . . .*

And I got an outside job. So I went in the Forestry Commission. I was, nearly seventeen when I left school. So, I was seventeen and getting this job with the Forestry Commission. You're a young fellow, keen, and you're wanting to, you know, show people that you can work. So...In actual fact my first day, I got picked up, it was the, it was called the Co-op... we had a Co-op [person] at Galston, there was a garage there and it was called the

Brian Speirs demonstrating hand-draining tools   Photo: Ruth Tittensor

Slicing down with the rutter to form the vertical drain side

Digging out the drain with a bottoming shovel

Lifting the 3-pronged howk to....

....pull out the loose vegetation and peat from the drain

Bobbin then. And, I used to get picked up there, and I'd get picked up there in a Land Rover, with the rest of the squad. And we carried on up the Irvine Valley, picked a couple of other guys up, some of the old sweats that had been working in the Forestry Commission for a number of years. And they carried on to High Allerstocks.

*So, of course when they opened the back door, I sprung out, raring to go and do some work, and because it was raining, they all went into a caravan. (laughter) Because it was some, it was to do with the union and stuff, that you didn't work in the rain, which just seemed a bit strange to me you know what I'm saying? So, I had a bit about a week of that, champing at the bit, dying to go and do some work, but the old sweats were saying, "**Oh no, it's looking like there's going to be a shower coming up the valley**". (Laughter)*

But I eventually got the chance to do some work, and, it started off with, it was draining.

A 'Backacter' (Tracked Excavator) makes draining easier
Photo: Forest Research, Technical Development

Ruth: Right, that was the first work you were introduced to. And can you tell us why draining was needed and how you did it?

Well what had happened, I mean when I was, when I came to the Forestry Commission I was sixteen, a lot of it was still being established, a lot of the main block. So there was a lot of new ploughing, and furrows for the trees to be planted on. So, when the machine goes in, the 'Backacter' goes in and the plough goes in, to drain the ground, you've got...

What's a 'back actor'?

Well, it's just a, it's just a big machine that puts the main drain in, to, to drain the water off the plough, the ploughed area. And, what would happen, what would happen was that, a lot of these drains would get blocked, and so, you would have to go and finish the drains off. So you would use a howk, which was like a, it's like a garden fork, but bent at ninety degrees, and that was used to kind of, pick out the sods and stuff. And, we also used a Rutter, if there was a particularly big blockage you would use a Rutter that just looked like a huge big spade. And, you would use that to, to cut through the peat.

So, I mean it wasn't just a bit of silt blocking the drains, it was big, thick stuff that had fallen in?

Aye. Aye it was good... Aye, it was good, for a young boy that was wanting to do a bit of work, there was plenty there . . .

Can you tell us how deep and, sort of how long the drains were?

Oh well the drains, I mean some of the Backacter drains just went on for hundreds of metres. And, I mean some of the block... I mean, you were kept fairly busy all day, basically. You would stop for about half an hour for your piece, but, there was a lot of work involved . . . And, and then, my first wage was £50, which was quite a lot of money then.

And was that, that was one week's money?

That was one week's money.

That's a lot of money, wasn't it?

Yes. And I can always remember my wage after that, which was £48, and for a young boy, that was quite a lot. Because my, my Dad worked night shift, and I bought in my first wage, I gave it to my Mother, and she, she thought, **"That's an awful lot of money, that".** *So she went upstairs and woke him up to show, show him my wage packet. (laughter). Aye, she was, she was pleased, and thought* **"... good grief, there must be more to this forestry work. There's money in them there hills.** *(laughter)* **In amongst the peat".** *Yes.*

Yes. (laughter) Gold somewhere. Mm. Was it piecework?

It was, it was piecework, aye, so... Supposedly the harder you worked, the more you get, so, that was an incentive. And when you're keen, you're that age, you just, you want to impress the old sweats and you want to let them know that you're not a layabout, so, you just get on with it. (laughter) . . .

Jim, Jim Young would show us how to operate the Howk, and... the Rutter and stuff like that. But most of the time, because I was a seven-stone waif... Well, no, not exactly, I was a bit, maybe nine stone. I was just a wee fellow, and...

You... the Rutter was nearly bigger than you were.

Aye, that's right, aye. But I was strong enough, like, to do the work, don't get me wrong, but... Jim was bigger, and he could work the Rutter and I could work the Howk. And we had a system going where we could just battle on at it. So it was good.

Planting Contractors

Willie Malone was a local contractor whose chaps worked in the young Whitelee Forest between 1963 and 1965. **George Young**, a countryman born and brought up in the hills just south of Darvel, worked for Mr Malone in 1965. His memories of his time spent working in the new Whitelee Forest were written as he spoke.

A squad worker with his planting bag walking the ploughed ridges, Whitelee Forest 1976
Photo: Courtesy Norman Davidson Forestry Commission

The area concerned was in that part of Whitelee Forest between Whiteleehill Farm and Pley Moss. . . So in that year, he took a job in Whitelee Forest, an area he already knew well from his childhood and youth. This is how he came to be involved in Whitelee Forest.

Mr Young picked up the rest of the squad at 6.30 am every morning and took them to Whiteleehill Farm in a van. At Whiteleehill Farm, the tree seedlings, 'shrubs' or 'sprigs' were stacked in sacks beside the building. Each worker loaded himself up with enough sprigs for the day's work. They loaded up tree seedlings with "more than you could carry".

'More than you could carry' consisted of "two big bags over the shoulder, and your arms full too".

Two or three days a week, Mr Young, instead of tree-planting all day, left the tree-planters at Whiteleehill, and drove the contractor to West Kilbride. Here there was a massive tree nursery, where the seedlings for Whitelee Forest came from. The contractor's van was "loaded to the gunwhales" with seedlings by the fellows at the nursery. Despite being so full, the van took only enough for 2 or 3 days work at a time! The two men then drove back from

West Kilbride to Whiteleehill Farm, where they put the sacks of tree seedlings out of the van onto the ground. Each sack contained thousands of seedlings. Then the two men got themselves loaded up with seedlings and went off to the planting area to spend the afternoon planting with the rest of the squad. Most of the squad planted all day, every day.

There were 6 to 8 men in the squad – no women. They started work at 7am and finished at 6pm. They each took a piece and a flask, and "just stopped whenever" for their lunch break, not at a set time . . .

The planting area he worked in during 1965 was enormous: from Whiteleehill Farm in the west to Laigh Overmuir in the east and High Overmuir in the north. This could involve a very long and arduous walk to the day's planting site, even before the planting began. Often this meant heaving oneself across the quaking Staàmire Moss and over – or through – the large Staàmire* Burn, an area that is so soft that it was never itself planted! They had to climb up and down the peat hags, over or under fences, across smaller burns and along ridges. Where possible, they walked along, inside the ploughed furrows,

which are 3 feet down from the top of the planting ridges. All this time, they were carrying two very heavy bags and handfuls of tree seedlings. * [Stagmire]

Mr Young reckons he "planted plenty of trees" in 1965. But the working conditions were difficult. It was often wet and cold and it was open to all the elements. This is because the Whitelee Forest area is high up (above 900 feet altitude), with no higher hills or mountains anywhere around, including towards the sea. There was no shelter from existing woods or forest, or from any topographical feature. The squad just had to carry on whatever the weather . . .

They had to provide their own clothes and rain gear. Oilskins are not much use when you are constantly bending up and down and using a spade. Thus they often got wet, and even had to sit on the wet peat to have their piece.

There were good days of course! But when there was a puff of breeze down in the Valley at Darvel, there was an enormous gale on the hill! However, that at least meant that they were not troubled by midges! Neither were they troubled by clegs, because the stock animals had, of course, all been cleared out.

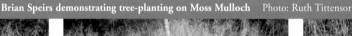

Brian Speirs demonstrating tree-planting on Moss Mulloch   Photo: Ruth Tittensor

Counting 6 paces between planting

Digging notch in the peat with
the Planting Spade

Placing the seedling into the notch at the
same time as heeling it in with his foot

Having arrived at the planting site, the squad would drop their bags to the ground. Then they would pick up enough seedlings to get to the end of the planting line and back. After all, if you got half-way, and ran out of seedlings, you had to walk all the way back to the start of the line, to get more!

To plant a tree seedling, the tool you used a large 'V' shaped planting spade. You put it into the ground in front of you and then put your foot down hard on it to make a deep 'V' shaped slit in the ground. You eased the spade forward somewhat, put the sprig into the slit, roots down, took out the spade and trampled the turf down hard to hold the seedling in the ground securely and keep the turf in place. Planting tree seedlings was not really as hard as carrying the two bags to the planting site!

The tree seedlings were planted on top of ploughed ridges. The ridges and their furrows formed straight lines and had been formed from ploughing. The plough had overturned the original turf or vegetation surface (of grass, heather and rushes), which was now underneath. The peat soil, originally underneath, was now upturned and ready for little trees to be planted in it.

You walked down the line of the planting ridge with your spade and sprigs, planting sprigs every six feet. When you got to the end of the line of the ridge, you climbed down into and across the furrow, then on to the top of the next parallel ridge. Then you went back down the line, parallel to the previous ridge which you'd just planted. That went on all day for 8 hours, except when it was time for your piece.

"You planted thousands of tree seedlings a day. All day"

Later Plantings by the Forest Squad

By the time Alex Fenton was learning to plant trees in the late 1970s, some of the jobs were easier than for George Young. He described his tasks and tools.

Alec: *Well, again it was, it was Sitka spruce which was the main crop, and that was, predominantly was planted. And you can see that in Whitelee, and you see it's wall-to-wall Sitka basically. And the, the plough* was planted*

with Sitka. Now the spacing was around six foot apart; the trees were maybe, somewhere in the region of five, six inches to maybe eight inches. Depending on what nursery they came from. So, you were given a specific area, and again it was a piecework rate, so you would try and go as hard as you could, and... * [the ploughed land]

Ruth: Right. And did you plant them, did you have to dig a hole, and, did you plant them on the, on the furrows, or where did you plant them?

Yes. Yes it was on a furrow. The reason for putting it on the furrow was, is, the plant (Pause) when the grass grew, and how you've got this furrow, the grass wouldn't fall over the tree. It wasn't planted straight into the ground, then you'd tae go and weed it. Although we did have to do weeding as well. Thus, you knew exactly where the planting was; once it was planted, if you had to go, say, and give it some fertiliser, you've got a nice big furrow of wee trees every six foot . . .

Planting Sitka spruce seedlings in another forest, Strone Holdings
Photo: Forestry Commission Picture Library

So it was easy to, easy to follow.

Yes. Mhm. So you could... Maybe one furrow, maybe it was 100 metres, 100 metres up, and 100 metres back down, then just go, just cross over to the next one.

And did you use the same sort of tools?

Yes, just a small Planting Spade, sharpened with a Rasp, just to put a good edge on it for cutting the peat. And, it was usually an 'L' notch you would cut in the peat, to put the plant in. Then you would just kick it, kick the 'L' notch back in... to secure the plant. Try to leave the plant straight up and not lying on its side . . .

Again I worked with Jim Young, Jim Young worked with a Circular Spade. Sharpened up and 'at. The handle maybe about eighteen inches. And you would stick that in and you rotate it, and you pull out a plug, and you put the plant in and you put the plug back in.

That was just what he preferred, was it?

Aye, but that was a bit time-consuming, compared to the planting spade. The most of the contract planters who are good planters just use the small, just looked like a smaller garden spade, sharpened up.

And, the plants, how did they get to Whitelee Forest, and what happened to them?

Well, they were brought, they came from the nurseries. They were grown from Forestry Commission nurseries. And, what would happen is, there'd be an area, the Forester would look at the area, and gauge how many plants he needed for that area that was ploughed. So say if it's a hectare area, that would be somewhere in the region of two and a half thousand to 2,700 trees, and, so he would get that order in. They would come on a lorry, and all the squad would be there to 'shoch' them in. Now that's when you would get the plant, they just came with a string round them, in bundles of 100, and you'd put them into a wet drain, and you would just, say if you'd got 30,000 plants, say, you would put them in a drain, and stop it up, so they wouldn't dry out, so the roots wouldn't dry out.

And you just took from that drain as you needed.

Yes. Yes. And when you went out of a morning, and you picked up bundles of these Sitka spruce seedlings, how many did you pick up at a time, and, were you carrying them in your hands?

Well what would actually happen is, they would bring in a machine, it would be a Muskeg, it's just a tracked vehicle that can go on a hill, and it was specifically designed to carry plants, and carry fencing material out and that sort of thing. So we'd put as many plants into that. And say there was an area that was needing planted, you would put out so many thousands strategically round this given area, so you could, you could walk to these areas, you put the plants out, say 1,000 at a time. And, that's how they did it. But you had a planting bag, and you would put a, normally 100 plants in that at a time. Because if you put too much in you ended up with too much weight, and it kind of slowed you down a bit.

Ruth Tittensor asked **Alexander Fenton** what happened after the trees were planted.

Ruth: Right. Right. OK. And, once the trees started growing, I mean I don't know what time of year you planted them, but they obviously started growing. Were they just left alone, or what happened?

Alec: *Well, the planting usually happened in the 'back end', like autumn time, and into the spring. And you would maybe finish for April with your planting. Because if you start getting later, the plants, the trees would start to bud, start to get growth on them. And they go back a wee bit if they're planted too late. So, getting into spring, into summer, we would, some of the areas that were maybe, previously planted a year or two before, we'd get these areas, and weed round about the tree.*

And how do you do that?

That was just a, a Grass Hook... Or a 'Hyock'. (laughs) That was, that was a name for it, a 'Yock'*, always called it a grass hook. Aye, it's a funny kind of name. But you would, again you would have a Rasp, you'd sharpen it up,* *and you would just pick a line and just do a line of trees.*

* [Transcriber: also 'Heuk']

And was this a sort of circular, like a bill-hook?

Yes, you would just, you would... Aye, a circular Bill-hook. And, you would basically cut the grass round about each tree, to... Because, and, specific areas of Whitelee you get that tall grass, and it's as tall as me just about. And when that that falls over, especially when it's wet and in the winter, it falls over the terrain, it can restrict growth.

Yes. Right. Right. OK. And all these tools you've mentioned, did the Forestry Commission supply them?

Yes, they were all supplied. We had a store, we had a shed at Waterside. In fact, the shed was next to the Forester's house, he had a Forestry Commission house, and, I think eventually he bought that house from the Forestry Commission when they were selling a lot of their housing stock. And that was, that was a shed where we had our stores, be it fencing materials or tools for specific jobs within the Forest.

Yup. Yes. What about clothing?

Clothing, well, you got a pair of black Dunlop wellies, and a set of waterproofs, and that was it. They were just the oilskins, yes.

Right. Right. Right. So anything else? Gloves, you had to provide yourselves then did you?

Well, yes, gloves, and, especially in the planting, in the planting you used to put eh use 'Marigolds'. Aye, because when you're planting, you're planting...

Yes. Kitchen gloves you mean?

Yes, aye. Because, what would happen is, you're putting the tree in the peat, the peat would get up under your nails and in the quick, and, you had a hellish time trying to clean your hands. So, this prevented that.

Right, right. But you had to buy them yourselves...or get them through your wife or your mother.

Aye, just my mother, just borrowed some of hers. (laughter) I'm quite sure she wondered where they went over the years. They would crack a light a bittie anyway.

Three different types of planting spade were described. These, and the other hand tools used by contributors, are listed in Table 6.

Table 6: Hand Tools Used

HAND TOOLS	USE
Rutter	Draining tool: to cut drain sides; to break-up drain blockages
Howk (Hawk or Drain Drag)	Draining: to pull out material from drain and fling onto ground alongside
Bottoming Shovel	Draining: to clear and level the drain bottom
Border Spade	To plant young trees
Semi-circular Planting Spade	To plant young trees
V-shaped Planting Spade ('Glentrool Spade')	To plant young trees
Rasp or File	To sharpen tools
Grass Hook (also Hyock, Yock, Heuk)	1. Heavy 'sickle' shape blade for weeding (cutting) rushes 2. Finer metal blade for weeding grass
Planting Bag	To carry up to 2000 young trees to and on planting site
Pail and Measuring Container	To fertilise small trees by hand
Knapsack Weed-killer Apparatus ('Bagpipes')	To kill weeds around young trees
Oilskins and Wellies	To keep dry
Kitchen Gloves or heavy Gardening Gloves	To keep peat off hands and to protect hands from spruce needles

Source of data: contributors

Other Whitelee Workers

Six to twelve men from Dungavel Prison sometimes came to assist with tree-planting. The warder brought them each day at about 10am and left them there until about 3pm. Ian Peter and Brian Speirs showed them what to do and kept an eye on them. They caused no problems to the regular squad. One summer, two young women spent their college holidays working in Whitelee Forest.

Fertilising and Fencing

The young trees needed fertiliser to encourage their growth on the poor peaty soil. **Brian Speirs** worked at fertilizing the young trees by hand.

> **Ruth:** You've explained how you planted trees in the early years, uh, in the ploughed – on the sides of ploughed furrows and all the details of that, and after you finished planting the, eh, designated area for the year, the next job? What was the next job you did after that?

Brian: *Fertilising the trees.*

And what did that involve, what sort of fertiliser was it, was it liquid…

Rock – it wes rock phosphate.

Rock… what does that look like?

Fine sand.

And did you have bags that you carried it in, how – how did you –how did you apply it to the trees?

Pails. The bags – the fertiliser came in half hundredweight bags. And one ae the local farmers wi his tractor would lay them out along the brakes, an we went along with pails and measurin containers. And carried thur, this pail up an down the rows, juist pittin a circle round each tree wi the – the fertilizer. That's how it wes done.

Right. And were they the sort of pail that you might use in the house and garden or was it bigger than that?

Well it was bigger than that. Mebbe the kind that the farmers would use. And, I mean, they were heavy.

Yes.

They were heavy.

Yes yes, so instead of walking up and down the rows with, uh, bags of little trees you were walking up and down with pails full of rock phosphate and putting little cupfuls. Round the bottom of each tree, right?

That wes it. Again there wes a, a piece work rate. So ye hud tae really move up an down. Quite swiftly. Tae earn some kind o money, so it didnae take too long. A lot quicker than planting the trees. A lot quicker.

Yes yup, and when the fertilising of all the little trees planted that year had been done, what was the next thing you did?

Well, there's a lot o the – the wee trees, if they're planted in a, a kind o grassy bank. We hud tae go along an – an cut the grass round about the trees. Tae give them a chance. That wes a – a job, because there wes a lot o these grassy banks, there wes wee areas scattered everywhere. So we hud tae go along an do that an then move tae the next site. An do the same again. We did that. After that, as I said, there wes fence repairs. Here wes some o that. Then we would go back tae the drains. An do that kind o thing again.

An that would be, by then it would be autumn? Summer?

Autumn.

An when you talk about fencing repairs you said that before the forest there were March Fences up on the moor. Is it other sorts of fences that you were mending – what fences were they?

No, it was the March Fences. Because initially once the stock in that particular area was off. The grass really grew quite lush. So the neighbourin stock. Was really pushin the fences tae get at the fresh grass. So there wes a lot o fence repairs in that respect. An that's why there was a lot of grass that you had to weed round the trees. Cos there wasn't anything grazing.*

* [There were no sheep or cattle to graze the grass so it grew very long]

116

In the very early years, tree seedlings, fertilizer and fencing materials were carried long distances to where they were needed by the squad. **Brian Speirs** explained how it was done later on.

A 'Muskeg' was an important vehicle to carry fertiliser or tree seedlings to the working site, moving over peat without breaking the ground surface
Photo: Forest Research, Technical Development

Brian: *Initially we would get a local farmer there wi a tractor, a farm tractor, to take them as – out to the planting site, eh, but as the, the planting sites got further away, that's where the Muskeg come in, it could go these – wi it being tracks, it could go in the better, wetter ground than what a farm tractor could.*

There was what wes, what we termed anyway, the 'Muskeg', which was a small tracked vehicle. That was brought just to put the trees out, we used to load it wi trees, and that would go round the planting area laying the trees out and occasionally fencing materials if there wes a fence to sort, out the way, it would use that as well.

Eh, some o the ones we had had a great big cab on, eh, with panniers on each side so you could load the trees onto the panniers and you could go in the cab and go out with the trees, eh, the other one hud just the big panniers and aa cab for a driver, and that wes it, so to go out wi these, ye had to walk behind it.

When the trees grew bigger, thicker and prickly, the Forestry Commission hired a helicopter and pilot to spray artificial fertiliser from the air. **Tom and Janet Grant** Remembered it well.

Ruth: So did you ever have em the helicopter em which brought in fertiliser…[all talk at once – end of question indistinct]

Tom and Janet: *Yes, Yes. Every so oaften.*

Ruth: Right. Did they use your land?

Tom: *Yes, sometimes.*

Janet: *They wid bring the bags of man-ure** [equally stressed syllables]. *Well they used to put it down at the grid. On the level and eh the children and I would go down an watch them.*

* [manure used here to mean artificial fertiliser]

Tom: *Aye.*

Janet: *Spreading the manure…They havnae put manure on for many years now …*

Tom: (interrupts) *No for a long while now . . .*

Ruth: But before that they did put it on quite regularly?

Tom: *Yes, yes.*

Janet: *As I say my children would have been fairly young when they did… yer talking about 70s into 80s.*

Tom: *That wis until the trees got up they did it that wey. When they were small they gave every tree an egg cup… but then when the trees got up ye couldnae get walking through them the helicopter did it.*

Removing Heather

The extensive moorlands of the Carrot Estate on the north of the Plateau were bought by the Forestry Commission in the 1970s. As top grouse-moors, they grew excellent heather – good food for the grouse and the sheep which grazed the land.

The sheep had been removed, the moors ploughed and drained in the usual way and Sitka spruce planted. However, the heather continued to grow well, taking up nitrogen from the soil at the expense of the little spruce trees. Spraying nitrogen fertilizer from helicopters, to increase its availability to the trees, had little effect on their growth. So the forest squad was sent up one summer to spray the heather with a herbicide, Glyphosphate ('Round-Up'), to kill it. This herbicide kills heather but the needle-leaved Sitka spruce is unharmed. Spraying by hand was a very difficult job because of the wind on the Carrot moors, and spraying is not permitted in windy conditions. Frequently, the squad got all

Forestry Commission's knapsack kit for spraying weeds round young trees. The Whitelee squad had bright orange, not white neoprene suits
Photo: Forestry Commission Picture Library

their gear (protective suits, knapsack sprayers, spray and a lot of water to dilute it) out of the machinery shed at Waterside on the calm plains below, drove the very full van on minor roads round the edge of Plateau and up the Carrot track to the young plantations. They would then find it was too windy on the Plateau to spray, or they started spraying and the wind got up after half an hour!

Working as a Banksman

Brian Speirs undertook yet another role in the early Whitelee Forest, as a 'Banksman'.

Brian: *Well, it was a job. That if one tractor come in tae do the ploughing, one of us hud tae stay with that tractor – what they called a banksman. In case of accidents. But later on they come in in twos an threes, tractors, an then it wasn't necessary to have a banksman. But initially it was.*

Ruth: And what did the banksman do? (Brian amused) Just stand there?

The first time ah got that job I walked behind the plough. Up tae the top o the row an walked back down an walked back up. An eventually the tractor driver stopped and said **"What are you doin? Wait half way. Ye don't need tae walk. Wait half way".** *An that made sense as long as ah could see him. An that's what it entailed fae then on.*

Yes, so he was ploughing quite long distances was he?

No, three hundred yards? On average?

And an what sot of accidents were they trying to prevent, using a banksman, what – what might happen, or have...

The plough was worked off a winch rope attached tae the back o the tractor. An a lot o the time, that wes a dangerous thing, workin that winch rope, that wad hae been a big accident if it hud broke. Because it wad hae come right back on the driver. That kind o thing.

Yes, it would have whiplashed sort of.

Yes.

Right I see, so, um, does that, does that mean you had, you had a ra- you were in radio contact?

No.

So you – you just had to administer first aid if an accident happened or ...

Well, even at that time we did not have any first aid training so I suppose you made sure the driver was reasonably all right. An then ye – ye ran back tae get the forester.

The Squad Members

Whitelee squad workers Hugh McClymont (left) and Grant Peter early 1980s
Photo: Grant Peter

The squad members whom contributors remember are listed in Table 4 along with the three remembered members of Willie Malone's squad, the tractor and digger drivers, trappers, rangers and other known workers. The Peter family, consisting of father Alf and three of his sons Grant, Ian and Robert, worked for many years in the squad as well as running the Forest Workers' Holding of High Overmuir. Jim Young ran the FWH of Croilburn as well as working in the squad, while the Kennedy father and son, Lawrence Senior and Lawrence Junior, worked in the Forest and ran the Whiteleehill FWH. Brian Speirs ran the holdings of Craigendunton and High Allerstocks (Alderstocks) in

succession. Tom Grant of Brocklees, when a young man, worked for the contractor Willie Malone planting trees, and earned money transporting seedlings and other materials on site with a farm tractor.

The squad was not always complete during the planting years. Forestry was apparently not attractive work because the Job Centre in Kilmarnock is said to have had permanent job vacancies for Whitelee Forest workers. The Forest Workers' Holdings were intended to attract long-stay workers. Three of the five tenants of FWHs came from far afield in southern Scotland. The majority of the squad and contractors stayed close by Whitelee Forest, to its south and west, particularly Darvel. Most tractor and digger drivers were from elsewhere in Scotland, working at Whitelee Forest only when needed.

Working Weather!

Weather was a major factor in the lives of the forest workers and in what work got done. **Brian Speirs** described the difficulties.

When I used to walk up there as a young fella. The worst wes the mist comin down. That wes the worst. Eh, started work up there: a really wet day wes worst. Because ye would go out in the mornin an work an (Coughs) *in that time we hud shelters out on the hill where ye could go in [on] yer lunch break. But ye would go in there an have yer lunch break. But the worst thing ever wes tae put the wet*

Young plantations on Blood Moss behind the Brocklees family, 1981
Photo: Janet Grant

waterproofs back on tae head back out, that wes the worst feelin ever. Definitely. But as I said, apairt from a really wet day eh, that wes it. I mean a mild still day ye used tae get a lot o midges. There were a lot o midges [unclear] an they were bad, they really were bad. Eh, eventually The Forestry supplied ye wi midge cream went in that kind o thing which made a big difference. But prior to that, that wes it, even the – the snow or the frost. It There must o been wes juist one o thae things, ye'd tae gae oot an work in an that wes it.

He then mused on the possibility of nice sunny days.

Brian: *There must o been. But very few. Very few. Because, if it wes dry an sunny ye didn't do much work.*

Till you were really sweating. And at that time, even – a really warm day they hud no shade. The trees wes that wee there wes no shade. So ye wur stuck oot there all that time an there's nuthin ye could do about it. There's nuthin ye can dae. So, as I said, there must hae been some ae the days when the sun wes shinin Wi mebbe a nice wind blowin or sumthin like that. That wad hae really hae been enjoyable, but they were few an far between. (Laughs)

Ruth: (Also laughing) So on the whole the weather – the weather wasn't very helpful.

No. No. No.

Young plantations in winter snow on the slopes of Whiteleehill [with the Isle of Arran in the distance] early 1980s
Photo: Grant Peter

120

One way or another. Yes. If the weather was too bad to work, what did the squad do? I mean, were there any occasions when you could stop work?

It wes a rule . An I don't know whether it was an official rule or not, that if ye were out workin away an it come on rain ye'd to give it three quarters of an hour and if it still rained then ye could go for shelter. But it wes three quarters of an hour at least before you could say **"Right. Shelter"**. *That wes it.*

And what sort of shelter did you have? Was this the shelter you went into at lunchtime?

It used to be, The Forestry supplied, I think it wes three shelters. It wes like round (Pause) *wee huts I suppose ye could call them – that would hold aboot six people and light enough to shift round the hill – once you were finished an area ye could move this wee shelter tae the next area. Eh, as I said, there was one probably for a fair area o ground so it wasnae always feasible tae go to there. It wasnae always feasible. nd eventually the wind got them an – dismantled them.* (Laughs) *They didnae last that long.*

What were they made of?

Aluminium.

Comment

Forest squad and contractors carried out many tasks in the planting phase of Whitelee Forest (1961 to 1992). Several have described in extraordinary detail their daily work, their schedules and tools, and the conditions they encountered. A picture emerges of a group of skilled, practical men, working day-in and day-out: continuous sheer hard work that today we can scarcely imagine. They worked very hard in difficult conditions and for low pay. Without such men there would be neither a Whitelee Forest nor any other modern forest in the Scottish landscape.

For men who also ran Forest Workers' Holdings, there was an 100 acre farm and its stock to see to before and after the daily forestry work and at weekends. Few took the three weeks' unpaid leave allowance for harvest or lambing, as they could not afford to. Wives and families were absolutely vital in running Forest Workers' Holdings. They lived in remote places far from shops, schools and work, and their vicarious part in the development of Whitelee Forest is acknowledged.

Whitelee Forest contains about 10 million trees of which Brian Speirs planted over 1 million, with the Peter family and Jim Young not far behind. The men are proud to have seen their handiwork developing into a new forest, as summarised by **George Young**.

"It is good to know that I was at the instigation of that"

CHAPTER 10

'This Great Curtain Came up from the Ground'

Outside Attitudes to the Growing Forest

From his home nearby, Richard Roberts noticed Whitelee Forest starting to grow both upwards and in area.

Yes, I, I think, well I think the, as the ehm Whitelee, the, the earlier plantings of Whitelee... began to mature... I became aware of, quite a change. This was visible to a degree, travelling south on the A77. From, from Glasgow, as one approached the Eaglesham Road end, you could look across. And suddenly these... Well at that distance I assumed they were Sitkas. They certainly... it was not Abies*. And ehm, it almost seemed like this great curtain came up... from, from the ground.   *[Fir trees]

And ehm, I must say, that's when I started having er, second thoughts about the utility of the Forestry Commission and its ideals.

Being a foot explorer, **Bryan Simpson** had difficulties actually traversing the new Forest in his quests for plant and animal life. He explained to Ruth Tittensor how he felt about the changing landscape.

Ruth: So, can you remember anything about the first ploughing, did you see tractors ploughing? Huge furrows appearing?

Bryan: *Yes.*

Young plantations of Sitka spruce on Loch Hill; the heather expanse is Flow Moss, Lochgoin farm hidden by the tree clump 1980s
Photo: Brian Speirs

What did you feel about all that?

Well, I... It's hard to remember how I felt about it, but... I found them interesting actually, because, what happens is, in the early stages you often, you often used to get large concentrations of various birds associated with these things. And you used to get moor owls, short-eared owls, more often than not if you cut through these young plantations, very young ones . . . but they were terrible places to walk across, because they were all ridged and furrowed. And they were absolutely murder to walk over. But in some cases, if you didn't walk over them then you had a long detour to get round them you know.

But, I think probably I was a bit, I don't know, a bit taken aback perhaps by the extent of these things. I saw the first ones, the ploughings then, I thought, that was quite a good, because it struck me as a very bleak spot. And I thought, well these trees, although they're conifers and they're all going to be spruce, it should make a difference to the landscape you know.

So, I don't think I was too negative about it actually. I thought, well... I don't think then I fully realised, in fact I'm quite sure I didn't fully realise, the extent of the Whitelee Forest, what it was going to be eventually you know. That it was going to stretch for miles and miles and cover nearly all the hill country that I used to walk on. I think I might have been a little less sanguine about it if I'd realised the extent of it you know. Losing all this peat bog.

And **David Findlay** remembered as the Forest grew into a wall of trees.

Yeh, ah was, eh, first of all ah can remember wanderin throu it when it wis tiny wee trees an then the trees got bigger as the years went on, eh, an they got bigger an bigger an – at one stage it wis really pretty because at one, they plantit the trees at different rates an one right hand side there wis big trees an then in the middle there wis a lot a little trees an there wis like valleys an curves an it looked quite, quite pretty, . . .

Sitka spruce planted close to the Little Calder
Photo: Ruth Tittensor

Sitka spruce turning brown on the quaking bog of Moss Mulloch
Photo: Ruth Tittensor

But now it's just thirty-foot trees, eh, so it's, it's a bit bland, it juist stum-, it's juist a wall o trees now.

On part of Moss Mulloch **Jim Kennedy** reckoned that there was extremely poor tree growth.

Jim: *Now, in 2005, this owner is keen to get rid of his area of forest on Moss Mulloch, because the trees have not grown well, and the price of timber is very low. In fact, on one part of Moss Mulloch the trees have grown to only about 6 feet tall and then stopped growing or even shrunk!*

The average growth rate would be 0.24 feet, or less than 3 inches, per year!

Foresters and Other Managerial Staff

When Whitelee Forest was instigated, the Forestry Commission had a 4-tier managerial structure for practical management: Conservancy headed by a Conservator; District with a District Officer; groups of forests or one large forest run by a Head Forester; individual forest run by a Forester aided by an Assistant Forester. These people were trained at British universities or forestry training colleges.

The Forestry Commission moved its forestry managers every few years, so a number of men were involved in running Whitelee Forest to the end of the 20th century. The first forester was George Caird, who has already been mentioned; his boss was head forester Mr Bert Mitchell, who was also in charge of Leapmoor Forest at Wemyss Bay. His boss was district officer Bill Sutherland who worked from the

Whitelee Forest Office in Waterside
Photo: Ruth Tittensor

Table 7: 20th Century Managers

FORESTERS

Head foresters	Office	Date	Foresters	Date	Specialist foresters	Date
Bert Mitchell	Wemyss Bay, Leapmoor Forest	1960	George Caird, Whitelee Forest	Early 1960s	Roy Harvey Ploughing Forester	1961 on
Tony Polwarth	Whitelee Forest	?	Duncan McCallum	Mid-Late 1960s	Ian Reid Ploughing Forester	1980s
Alex Smellie	Whitelee Forest	1970	John Clark	1970-1973		
Fred Cowie	Waterside, Whitelee Forest	1971-1975	David Gregory	1970s	Bill Mason Forestry Instructor	1970s
Pat Armstrong	Waterside, Whitelee Forest	1975-1987	Bill Meadows	1977-1984		
Kerr Robertson	Isle of Arran, Arran & Whitelee Forest	c.1992-1999	Ken Whitaker	1987-1990		
Andy Walker	Isle of Arran, Whitelee Forest	2003-2004				

DISTRICT OFFICERS AND MANAGERS

District officers and managers	District	Office location	Date
Bill Sutherland	Kilmun District	Cowal, Argyll	1960-1966
Ian McIver	Stirling & Arran District	Stirling, Stirlingshire	Early 1970s
Brian Roebuck	Stirling & Arran District	Stirling, Stirlingshire	Late 1970s to 1984
Alister Jones	Ayrshire & Arran District	Straiton, Ayrshire	1986-1992
Jim Hamilton	Ayrshire & Arran District	Straiton, Ayrshire	1992-(not known)
Tony Burns	Ayrshire & Arran District	Straiton, Ayrshire	Not known
Christina Tracey	Cowal Forest District	Dunoon, Argyll	To 1999
Michael Wall	Scottish Lowlands District	Lanark, Lanarkshire	2001-2007

Source of data: contributors' memories

Kilmun disitrict office in Argyll. And his boss was the conservator in the Glasgow conservancy office, Mr George Stewart. George Caird had no assistant forester or secretary, doing all his own paperwork in his digs at Laigh Hapton.

Table 7 lists the managers whom contributors remember. George Caird 'digged' with Alec and Betty Kenyon in their farmhouse of Laigh Hapton close to the new forest plantings, but eventually a forester's house was built in Waterside to the west. A large wooden shed in the garden of the forester's house acted as forest office and machinery shed. Assistant foresters lived elsewhere in the community.

Head Forester **Fred Cowie's** memories of the reason he was sent to Whitelee in 1971 were written as he spoke them.

He came to Whitelee Forest in October 1971 from Aberfoyle, and left in December 1975. He was sent to Whitelee because of his experience in soft ground/deep peat ploughing and planting at Buchlyvie in Harders Moss. Harders Moss has peat 45 feet deep! Whitelee Forest has deep, wet peat, but nowhere near as deep as Harders Moss . . .

He had a shooting lease over a big area at the east end of Whitelee Forest, approximately between High and Low Alderstocks and Logoch. A person named Brown raised pheasants and put them in the Forest at Logoch. Mr Cowie lived in Whitelee House, Waterside, and the Forest Office was there too.

Mrs Cowie was not as happy at Waterside as her husband, but the children liked it.

She said that she quite liked living there (near Whitelee Forest) but it was the least favourite of all the places she has lived, for 2 main reasons. Firstly, she was the main dog-walker, and there was no pre-existing forest at hand in which to walk. Secondly, she did not like the smells from the farms nearby. It was also very wet and windy.

But the children (2 boys and 1 girl) liked it. They went to school in Waterside and Fenwick (primary) and Loudoun Academy (Galston, secondary). None have gone into forestry. The kids liked guddling trout from the nearby burn. There was one shop in Waterside at that time.

The Work of a Forester or Head Forester

Fred Cowie wrote answers to questions about his work at Whitelee Forest.

Who worked in the Forest office?

Forester, Assistant Forester, Secretary – not staffed full time.

Did you have a Secretary, Assistant Forester or Foreman?

Yes, all three. Secretary only part time.

Can you describe to me what your job was as Forester in charge of Whitelee?

Inspecting areas proposed for acquisition. Planning and budgeting. Liaising with neighbours. Checking fence lines and agreeing renewal. Inspection of ongoing work and supervision of ploughing and draining operators. Checking performance against budget and preparing reports. Ordering stores.

Who was your boss?

District Officer

Where was his office?

Stirling

Did you get lots of freedom to use your initiative?

Yes

Where did you live?

Waterside – next forest office

How many squad workers were employed?

8

Were they local chaps?

Yes

What other types of workers were employed at Whitelee?

Smallholders who were employed by the FC but allowed time off as necessary to run their farms.

Acreages and Species Planted

All the land for Whitelee Forest (except a tiny parcel for a footpath) had been bought by 1984. By 1994, 5953 ha had been planted with trees leaving about 150 hectares of open land along burns, on rocky knowes and bogs.

As a Forestry Commission acquisitions officer, Bill Sutherland was expected to survey the land being bought and recommend tree species to plant there.

He usually suggested that Sitka spruce would be the tree species most suited to producing a quick, harvestable crop in the Whitelee environment.

The high productivity required from state forests was emphasized by **Gordon Cowie** when he discussed choice of tree species for Whitelee Forest.

The... Whitelee, as I've mentioned earlier, was very much a large-scale afforestation area, in common with much of south Scotland. And it was envisaged right from the beginning that we could create a critical mass of forest production, of timber production, which would encourage inward investment.

So, this was the, the objective right from the beginning. Inward investment in timber industries . . .

Primarily Sitka spruce, because it is a tree that is very very suited to the site. It grows very well, it's wind resistant, although if windblow starts, it can continue. But it is in fact the only commercial tree that will grow there. I say... Apart from small hollows, there's no other commercial tree would grow in Whitelee. It's a tree that is much in demand, it produces the best paper. The fibre of Sitka spruce is wonderful. And it's very long fibre, and this is, was one of the attractions for Caledonian Paper building its plant at Irvine. It's a tree which produces good structural timber. The sawlogs. And, the big sawmills tend to be in the Borders, there's a big one at Lockerbie, and it's just announced major expansion, I think another twenty-odd million pounds' expansion, and, it started after I left, and that was '97, so, that's a measure of it. It's a very versatile timber . . .

But if it wasn't for Sitka spruce, Lodgepole pine was very much a tree of the Seventies, it was a tree that was expected to have a lot of potential, but it had a lot of problems. And, both insect and quality. So, Lodgepole pine went out of favour by the Nineties. It's a tree that will grow on very poor sites, and doesn't need much fertilizing. But, it went out of favour. And apart from that, larch is about the only other commercial species, and in Whitelee it was limited because of exposure. But it was used in places. It's susceptible to, to wind and... It's not a timber that's in great demand just now, unless it's good quality. And I, I couldn't grow good quality larch up in Whitelee.

Sitka spruce seed came originally from two sites in North America, Queen Charlotte Islands near Vancouver and near Washington. The former provenance of the species grows better in conditions of very poor weather as at Whitelee Forest, while the Washington provenance grows better in milder conditions.

Fred Cowie's comments on his practical difficulties of getting exactly the right Sitka spruce trees were written.

He wanted to plant Sitka Spruce of "Queen Charlotte Island" Provenance at Whitelee Forest, but he was given seedlings of "Washington" Provenance, which grows too fast and does not therefore provide good final timber quality.

He, the Forest Commission, at Whitelee Forest stopped planting Lodgepole Pine because it was susceptible to windblow, especially when planted in mixture with Sitka Spruce.

Pat Armstrong was the longest serving head forester. Ruth Tittensor wrote down what he said of areas and species planted.

The peak time of plantings was in 1962. The other main plantings: were in the mid 1970s – 1980s. About 1000 acres (400 ha) of trees were planted each year at that time. The major concern at Whitelee Forest was the choice of tree species. Sitka Spruce was the logical choice. Sitka Spruce is from West Coast America. 90% of Whitelee Forest is Sitka Spruce. The Forestry Commission tried Larch where conditions seemed suitable. During the 1980s, there were attempts to plant hardwood tree species in potentially suitable areas. Mr Armstrong tried Nothofagus (Chilean Beech), birch, rowan, sycamore and willows in wet places. He did not try oak . . .

It is a very difficult area for a forest. The particular difficulties are the peat 'soil', the high water-table, the high rainfall and the high winds. Plants are damaged easily, the soil is unstable, and windblow occurs.

The Conservancy office in Glasgow also expected **Fred Cowie** to plant hardwoods (broadleaved, non-conifer trees) and he recounted another story of difficulties with tree species.

The Hardwood Plantings were not good, and he wanted to persuade the chaps in the Glasgow office to stop having hardwoods planted. He took a scientist from the Forestry Commission Northern Research Station at Roslin, near Edinburgh, to see them.

The Scientist said to him **"Would you plant hardwoods here if you didn't have to?"**

Fred Cowie said, No!

"Quite! When would you plant hardwoods here as you have to?"

In a few years time when the Forest has grown up a bit, to provide shelter

"Quite!"

So Fred Cowie said to the scientist "Will you write to the Glasgow Office and tell them?"

and the reply was **"Not on your life!"**.

Squad planting amenity hardwoods in grow-tubes near Logoch 1980s
Photo: Grant Peter

However, **Brian Speirs** told Ruth Tittensor that he really loved planting broadleaf trees, and thought about how beautiful they would look in the future landscape.

Ruth: You worked at Whitelee Forest for thirty-three years, um, are there any parts of the forest that are special to you from those, all those years that, um, have special meaning to you or you remember particularly well, things that happened particularly?

Brian: *Well, it's hard tae say. The area at Lochfield which was originally a loch, it was decided then to dam the outlet and return it from a, a marshland, a wetland, back intae a loch. Now that at the time I thought was a great idea, but it never materialised. Other th-, areas, streamsides, riversides, were, to the latter end were planted with broadleaf trees, eh, in growtubes,*

Oh right.

Amenity oaks sprouting from their tubes below Drumduff Hill 2006
Photo: Susan Anderson

128

Quite a lot. Some areas it wes thick wi thousands planted down [a], which when ye're planting things like that, ye try tae envisage whit it would be like fifty–eighty years from then, which really would hae been a nice place, but wi the manpower an the cutbacks, whether these trees are being maintained and still growing ah honestly don't know, ah don't know.

What sort of broadleaves were they on the whole?

Mixed. Eh, rowan, birch, sycamore, ash, cherry – or gean was the wild cherry – mostly them.

Right. Any alder as it was along the, um, streams?

There was some alder in some areas, but the broadleafs were not planted right down to the stream. Juist on the slope at the side. The stream itself wes left, it wes left. Deliberately left open, yes, yes.

Managing the Workforce

As head forester, **Fred Cowie** understood his workers' skills and hard work; he had high regard for his tractor drivers.

The squad spent almost all of their time planting and fertilising trees by hand. Some learned to use the planting spade better than others. Some of the squad could do it very fast to make it look easy, but they were well – practiced, and it was very hard work . . .

His tractor driver was a very good machinery person. If a piece of machinery was bent or broken, he would explain very carefully to Fred Cowie what he wanted. Fred Cowie would then take it to one of the small engineers which were common in Kilmarnock at that time (there was a big Massey-Ferguson and lots of small supporting engineering firms). Kilmarnock was a very nice, busy town then. They would do the repair or make a new piece exceedingly well.

Mr Cowie once had a special tractor driver over from his previous patch at Aberfoyle, after one of the Whitelee tractors got stuck deep in the peat . . . The Aberfoyle tractor driver was used to ploughing on the 45ft deep peat Flanders Moss. He just had a knack! He was a difficult

character, but worth his weight in gold. He could tell from the ground when not to go forward i.e. he left open areas where there was very soft ground.

Forest Workers' Holdings

High Overmuir steading, a Forest Workers' Holding run by the Peter family
Photo: Andrew Tittensor

A stable squad was a very important asset to a forester overseeing the long-term development of a forest, so Forest Workers' Holdings were available for some squad members, to encourage them to stay long-term. Tenants of FWH are listed in Table 4. Brian Speirs described to Ruth Tittensor life as tenant of a FWH.

***Brian:** Well, in ma time up at Whitelee, I wis the tenancy o two different smallholdings – I'd like to call them smallholdings. They were difficult working because at the time The Forestry let these smallholdings to the workers, the land was pretty neglected. So it wasn't very good growing-wise, plus, wi it being hill land, you were very limited to any crops you could grow, very limited. I mean most of us tried hay crops and dependin on the season quite often you didn't get it, ye juist couldn't get it. So, again bein up at the top ae the hills*, it wes a long winter an a short summer. Consequently most o the feeding an the keep for the, your livestock come up the road on the back of a lorry fae the grain merchant.*

* [340m or 1122 ft altitude]

Ruth: Yes, yes. Um, so it wasn't, it wasn't easy, um, and presumably it wasn't eve- easy for the farmers who were the there before the forest came along to make a living either. Um, how many acres did you have?

The first holding ah had, in Craigendunton, I hud a hundred and ten acres. Ah then moved tae High Allerstocks with a hundred and fifty acres, an the hundred an fifty acres was the average for any o the smallholdings.

And can you describe to someone listening maybe in twenty years time, or somebody who doesn't know about hill farming, can you describe, um, what it looked like and what you did with your hundred and ten or hundred an fifty acres?

Whit we did, we all did, we had beef cows, eh, and sheep, and that wes it. We, we – ah hud one or two fields set aside for hay, but the rest was like a free range for the sheep and the cows, eh, at that time. It wes a situation where at, like, lambing time, the weather can be really severe an ye would lose quite a lot o lambs because o that. The other drawback, especially for the smallholders, ye had yer store calves an yer

1946 air photo of High Allerstocks at 325m altitude on the remote Allerstocks Moor
Photo: Courtesy of RCAHMS (RAF Air Photographs Collection)

lambs go on to market an if the buyers weren't there at the time ye didn't get a very good price, but that wes yer income for the following year which wes a big drawback, but it was hard work for little reward, that wes it.

Right. It was meant – was it – why did the Forestry Commission let these areas of smallholdings then?

When The, The Forestry bought a hill farm, they used the, the hill ground for planting trees, but they used the house, the outbuildings an the fields round about the outbuildings, they let to the forest workers to try an give them a wee bit extra – well both income, and incentive to stay in the forest, to work in the forest, that wes the idea o that, that wes it.

Yes, okay. With this work was it, was the work on the smallholding on top of a – your full time work at the – in the forestry or, or, or did, did you get time off from the forestry to look after the smallholding?

Largely the work wes on top o the, the forestry work, early in the morning, later at night, weekends. You did get unpaid, what we called holding time, which wes unpaid. Eh, very few of us actually used that, but we used wur annual leave to work the hay and mebbe go tae the market, that kind o thing, we used the annual leave.

Goodness me. Mm. And did wives and families help with the smallholdings generally?

Oh yes, oh yes. Oh definitely. Eh, lambing time wes – well, the wife was involved in that, eh, because to really do it, ye hid to do it mebbe three, four times a day, go round the sheep, check and make sure, eh, that kind o thing. Eh, hay time, a lot o the wives would probably even drive a tractor with a tether or something on the back to work the hay, that, that, but, yes, they, they, the wifes, definitely. The families as well if they were old enough did a lot o work, if they were old enough, they helped oot a lot, so it was family affairs, definitely family affairs.

Firewatch and Forest Fires

Fire is perhaps a forester's worst nightmare. Brakes separating blocks of trees were very useful when it came to forest fires. Ruth Tittensor asked Brian Speirs about fires in Whitelee Forest.

Ruth: . . . now, as far as I can gather, once you get a forest and there's a lot of long grass because there's no grazing any more, um, it becomes liable to, to fire and um I don't know whether natural fire or fire caused by human beings so, um, did you have any duties connected with, um, fire or were there any fire towers you had to build or use?

Brian: *There wes no fire towers. Fire training was based down at Straiton and that involved helicopter work, and the idea o the courses, there would be, mebbe four or five of us wi fire brooms, we would go in the helicopter and get moved up to the hill and dropped off and this exercise was in case there was a fire where they could get us there quick, eh, at Whitelee we hid no sort thing like that up there, but we had a trailer specially with knapsacks, hoses an a big fire pump, that was all this trailer wes used for, in case there wes a fire at Whitelee, we could just connect the trailer an head out as near as we could to the fire, but mostly it was fire beater work, an that wes it.*

Right. So can you explain to people listening who don't know, what, what is a fire beater, or broom, what did you call it? Um, what's the tool that you're using and what are you doing with it?

Well, earlier a fire beater was a st–, a fairly long straight bit o birch, possibly a young tree, aboot eight foot long, an at the top ae that was the branches tied in bundles ontae the stand, ontae the main trunk, and that wes the fire beater, that. It evolved later with straight young trees, but the top hid [the] old matting, rubber matting, that I think the open cast mines provided, eh, and these were cut into, big squares and bolted onto the top o thir trees, these wur used lately, err, tae the latter end, and that the birch broom as such wes done away with, it wes done away with.

Right. And what did you do with this tool, this thing?

Whitelee squad on fire training near Straiton 1980s
Photo: Grant Peter

Making rubber fire beaters was winter work
Photo: Ruth Tittensor

Mesh and rubber fire beaters colonised by lichens, Craigendunton
Photo: Ruth Tittensor

131

These, these were spread out in stands throu-out the younger trees in the forest, eh, six or eight o thir in a stand, eh, and the idea o that is, if there was a fire you would go up and you would take one and head along the brake, the ride line, trying to put the fire out on the ride line wi this, beating it to make it out, and that, that wes the idea o the fire beater.

So, does this mean that the fires were mostly on the ground and not at the tops of the trees?

Initially they were on the ground, because the trees weren't big enough, but later as the trees got up to Eh fifteen foot high, they would take what was, was described as a crown fire. They would sweep through the trees because when the trees were that height, there was very very little if any grass or cover at the bottom, so it would go along the tree itself, frae one tree tae the ither itself, and when that happened, the fire beater wes no use.

So what happened in, in that case, what, when there was a cr- crown fire, what did, what did you do, or nothing?

Well, at Whitelee, as I said, what we did, we waited at the fire breaks, or the ride lines, an if the, the grass caught alight in these, we tried tae contain it . . . that's where the fire-beaters come intae effect, an between ourselves and a lot ae the squad from Dalmelliton comin up to help, plus the fire engines – an there could be as many as four-six fire engines from the district doin the same work – an that is how we fought the fires up at Whitelee.

But if there were no roads, or very few roads, how did the fire engines get to the fires?

The fire engines theirself got as near as possible an the men walked. They walked out to the fire, that wes it.

Right. And the trailer you mentioned with the knapsacks and so on on it, where was that kept?

That was kept at Waterside, in the store at Waterside. It was sittin there.

Um, what I'm - don't quite see is, umm, the fire engines and the trailer with the knapsacks and so on, uh, didn't they need water to put out a fire, where did the water come from?

As far as the fire engines or the firemen concerned, they were equipped the same way as us, wi fire beaters. Because, every winter, if the weather was bad an we couldn't go out to the forest to work, we used to be in the store making fire beaters. And a lot o these wur taken round an supplied to the fire stations for that thing, so the firemen relied on the beaters the same as we did.

Okay. And, um, now that the forest is – parts of it are getting mature and it's started to be harvested, do you think the fires are still the same sort of fires, would they be the same sort or would they be the sort that needed helicopters?

They would be what we would term crown fires which definitely helicopters [unclear word], definitely that. A fire beater at the stage the trees are at now would be useless, would be no use.

Jim Newall emphasised the difficulties of trying to put out a fire in a forest growing on peat – which was after all, a commonly-used fuel for burning in home fires!

Jim: *Right, the first time a seen Whitelees Forest it wis on fire. It hud a massive fire, that wud be about eighty-three, a wis workin wi ma plantin squad an we got a radio message sayin Whitelees wis on fire, so we came up, full squad o us, we came up here on the Friday night, aww, it wis an awfie state, but we managed to mair or less put it oot on the Friday afternoon late, but the problem is Whitelees[is] on peat, so there wis always the fear it would brek oot again, [so the]*

Ruth: Right. Can you explain why?

Well peat – the kinna stuff that peat is built wi, the mineral that peat is built wi, is actually a fire, it's, up in the Highlands o Scotland it's uised actually for, for makin fire. For heatin the house… So what we end up wi was, a fire wis breakin back oot, the embers o the fire, so we'd to keep an eye on it for so many days. Sae anyway, we were here all day Saturday an all day Sunday. That wis ma first time a seen Whitelees . . .

Right. Where was the fire?

The fire wis all ower the south section, it wis massive, massive damage done. That time o day there wis a full squad here an aw, a f-, a Whitelees squad . . .

They were tryin to put it oot, but, at that time there'd mebbe wud be aboot sixty men there plus four-five-mebbe-six fire brigade.

Tom and Janet Grant described a frightening fire in the mature Whitelee Forest close to their farmhouse and steading.

A fire destroyed maturing plantations at High Hapton in 2002
Photo: Ruth Tittensor

It wis such a dry Easter it wis so dry . . .

Before yer sayin [indistinct] that wid [wood] wid never burn…it just shows ye. It wis so dry and we had, what? About 8 or 9 fire engines the chuck wagon, police, Forestry Commission, police helicopter. Aye, the forester he wis here …three years ago.

And em then they started tae take water out the loch and by helicopter they dropped, aye they bombed the fire. They came off last thing at night and they said the fire wis out and Matt Mitchell phoned... wis it the next morning? and said **"Mrs Grant have you been burning the toast up there?"** *and I said that* **"I think they've got it out,"** *he said that he wis in Australia and he'd experience of forestry fires and he said last thing at night he says the winds change and it dies down and it seems to be dead but he says see by lunch time the next day when the daylight*

comes and the wind changes, he says, it'll start tae burn again. And that wis correct that wis unbelievable … And it burned for, Ruth, aboot a week. It wis unbelievable how how they would say it wis out an by eleven o cloak it wis whoosin up the trees.

It's a sight tae see that Ah micht never see it again in ma life. It wis unbelievable how it could shift as much an spread as much but ye see when they firemen got coat* wi a wee chynge o wind.   * [caught]

Fox and Deer Control

Local people or forest employees took on shooting leases in early Whitelee Forest days. But the Forestry Commission took responsibility for controlling certain species. **Bob Logan** has been a ranger on the Isle of Arran for more than 30 years. He explained that in the late 1970s, he was sent to Whitelee Forest to carry out fox control. This was not because they damaged trees, but because adjoining farmers reckoned the growing Forest harboured many more foxes, which killed lambs in the spring.

In the young Whitelee Forest deer of any kind were rarely observed. But by the 1980s, numbers of roe deer had increased to several hundreds. Along with rangers from the Straiton office of the Forestry Commission, Bob Logan was sent to Whitelee on many occasions to cull the deer population. And from 1997 to 1999, Alec Fenton was full-time stalker. Nowadays, the deer-stalking is all let to several private syndicates under strict conditions which are rigorously monitored by senior ranger Jim Newall.

When Jim Newall's apprenticeship as a slater came to an end, there was no roofing job available, only forest squad work. At the age of 20, after several years of 'hard manual labour' in the squad, he had the opportunity to become a trainee ranger. With head ranger Robin Heaney, he went to Whitelee Forest in1985 for his first day of training. He eventually specialized in deer stalking and became one of the part-time stalkers in Whitelee Forest, based on the Straiton office.

Alexander Fenton described to Ruth Tittensor how he came to be a stalker, why deer need culling and what the job involved.

Alexander Fenton, wildlife ranger in Whitelee Forest 1997-99
Photo: Courtesy Alexander Fenton

Ruth: So why did you go into deerstalking?

Alec: *Right. Whilst I was at Whitelee as a squad member, I had...the Forester there asked me what sort of, what I was interested in, and I says, 'Outdoors and hunting and that sort of thing' He says, 'Well, we, we've got guys that are trained as Trappers,' they called them Trappers; they're called Wildlife Rangers now because it sounds better. And sounds more PC* (laughs). *And, they were called Trappers in those days, because they trapped foxes and stuff like that, and, they stalk deer and such like. So I, I told him that I'd be interested in that if there was any chance of a position. And, there was a trainee's position in Inverliever Forest in Argyll, whilst I was at Whitelee. And, the head man from up there came down to see me, and there was fifteen applicants and I got it.*

Great.

. . . The Forester put a word in for me, I got the job, I got the position, I moved to Inverliever. Did my training there, being another Forest District, came back to Whitelee Forest in 1997, till 1999, as a leading ranger . . .

Yes. So can you explain to the people who are going to be listening to this what stalking is and what trapping is, and, and what you did at Whitelee?

Well when I came back to Whitelee, the policy in trapping had stopped, there was not to be any snaring of any animals at all.

Oh. Had there been previously?

Yes, aye, yes a number of years previously. The political climate had changed then, there'd been a government organisation that didn't like to be seen to be doing things that the public maybe didn't like trapping foxes and stuff like that. Although foxes were causing the neighbours with, around the beat, the beat of Whitelee Forest major problems, because they, that's where the foxes were harboured, in the forest. So... In some instances I would get a call by somebody that was losing lambs, and I would go and shoot the offending fox, or foxes.

Yes. But other than that, you didn't, you didn't… you weren't proactive so to speak in going out and trapping?

No, no, no, because the Forestry Commission even now, they're not, they don't want to be seen to be killing foxes. Although we shoot deer. And at Whitelee, at Whitelee I had a cull, well, they didn't set a cull for Whitelee because they'd never had a, a full-time stalker there, so they weren't sure what they were going to get out of it, any given year. So I would, I would be shooting about 200 roe deer out a year, out of Whitelee.

Roe deer increased to about 600 during the Forest's first four decades
Photo: Alexander Fenton

That's quite a lot. And that was your job, basically?

That, that was my job. Well eighty per cent, eighty per cent of my job was deer culling.

So this was quite different from your work with the hill squad. So, did you sort of see your mates, your mates from the squad, or...?

No, well, by the time I came back, there was no squad in Whitelee. I was the only man on Whitelee on the ground. That's why I called, when I, when I came back to Whitelee I called it the 'Forgotten Forest', because, people just forgot about it. But I mean people, I mean the hierarchy within the Forestry Commission . . .

So, can you describe what happens when you go out and stalk deer? How do you decide when you go out one particular day where you are going, and what do you do?

Well obviously, there are shooting seasons. But with the Forestry Commission, we get out-of-season shooting. That means that we don't, we're not required to stick to the, the law for, say, a recreational stalker. We can shoot outwith the season, if there's a problem. This being a commercial forest, deer weren't professionally stalked and weren't professionally shot; they were poached around the periphery. And there was not many people knew about Whitelee Forest and where it was situated, except for the poachers, the local poachers in the Irvine Valley and surrounding areas. But they tended to shoot round the periphery, in the fields adjacent to the Forest block.

So I would go in, like this time of year, like this morning for instance, I was out the door at half-past three this morning, getting into an area of ground for a shot, when the deer aren't moving, when I know they're going to be moving.

So, it was the same at Whitelee, I take down there at the crack of dawn, knowing when the deer weren't going to be moving, and, when they were going to be lyin' up, because when they lay up, I would come home.

And, at this time of year, in the summer, you'd go back out

again at night, and you'd be out till midnight, then back again. And you just do that, it was just perpetual.

And did you shoot on foot or from high seats or, how?

No, most of the shooting was, walked-up stalking, actually going in and locating deer, and, shooting them, that way . . . I would have a, I would just go in there, this time of year it would be roebucks, does, the roe does, would have eh kids at foot. So, I wouldn't shoot, obviously not shoot them because they've got dependent young. So it would just be the males.

And then, having shot it, what's then? You're stuck in the middle of a forest, high up on Whitelee plateau with a dead deer. What do you do then?

Right. Well, OK, I mean you bleed the animal, you gralloch it, gralloch's removing the intestines and the stomach. And, from there, you keep that beast intact, put it in your roe sack, and carry... a roe sack's like a rucksack, specifically made for carrying roe deer. And you would move off the hill, or move out the forest to your vehicle, and then that beast was taken straight to the game dealer . . .

So, you carried this animal, this dead animal, on your back?

Yes. Yes, in a roe sack. Yes. Yes. To the vehicle, from the vehicle straight to the game dealer.

Right. Right. So, the game dealer got it pretty soon.

Aye, it got it quite fresh, aye (laughter). *Because Whitelee, although it's a 6,000-hectare block of forest, it didn't have a larder, a deer larder. In the present place I'm in now, we have a, a quality assured deer larder, it cost us about £150,000 to put in . . .*

Did you ever meet anybody as you walked back to the vehicle with this roe deer on your back?

No, because, a lot of the times that I was in the Forest, I would be out before people came in. More up the East Kilbride end, up near the Eaglesham end, there tended to be more people out early in the morning walking their dogs

A modern Scottish deer larder where carcases are processed according to strict European rules   Photo: Alexander Fenton

Mhm. OK. And will it continue to be ideal as it matures and is harvested?

Yes, when it's harvested, because when it's harvested, not so much when it's ma' . . . they'll ruminate in the mature timber, and, they've got a lot of stuff at thicket stage. I don't think there's anything at pre-thicket. There's a lot, there was a lot of check in some areas up the Eaglesham end. But, they like to come into the open, but some areas they don't have to if they've got shelter and food, they won't do that. As the timber gets up and the timber's felled, you're creating an open area where the light's getting to it and you start getting rank vegetation coming up. So you're getting various types of grasses and plants, bramble and stuff like that coming up through.

And they eat that, will they?

And they just love that, aye. Mm.

By and by, Alec Fenton left his job at Whitelee Forest for ranger work elsewhere in Scotland. The Forestry Commission changed its deer control policy once more. **Jim Newall** became the trainer and mentor of shooting tenants who are nowadays the deer stalkers of Whitelee Forest.

and stuff like that. So I, I would maybe meet, meet some of them. But I got kind of friendly with these people, and they knew what I was about, and they were kind of country people anyway, so they weren't in the least bit worried about what I was doing.

And you say you shot about 200 a year . . . And can you explain to people listening why it was necessary to shoot deer? Were you trying to make money?

No, I wasn't... You see that's a... Within the Forestry Commission, deer are a by-product of growing trees.

If you're growing a commercial crop, if that commercial crops getting damaged, well you've got, if there's a problem there, you've got to attend to it. So... And plus the fact, within an area, if there's too many animals for a specific habitat, that's detrimental to the animal . . .

Yes. Yes. So, deer damage trees, do they, or what do they do?

Yes, well they do damage trees. And in some areas of Whitelee there was hardwoods planted, and, the hardwoods just get hammered basically. Because when the hardwoods are growing, especially in the spring, at this time of year the leaves unfurl, they're nice and juicy, and they're soft, and roe deer just love to pick the leaves off the hardwoods . . .

Bark of young alder frayed by roe deer antlers
Photo: Ruth Tittensor

Jim: Mm. So anyway. They left that. Alex startit in here an he did a really guid job killin an awul lot o roe in this area an he got the population doun. He also got rid o aw the auld wans that shoudae been shot years afore a- an mangaged to dae sumthin to increase the quality o the roe in the area. Nou Alec wis here for a number o years. At that time the Foli-, Forestry Commission

136

chynged its policy an they decidit to lease oot areas for stalking. This wis a new venture we were in which has proved up to the nou to be successful. Hou it warks is, ye take on mebbe six people in – well, no s-, no as many as six, usually about four – in one area.

Ye skills test them tae make sure they know what they're doin, their paperwork [an] insurance is in order, an they take it on for a period of up tae eleven month. To manage them ye do spot checks, an at wan time we were collectin the jawbones, just ti make sure they were shootin what they say they were shootin. They have a cull figure set an then try an obtain that every year. So the bottom line is they're now payin to do ma job. It suits the Forestry Commission quite well.

Ruth: (Laughing) Absolutely. But, but if it's leased out, you don't have the work.

That's right, so whit they said was, if it wis leased oot ah could concentrate on ither things, ither duties. So, we stertit gettin involved in batboxes, birdboxes, blackcock, different conservation projects, which a found very interestin.

Like other workers at Whitelee Forest, **Jim Newall** loved his training and work as a ranger.

Jim: *The trainin wis hands on, we hud a gentleman worked wi us cawed Robin Henney. Robin had been a – hus been a ranger aw his life. When ye were daein yer trainin ye were sent wi him. Ye were wi him for a period o anythin up ti a year, an it wis hands on all the time. When it got ti the larder, he handit ye the knife, he watched ye. He h-, he could dae it so you had ti learn ti do it. He wis strict but he wis fair. There wis nuthin he didnae know about it.*

Ruth: And you enjoyed all this?

Oh ay, ah loved it, ah loved it, it wis ma dream job. As for the rifle. Well, ye went to a range wi the rifle ti start wi, but there's a big difference in shootin a range an shootin a deer because ye never do the same shot twice, so every day wis a school day, every day ye learned sumthin different.

Sitka spruce with lower twigs eaten by roe deer, Low Overmuir
Photo: Ruth Tittensor

Shooting Tenants

In the 1960s, John Golder a non-resident of the locality took on the first shooting tenancy of the new Forest. In 1981, when the Forest had grown somewhat, the shooting was divided into several lets, and this is how it has continued. Local resident Hugh Hendry tendered for one of the leases, but was not successful. He was not disappointed however, because he was sad at what he felt were deleterious effects of the Forest on game and wildlife.

Robin Chambers has been a shooting tenant of the Forestry Commission since 1987. Ruth Tittensor wrote down his memories of the changing situation as he spoke.

> Mr Chambers had also obtained from the Forestry Commission a game-shooting-tenancy of most of the northern side of Whitelee Forest by 1987. He and his brother formed a syndicate for game-shooting. At that time, The Forestry Commission stalked its land with in-house stalkers, in this case a stalker from Arran named Mr Bob Logan, and then Mr Jim Newall and Mr Alex Fenton. In the early years of planting, a Forestry Commission officer had come from Dalmellington to control the white hares.
>
> In due course, Forestry Commission policy changed and its in-house stalkers were withdrawn. It no longer permitted its shooting tenants to shoot game in Whitelee Forest. Deer now became the only legal quarry. Mr Chambers formed a syndicate of three and they became deer stalkers trained to the Basic Level 1. By now, the Forestry Commission allowed its shooting tenants at Whitelee Forest to shoot only deer and no other species.

Income From Whitelee Forest

By letting shooting of game or deer in Whitelee Forest to outside tenants, the Forestry Commission brought in income during the period before trees became harvestable. Income came in other ways too. District officer **Alister Jones** remembered a small Welsh firm approaching him.

> One of the innovations of this kind we had in the Forest District during my time was moss picking. What happened there was, a chap rang me up one day and said he was interested in collecting moss for the horticultural trade. And he had a little factory where they would make up these moss poles and, hanging basket frames and things, and could he go and pick the moss? And actually I had to say to him, **"Well you'll have to come here and show me what you mean,"** because I, I didn't really know much about it. And what it amounted to was that, he had a squad of men who would go into the woods where the trees were, oh, six to eight feet high. That meant that the ground had developed since it was enclosed and the trees planted, and the moss had grown fairly luxuriantly. Had he left it any longer then the trees would gradually kill off the moss. So that's when it was about best. And he would pick… there's different kinds of mosses of course, and he would pick the type of moss that he wanted. Put them into polybags, take the polybag down to the forest road, and then he'd come along at the end of the week with a lorry, load the bags and off he went. And he was quite happy to pay quite a lot of money for this. And, it was a coincidence that, I being Welsh and he was Welsh. (laughter) And he did this very regularly in North Wales, in the forests of North Wales, and it was something that we hadn't heard of in south Scotland. And I said to him, **"Well,"** I said, **"yes I'm quite interested,"** I said. **"I think this will be possible, but I can't just let you have this; I'll have to advertise it, because there could well be some other people out there who would like to do it as well, but haven't actually asked"**. So, it was duly advertised, and bids were invited. It happens, he was the only bidder.

And of course **Brian Speirs** saw it happening on the ground in Whitelee Forest.

> It was between 1988 and 1990 that workers appeared in Whitelee Forest to collect Sphagnum moss commercially. They were employed by a firm from Wales, which was apparently one of the main market suppliers of Sphagnum in the whole country. The workers were lads, not Welsh, but from the general area of Kilmarnock and were mostly young – in their late teens or early twenties. They arrived

in Whitelee Forest in the autumn and worked through the winter, spending a couple of months clearing each area before moving to another mossy area. At the end of the winter, they disappeared until the following autumn. At any one time there were 6 to 15 young men employed and working together at moss collecting in the Forest . . .

When collecting Bog Moss, the lads would go into the young trees, rake up the moss and stuff it into bags about 1½ by 2½ feet in size. The bags were a sort of woven plastic. They would then carry the full bags to a Forest ride or track in a vehicle resembling a "Muskeg". The full bags would be piled and stored until there were enough for a lorry to come and fill up with them for carriage to Wales. Apparently the lads earned good money but did not last long in their jobs, so the faces which the forest squad saw changed frequently.

Comment

Running Whitelee Forest involved many operations in which the choice and planting of trees was only a small part. The Forestry Commission tried to ensure a constant supply of work for the squad and rangers all year, every year, in the long term. The squad and rangers who have given testimony enjoyed their work and stayed in their jobs for long periods. The Forest Workers' Holdings (most of them the size of a small farm) helped keep a core squad. However, their dual jobs gave little time for anything but constant hard physical work in the Forest and Holding: even annual leave was used for lambing or hay-making. Neither Whitelee Forest nor the Holdings would have succeeded without wives and families to help produce an income from these left-overs of previous farms.

The rangers worked very unsocial hours, at times of day or night when few people are about. They loved their jobs and are still employed by the Forestry Commission in outdoor work.

Fire was a constant hazard and 'firewatch' provided extra work for the squad, including at weekends. It involved sitting in a vehicle at Whitelee's high points, keeping an eye open for the start of fire, and contacting a fire-duty forester at Straiton. The risk season was and is spring and summer, especially at weekends. Squads from several forests could be taken to help with a fire if needed.

Whitelee Forest was a busy place full of things happening. The next chapter will describe how that changed radically when tree planting came to an end.

CHAPTER 11

The Time Gap and its Consequences

Need for a Minimum Forest Size

Expanding the area of a new forest would be the natural progression. To be efficient, a squad and machinery should be kept in full work and not left idle or made redundant while a forest is growing. A forest needs to expand to a minimum size so that there can be a smooth transfer from completing all the ploughing and tree-planting, to the start of harvesting. The original areas planted would then be ready for thinning or final harvesting just as the last plantings are finished.

As a result of the efforts of Bill Sutherland and other acquisition officers like Andrew Bearhop, Whitelee Forest expanded to 6,000 hectares. About 10% was not planted with trees, particularly the brakes, very wet or rocky areas and (later on) the margins of burns. From an ecological and amenity point of view, this was very desirable. But it was not only the size of Whitelee Forest that caused difficulties, but its environment: back to the peat problem!

Intermediate Management: the 'No-Thin' Regime

While a forest is growing, poorer trees are usually cut out or 'thinned' at selected intervals. This means the owner ends up with a 'final crop' of trees whose timber is of the highest possible quality for the markets envisaged. It also means some interim income for what is a very long-term investment (even when the investment is by taxpayers). There are other operations to be carried out on a well-managed forest while it is growing.

However, the management regime of the growing Whitelee Forest had been deliberately set as 'No-Thin'. Head forester **Fred Cowie** wrote answers to questions on the subject.

What intermediate types of management were envisaged for the Forest?

Remedial fertiliser only extra input envisaged.

Did fertiliser get used? How?

Yes, applied by hand from buckets. Remedial fertilisers (usually P & K) applied by helicopter where trees were too large for easy access. Also tried agricultural spreader.

What was the intended length of the rotation for the main species?

Approx 40 years rotation.

Were there to be thinnings at any stage during the rotation?

No.

What were the envisaged markets for the final crop?

Pulp.

'No-thin' management produces densely-packed trees with tall stems and small crowns, High Hapton 2001
Photo: Robert Graham

He indicated possible reasons for the 'No-Thin' decision.

> *. . . the combination of wind and soil plus single furrow ploughing . . . the Forestry Commission at Whitelee Forest stopped planting Lodgepole pine because it was susceptible to windblow, especially when planted in mixture with Sitka spruce.*

Pat Armstrong, who took over from Fred Cowie as head forester, reiterated the problems which produced the 'No-Thin' decision.

> *. . . much windblow of trees was both expected and takes place at Whitelee Forest. There is extremely high rainfall, of at least 60 inches per annum. This gives considerable drainage problems, because Whitelee is all peat ground. Plantings are therefore unstable and this adds to windblow problems.*

The effects of windblow were potentially devastating on such peaty ground if tree thinnings were taken from growing compartments at intermediate stages of growth. But with 'No-Thin' management of Whitelee Forest, there would be a time gap between the final planting of bare ground and the first harvesting of a fully grown crop from the first, 1962, plantings. It would also mean a longer interval before any income from timber was achieved.

Helicopter ready to have fertiliser containers attached, Low Overmuir 1980s   Photo: Grant Peter

Helicopter spraying fertiliser over a swathe of Whitelee Forest 1980s
Photo: Grant Peter

Helicopter returning with empty container for refilling 1980s
Photo: Grant Peter

Wind-blown trees create a gap, where trees continue to blow down like dominoes, High Hapton   Photo: Ruth Tittensor

Wind-blown Sitka spruce on Darvel Moss
Photo: Ruth Tittensor

Huge, root-plate of a wind-blown Sitka spruce on Whitelee Hill.
Photo: Ruth Tittensor

In the first years of the time gap (the early 1990s), the reduced Whitelee squad was kept busy with amenity broadleaved plantings, maintaining drains and fences, estate management and conservation. The men also spent time working away in Carrick and Kyle Forests and on the Isle of Arran, where productive work was available.

Bill Sutherland was unhappy with 'no-thin' policies in Scotland and wrote about them.

A renowned Graduate Research Forester, JAB MacDonald (now dead) invented a system of managing Woodlands known as "Eclectic Thinning" around 1956. Under this system, young plantations of 16 – 20 year old were brashed (lower branches removed using specially designed small chain saws invented by a Polish refugee forest expert at Forest of Ae). The Forester then selected, as I recall, about 140 trees per acre, and marked these with a spot (paint spray). Thinnings were carried out always to favour these selected trees, which would develop better roots and would thus create wind-firm timber. Foresters rapidly became enthusiastic about the system. They knew exactly which trees to favour when marking thinnings, and the results were rapidly (in 2 – 3 years) obvious.

142

But a "brilliant" forest economist "proved" that "Eclectic Thinning" was a nonsense. His view prevailed. Henceforth most of the Forests in Scotland were managed under a "No Thin" regime. The predictable result of non-management was that tree crops blew down before they reached an economic size.

Local people were unhappy too. **Tom Grant** noticed that there was no thinning going on in Whitelee Forest and became somewhat disillusioned with its development.

However, regarding the Forest itself, Tom feels that there has been neglect since the last residential Forester left. They did not ever thin Whitelee Forest. It has been badly managed. Tom reckons that the Forestry Commission should have planted tree species which grow better on Whitelee ground. Surely, after 50 years experience since 1919, the Forestry Commission knew which species would suit, what the markets would be and so on? He reckons planting Whitelee Forest was a big waste of money.

The Administration of Whitelee Forest from Afar

Whitelee developed into a large forest, but never became part of a forest assemblage such as the Trossachs or the Galloway Forest Park. Yet it was and is on Glasgow's and East Kilbride's doorsteps with a far larger urban catchment than Galloway, for instance. But Whitelee Forest became peripheral to mainstream planning.

In Scotland, the Forestry Commission had four Conservancies in 1961. The new Whitelee Forest was placed in the West Conservancy, in Kilmun Forest District, where Bill Sutherland was district officer. Between Bill Sutherland's time and the end of the 20th century, Whitelee Forest was administered from four other Forestry Commission districts and district offices: Stirling and Arran, office in Stirling; Kyle, office in Dunoon; Ayrshire and Arran, office in Straiton; Scottish Lowlands, office in Lanark. All these district offices were substantial distances away. It was also moved from the

"The Forgotten Forest": western part of
Whitelee Forest from Laird's Seat
Photo: Ruth Tittensor

West to the Mid and then to the South Conservancy. When the Forestry Commission was sub-divided into the Forest Authority and Forest Enterprise in 1992, Whitelee Forest became part of South Scotland Forest Enterprise. At this time, it was not regarded as an individual 'Forest', but as part of 'Arran and Whitelee Forest'.

The testimony of district officer **Alister Jones** shows that he was well aware of Whitelee Forest's isolation and the difficulties of administering it. Even as he arrived as district officer in 1986 the squad was down from ten to six.

> **Alister:** . . . *and Whitelee was almost, although it was physically very close to Glasgow, it was almost a little backwater. It was isolated from other forests in Mid*

Scotland. In fact it's, looking back on it, Whitelee has never entirely belonged anywhere. At one time the District Officer in charge of Whitelee was based in Stirling; then, it became somebody in Dunoon; and, and by the time, by 1986 when they decided to annex the whole of Whitelee to South Scotland, and it came into my patch, based in Straiton . . .

And as I think I said earlier on, later on it had Arran added to it. Now, Whitelee was roughly, the Whitelee Forest office was roughly twenty-five miles from the

"The Forgotten Forest": looking from Loudouns Water across Drumduff Hill to the 1980s experimental turbines
Photo: Ruth Tittensor

144

Straiton office. So inevitably, any management by me was done rather remotely. And I would rely fairly heavily actually on the, the local forester, a chap called Pat Armstrong at the time.

The last resident head forester, Pat Armstrong, retired in 1987, the Forestry Commission sold him his home (the residence of Whitelee Forest foresters), but the wooden shed forest office remained in forestry use for some while. From then on Whitelee Forest was never run by its own designated and resident forester. For a year or so, Kerr Robertson, forester on the Isle of Arran, visited once or twice a week to oversee operations. The squad continued its usual daily work under the watch of assistant forester Ken Whitaker and foremen Alan Mealy and Ian Peter. They all knew pretty well what needed to be done.

Local people felt Whitelee Forest was being forgotten. **Alexander Fenton** said what many others felt.

But I think, it's interesting that somebody's kind of taken it on board, and doing it, because, I mean I've always called it the 'Forgotten Forest', because people just... I mean, when it was part of Kyle district, it's now Scottish Lowlands, but it was part of Kyle district at Dunoon, I

mean it was just like, like, well you're just at Whitelee out o' the way, nobody bothered with it. Even the kind of higher management . . . You see what it is is, they don't have a squad there. They got rid of the squads. They did that in a lot of forest districts.

Possible Sale of Whitelee Forest

During the late 1970s and 1980s the Forestry Commission was expected to place more awareness on financial income than continuing to expand the area of trees planted. It was expected to get rid of as many of its 'disposable assets' as possible. Bill Sutherland experienced this personally, in two ways. Firstly, he found he could not buy the moorland farms still forming a big gap in the middle of Whitelee Forest. Farmer **John Telfer** explained this to Ruth Tittensor.

Ruth: . . . did you hear that the Forestry Commission was looking for land?

John: *Oh yes, Bill Sutherland* (pause) *came to Carrot you see. Looking for land. I knew they were looking for land you see, because, because eh,* (coughs) *the government suddenly had said that they weren't, the Forestry Commission were getting no land no land no more land.* (Coughs) *And* (pause) *Bill Sutherland came to me and explained the, and in fact you see he said,* **"So we'll swap you a bit over here and a bit over there".**

Right. Right. So you swapped some Carrot land for some Stoneyhill land?

Aye. And South Halls. But South Halls we went, er originally.

Was that a good swap? Was that in your favour?

Oh I think so yes. Well you see I was I was running out o land and so was he and he was scared that if the government stopped his money, forestry money as they said they were gonna do (pause) *. . . machinery and everything just lying going to waste . . . And then he came back and said he would do a an a an exchange for this farm here which is not a very good one but it's ten times better than Carrot.*

So they found a way round the stringencies which suited all concerned. But then **Bill Sutherland** found himself in an even more difficult situation, which he wrote about.

Around 1978 the financial situation changed. The Forestry Commission was forced to sell off surplus assets and to rationalise their forest ownership (i.e. dispose of smaller unmanageable properties or undesirable areas). I found myself trying to sell what I had previously purchased, and, as I was then approaching retirement age, I resigned and joined the EFC (Economic Forestry Group).

Tom and Janet Grant wrote about what they noticed at Whitelee Forest.

Attempts to sell Whitelee Forest. *In the 1970s, the Forestry Commission started selling the farmhouses, steadings and inbye of the Smallholdings. In all cases except one, the sitting tenant bought them; as sitting tenant, they paid only 50% of their value. The Forestry Commission also tried to sell Whitelee Forest itself. This was possibly in the 1990s. But no buyer could be found.*

Alister Jones explained how he was involved in the possible disposal of Whitelee Forest.

Ruth: Alister, Whitelee Forest, was it affected in any way by government, government desire at one point to rationalise and pin down statutory forestry in Britain and, and its wish to dispose of certain forest areas, for the Forestry Commission in other words to sell off some of its land?

Alister: *I suppose the answer is, yes and no. At, at my level of management, I was asked to consider and to suggest which areas of the overall estate, Forestry Commission estate, in, in my, in my patch, under my control, could be disposed of. Now a certain, certain criteria were suggested, such as, remoteness, poor access, not an important part of the current harvesting programme, say, just taking a five- or ten-year view, I can't remember the details . . .*

And so, it was fairly easy to begin with to list a number of areas that would meet most of these criteria. And the decision as to which would be as it were picked was taken at a, at another place. And, in my area of Ayrshire and Arran we did sell a few small, so-called isolated blocks.

Whitelee on the other hand, some people did suggest that Whitelee could be an area to sell in total, because, it was quite clear by the mid to late Eighties that it wasn't going to expand very much more; it was at least ten years if not fifteen before there was any significant start made on a harvesting programme. There was a question mark over the employment prospects for the, the men, as I was alluding to a minute ago.

Not that we wanted to go down the road of redundancy as such, and we did our best to try to avoid that. But, somehow, within higher levels of management, the idea of selling Whitelee didn't really take off. It would have been an extremely serious decision, big stakes you like to play for. But there was a rationale about keeping Whitelee. What you've got to think about is the fact that, in the 1980s a modern pulp mill was established at Irvine.

And, I'm not sure what the latest position is but it was built on a site and with a capacity to, with an ability to double its capacity in the medium term. There were also other timber-using industries being established along what was called the M74 corridor . . .

And so, really, Whitelee was not very far from existing markets for the type of timber that was being grown in Whitelee, and Whitelee together with similar forests from a wider catchment would be ideally placed for the possibility that another major pulp mill, and certainly sawmill, could be built in Central Scotland or along the M74.

And so, with its timber production being forecast for, say, the first ten years and twenty years of the twenty-first century, Whitelee could in theory be ideally situated. And, with a, with a, with that as a long-term prospect, Whitelee always went to the bottom of the pile as well as suggestions to get rid of it was concerned.

And that prevailed, well as I say, for the whole of my tenure there, and, as you can appreciate, there was, there was Politics with a big P behind this . . .

And, would there have been buyers, if you, if the Forestry Commission had decided to sell it?

Oh well, that we don't really know. Yes, the answer is, yes.

And **Hugh Hendry's** writings include a story recounted at that time.

Hugh Hendry said during the time towards the end of the Conservative government; the Caledonian Mill nearly bought Whitelee Forest. However, the talk of a potential Labour government probably stopped that happening!

Sale of Forest Workers' Holdings

Forest Workers' Holdings as well as some forests were counted as 'disposable assets' by the Forestry Commission, and so they too were likely properties for sale during the cut-back years at the end of the 1970s. **Gordon Cowie** discussed this subject.

Ruth: Well certainly the smallholdings seem to have been very much a way of life.

Gordon: *Yes. Some, some people really, it was an attraction. But, it became, as I say, more difficult to get people to take over . . .*

But, in that the tenants wanted them, the Forestry Commission didn't have any problem selling them, so why would it have sold them at Whitelee?

They were being sold generally because we were directed in the Eighties to sell all surplus assets. And these are any assets that didn't contribute to the primary objectives of the Forestry Commission. Sometimes we kept a worker's holding for strategic reasons. As I mentioned earlier, having somebody on site. I remember doing that in the Galloway Forest Park. But in a place like Whitelee, we had no strategic requirement. So we would have been willing sellers.

Yes. Right. Right. So this was to make money for the, for the Treasury.

Well, actually, holdings cost us money, on the whole. So it was to stop a drain on, on resources. And, also of course, there was the capital that we got. But generally we didn't get much money for the, the holdings.

Four of the five Forest Workers' Holdings at Whitelee Forest were sold, while Craigendunton became a ruin.

The Caledonian Paper Mill

In south-west Scotland, there were big expanses of state forests in Galloway, Argyll and on the Isle of Arran. **Gordon Cowie** spoke to Ruth Tittensor about the Finnish firm Kymmene setting up the 'Caledonian Paper Mill' near Irvine on the Ayrshire coast to accept the timber crops from these forests.

Ruth: And was it [Caledonian Paper Mill] placed there because of Whitelee Forest, or did it have nothing to do with that?

Gordon: *Well... Oh, very much, because of, not just Whitelee but all the forests in the south of Scotland, Arran, the productive areas. I mean, the pattern that we had with the investors was the, we had to satisfy them of timber availability for the next fifty years. On the basis that, that after fifty years... Timber is the ultimate renewable resource. Because you keep restocking.*

So, that was the primary objective. And, Whitelee, being such a large area, was part of the medium-term plan. So that, that was very much the case with Caledonian Paper.

Gordon Cowie even flew over Whitelee Forest with Kymmene executives to demonstrate to them the large size of its potential harvests. Thus there would be no problem with finding buyers for Whitelee Forest or its eventual harvest.

The paper-making machine in the Caledonian Paper Mill, Irvine, Ayrshire
Photo: Ruth Tittensor

The squad of course could not help seeing two besuited men from the 'Irvine Mill' being shown around Whitelee Forest by the head forester.

Reversal

Whatever did go on behind the scenes, Whitelee Forest was not sold by the Forestry Commission to the Caledonian Mill or anybody else under the government scheme for it to be rid of its 'disposable assets'. Planting newly acquired land with trees continued and the Forest carried on growing.

Forest Road

In the early days of Whitelee Forest here were no forest roads within it, so workers had to trudge daily across the moorland to their working sites. After the uncertainties of the 1980s, the Forestry Commission was still in control. This meant that the issue of transporting future harvested trees through the forest to a public road and a timber mill, as well as ingress and egress had to be addressed. Lorries loaded with harvested trees could not possibly traverse the peat bogs without a properly constructed hard core road. The time for harvesting the first final crop would come soon enough!

Alister Jones (with the new title of forest district manager for Ayrshire and Arran) described how and why the need for internal forest roading came about.

Much of the, many of the other parts of the forest had been bought piecemeal with separate accesses, and quite often these accesses allowed the Forestry Commission to come in to carry out the establishment operations and maintenance, but had not, were not suitable for the long, for the longer term and the days when harvesting would be needed.

And, if you wanted to get into the middle of Whitelee, you could get there from almost any point, leave your car or Land Rover and walk. (Laughs) And it, you know, it was a bit of a nightmare. That was not a very efficient use of, if you like, labour, because when they, if they were working in the middle of the forest, they would, it doesn't matter what time of day they arrived there, they would have possibly an hour's walk over rough land to get to the work site, and an hour, at the end of the day an hour to walk back.

The new forest road meets the public road at Ardochrig
Photo: John Struthers

149

But round about 1987/88, we had a fire in Whitelee... somewhere towards the eastern end. I think it was near Logoch. And, well, ironically, that wasn't very very far from a public road, but...

But, I pointed out to my superiors at the time was, **"Well, you were lucky that the whole forest didn't go up, and had, had there been a strong easterly wind that night, there would have been absolutely nothing we could have done about it"***. That fire could easily have burnt approximately a third or a half of the forest.*

And in terms of control and, from, say, Straiton where there was twenty-five miles via Kilmarnock, which is the best part therefore of an hour from office to the edge of the forest, and I've already said, possibly another hour to walk into the scene of the crime as it were, this really was a very unmanageable area.

Now, fortunately... Well, we were clearly aware of that, and, one of my first tasks was to, was really to make a case for a basic road, road construction programme . . .

Thinking ahead to harvesting. Well this hadn't really been done seriously. It was traditionally the case that when an area was planted, the forester would record what trees had been planted where; at some point after that he would assess how quickly they were growing. That would give an indication as to when the trees might be mature enough to harvest.

And based on this, there was a notion that quite large chunks of Whitelee would be harvestable by the late Nineties, 1990s. Now, quite honestly I think this was wishful thinking. I think quite a lot of areas had been totally overestimated, and so that became another priority for me, to ask for the first full forest survey... where we could get a detailed database of the areas, the species and the growth rates, and to use that information to, to get a decent estimate of when forestry production would start. And we did do that in the late 1980s. And that also pointed the way, the way to where the roads were required, or rather the sequence of road building . . .

And so the case was made for... Well, put it this way. Had the whole area been planned as a one-er, there would have been a basic network of road of approximately sixteen to eighteen kilometres . . .

And, because of developments at the north at Carrot, the possibility that harvesting, when it started, would be from the west, but that soils and roading conditions and quarries were better at the east, the whole thing began to make sense that we planned a basic criss-cross road system, but left the detailed planning of the network as a whole to follow the revised production forecast which would in turn follow the revised forest surveys. And by the time I left some of that road building had started.

Brian Speirs said that the squad had to clear a lot of trees blown down by the 'wind tunnel' created by the new forest road. And on soft peat, trees were laid flat to give a base for the road.

There was one road but towards the finish if you like, the Commission started building the roads using their own machinery, but we hud nothing to do wi that at all as a squad. They would, just did it theirself, eh, and that wes it, there was nothing at all as far as we were concerned. Nothing. They brought from Galashiels and all the way down, they brought them up from there, and lorries and thir diggers and thir bulldozers, these kind o things, to build thir roads . . .

But the one road that led towards Haptone was actually gaeing through the forest, so they cut a lot o the trees down the path o this, they actually laid the trees flat to use as a mat to put the stone and the brush on top o it.

Eh, they did that quite a lot o places actually, wi the softer ground the, the, the branches and the, the trunks were laid down, eh, they did that, but wi them gaun through like that, the first wind that got up caused a big wind-blow in the place beside it, each side o the road – a big wind-blow – and the squad boys were in trying to clear a lot o the trees that could possibly cross the road or partly cross the road – cleared that oot the road, to clear the road, but the rest ae it wes juist left. That wes it. That wes juist left.

The new forest road through Whitelee Forest met the Drumclog to East Kilbride public road at Ardochrig (Map 6 , page 153). It proved to be an unwritten, open invitation to the public of East Kilbride, Eaglesham and Strathaven to start visiting Whitelee Forest again, and enjoy what it had to offer. Without the Forestry Commission really noticing, public use of the Whitelee Plateau was increasing once more, though not in the same ways as the 1940s and 1950s.

Run Down and Redundancies

As conifer planting came to an end, the squad reduced to only four: Hugh McClymont, Ian Peter, Robert Peter, and Brian Speirs. Despite hopes for harvesting without a time gap, it became obvious that the first coup would not be ready until the early 21st century. Brian Speirs described the other sorts of work carried out by the squad while waiting for first harvesting.

Ruth: So did you at any time do any work connected with, um, providing facilities for walkers, um, or wasn't this part of your work if there weren't many people?

Brian: *It did not initially, wes part o the work wi walkers or the public, they were ignored. Later on, an, when I mean later on, I mean the past, the last two years. We did create, which initially wes a given walk which we called the Weaver's Walk, we tried tae improve that as much as we could, eh, that kind o thing, but only that kind o thing.*

Right, And what improvements did you, did you do, did you make any stiles or build any seats or um, clear the grass or…

We did build seats and stiles at both ends, we put down marker posts, and we – the path that a lot o people had walked we widened by cutting the grass. Any drains crossing it that had been overgrown wi grass and weeds, we cleaned tae let the public know the drain wes there, that kind o thing.

Yes. Right. Mm. Did you enjoy that sort of work?

I really did enjoy that kind o thing, really did enjoy it.

Despite the hopes of district manager Alister Jones that redundancy could be prevented, the four remaining squad

Whitelee squad preparing for a day's work, late 1980s
Photo: Grant Peter

The results of the squad's work: young oak and birch in autumn colours by the Pogiven Burn
Photo: Ruth Tittensor

members were given their statutory one week's notice of redundancy in 1994. After that, the only Forestry Commission staff to visit the Forest were wildlife rangers Alexander Fenton, Bob Logan and Jim Newall.

Despite guessing that it was coming, redundancy was a big shock to the squad members after their many years of loyal service. About 10 million conifers had been planted. These trees were growing and the first plantings would be ready for harvesting in less than a decade.

What an achievement for all concerned, considering the doubts of the suitability ('a stab in the dark') of Whitelee for a new forest thirty-three years earlier.

The Invisibility of the Forestry Commission

Whitelee Forest was complete, the last resident forester had retired, the squad run down and finally made redundant, and the Holdings sold. The familiar sight of Forestry Commission personnel in and around the Forest and surrounding communities became a memory. The trees carried on growing, the deer and foxes proliferated, other flora and fauna continued their lives in the naturally developing habitats.

Tom and Janet Grant were disappointed not to see anyone from the Forestry Commission again.

> There has been no one from the Forestry Commission seen on the Whitelee site since the last Forester left; he lived in the Forestry house at Waterside, to the west of the Forest. The Forester's house is in McKnight Avenue, Waterside. It was bought by the last Forester when he retired in the 1990s and called it 'Whitelee House'.

Gordon Cowie however, saw the positive side of post-conifer work which had extended the time that local staff were employed in Whitelee Forest.

> In some sensitive areas, the broadleaf percentage would go up to twenty per cent, and that was not seen as commercial, it was very much environmental. So, it wasn't a case, certainly not latterly, of putting the plough and sticking the tree in and shutting the gate for forty years.

152

Comment

Whitelee Forest's distance from successive administrative centres and from other big forest blocks produced isolating effects as well as feelings of it being forgotten. These feelings were enhanced by widespread knowledge of its possible sale in the1980s.

The Forestry Commission always compared it unfavourably with better-known forests. It was not managed by a resident forester after 1987. Its ecological, historical and archaeological significance were not realised by the Commission until the late 20th century. To local people there was cultural significance and traditions but the Commission showed little recognition of these and their importance in the neighbourhood. Little account been taken of the varied local uses of the Whitelee Plateau prior to its afforestation.

But **Alec Fenton** is positive about the future of Whitelee Forest.

What I think they need is, they need a, they need a team of people there, who are recreationally-minded and conservation-minded, and will go about and give talks, educational talks and stuff. And, start going that way. And, when the structure starts changing, it's going to be... I mean it's got a lot of potential... of the structure. It's changing. It will happen, but it's going to be a slow process.

And so is **Malcolm Crosby**.

Because it has been, it's been just parked around different places, nobody really knew where to put it, and now that, you know, it's, it's anchored very firmly to Scottish Lowlands, and it's a main part of our, our district.

So... its future is secure.

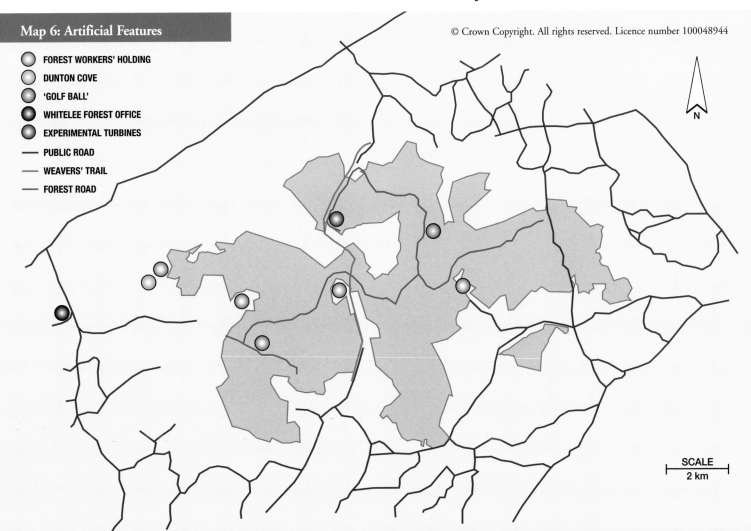

Map 6: Artificial Features

- FOREST WORKERS' HOLDING
- DUNTON COVE
- 'GOLF BALL'
- WHITELEE FOREST OFFICE
- EXPERIMENTAL TURBINES
- ⎯ PUBLIC ROAD
- ⎯ WEAVERS' TRAIL
- ⎯ FOREST ROAD

N

SCALE
2 km

CHAPTER 12

How the Forest Affected Local People

Widespread Effects

Planting 10 million trees on a this upland plateau gradually transformed the visible landscape. But people also felt the consequences in their everyday lives.

Farmers and Farming

The effects on local farms depended upon whether they were hill or moorland farms, whether all or part of the land was sold, and the proportion which went to forestry. Loss of any land to a farmer meant a rethink in the way the farm was run. And forestry operations on the recently-sold land still impinged on farmers in many ways. These matters were discussed by several contributors. **Jim Leitch** wrote about the effects on the hill farm of Gateside.

The new Forest gave shelter to Craigends steading
Photo: Ruth Tittensor

There were big effects of the coming of Whitelee Forest on local farmers. They could not resist the money offered them. But they knew their farms might not be viable afterwards, and they mostly had to get extra work – off their farms. They might work at places like nearby nurseries or tomato growers. Gateside farm has more lower-lying land than other nearby farms, so it was more of a 'mixed' farm, and did not lose so much land to the Forest.

Another farm, which had a huge expanse of very poor-quality moorland to sell, was affected differently. **Tom and Janet Grant's** writings assessed the reasons.

Mr Grant Senior sold some of the land of Brocklees farm to the Forestry Commission for Whitelee Forest. It was very soggy ground of moss and peat. However, selling the land did not affect the farm deleteriously, for two reasons. First, with skill, it was possible to keep the same number of sheep afterwards as before. The sheep were brought down to the nearer, lower, better ground. They did not have to sell the hill sheep. Secondly, the finances gained from selling the land were invested in other farmland. This was some of the better land of the nearby Burnfoot farm.

The growing Forest sheltered all Logoch inbye
Photo: Ruth Tittensor

On a more pragmatic level they suggested that the Forest provided some shelter from the weather.

Pauline: *So. Wis there any positive effects on your farm or or any negative effects on your farm.*

Tom: [softly] *Ah dinnae think so. Ah cannae think* [normal] *Ah don't think it's made a great lot o difference either way. In a richt wild nicht at lambing time if the*

Beef cattle at Brocklees benefit
from the Forest's shelter
Photo: Ruth Tittensor

155

wind's blawin the right wey we were thankful tae the forestry for shelter. Ye go oot at night there...ye go oot there . . .

The family of **Iain Hamilton** sold their own farm of Low Overmoor so as to buy their other, tenanted, farm, which was on much better soils.

Pauline: Did you sell land tae the Forestry?

Iain: *Ma faither did. By that time ma faither wis the tenant at Allanton farm and Low Overmoor wis sacrificed tae purchase it. Just, as Ah say, it wis an opportune moment there. They were offerin mair than ye could make off the bloomin place, break it tae plant trees on it. It's when yer business heid takes ower fae the romance, it whit ye caw the realities o life.*

An ye got a good price for it, obviously.

Och aye. He wisnae unhappy aboot it but Ah don't know if land [indistinct] hadnae hae been decided tae sell aff the ferms Ah wid probably still had it, that's somethin Ah don't know, ye cannae answer.

An he used the cash tae buy the...

Well that's right he got a chance tae buy the other ferm.

Jim Kennedy described the immediate effects on his farming when parts of Moss Mulloch were ploughed in readiness for forestry.

Jim: *The way they ploughed for, for forestry, the the – It wis so flat, of course, an there were – eh – hill drains – juist gutters as ye would say – goin that way. But for some reason, they, the way they were ploughin it, they ploughed across these, an they divertit the water, which startit floodin through the fence into the ground that we were left wi. So ah approached them an said, ai, here, ye'll need tae do sumthin about that. You've diverted the water. So wuthout any trouble, they come an put a big three-foot ditch, juist inside their ground, right round the, the fence, an it caught any water, an it [? drained]. So that's...*

Ruth: Yeh. yeh. They were good neighbours.

O ay. O ah couldnae, ah couldnae complain. They're no, they're no hassle.

And he noticed certain benefits when the trees grew up.

Jim: *No, ah wis delightit when the trees got up.* (Laughter from Ruth) *Ah mean it wis quite sheltered for the sheep. Because it was – a mean, when ye look at that, a mean, its – if you take a s, a wet sleety day wi snow, it's a bleak place up there, a mean – as ah sa(id), the nearest, the nearest shelter's Loudoun Hill, that's four mile away.* (Laughs).

Jim Kennedy noticed that although the growing trees gave shelter to the lambing ewes, one of twins often disappeared in the few days after birth even when it had been perfectly healthy and lively. He put this down to more foxes living on Moss Mulloch now it was forest-covered.

Archie Mitchell took over Whatriggs from Mr Mathew Mitchell Senior in 1972. He explained that they had very little contact with the Forest in earlier times, but his wife had put up a worker in the Bed and Breakfast in the 1960s.

Whatriggs took in paying guests Photo: Ruth Tittensor

Naw, as far as the forest wis concerned we ...that wis the only contact we had really were these men that stayed wi us, if Anne hadnae decidit tae start daein bed and breakfast at the time we would never have likely met these men. The came fae a bit away, they came fae Dumfries...

They were actually ploughin it so that the trees would be plantit oan top o the furrow that wis put oot by they great big ploughs. At that time that wis the only wey they could dae that. Noo they have what they call 'dollopin', they just go in wi a track digger an pu oot a dollop and plant the tree in the toap o it. Now that would have been a much better wey o daein for that kind o land because it's really soft up there.

And **Archie Mitchell** emphasised that the effects of Whitelee Forest on the landscape were minimal: having two forestry workers staying as paying guests was much more important to the family than landscape changes beyond the farm boundary.

Ruth: So to sort of summarize then; you don't feel the Whitelee Forest has really had much influence on your life and the farm, it doesn't affect you now and it doesn't affect the view or…

Archie: *The only wey Ah see that would affect the view, it would affect the view fae High Bowhill. Ah remember Mrs Blair, when the Blairs were there, Mrs Blair wis very keen on her garden an she got a winda put in facin that wey an it wis a winda at the toap o the stairs an she wis always gaun oan aboot the view she had fae this winda and it would look right ower the but then subsequently they built a shed oot there so that would've spylt the view onywey. But Ah quite sure that that view would have looked away over where the Whitelee Hill foarest is.*

It hasnae really affected us at the time these men were steyin here we would have been very grateful for the extra income fae the bed and breakfast…at that time Anne did supper at night …

And they were here five days a week?

Five days a week and then they went away hame.

And that was what? For a year or two?

Must have been for a year anyway.

So it wis regular.

Aye, ken, it wis through the winter as well as through the summer. Aye, we would be very grateful at the time for that. It wis something we could dae that didnae depend

oan the weather and we have a big hoose here which we werenae really needin.

Archie Mitchell's son, **Mathew Mitchell** now farms Whatriggs and High Bowhill as a unit. He spoke about several aspects of farming next to the Forest. Ruth Tittensor first asked him about the modern landscape.

Ruth: And what about Whitelee Forest today, um, and the landscape, um, around, y-, you farm close to the forest, an there are all these other farms around the forest, um, what are the views from this sort of area like? is it, is it a beautiful area?

Matt: (Coughs). *Well the top o Hyver Hill of course, ye don't get really much ae a view into the forest. But we're at the, the, what are we? the south-western edge, so a mean the views west are, are tremendous, an ye're up the top there, ye can actually see over the top of it to further up the west coast so a mean from our farm ye see right over tae Arran, eh, an then further, further south fae that tae the hills down there so, ay, we've a great viewpoint, eh, eh, the further up the farm ye go, eh, but the'r nuthin wrong wi trees either, I don't mind lookin at the trees,*

Right, good (both laugh.) So Whitelee Forest, does it r-, does it affect the views from your farm at all?

What? No, no, no; certainly no frae the steadings, eh, no; no at all.

So is the landscape important to your business at all?

No to any point o makin money, no . . .

And what about your bed n breakfast visitors, d'they use the forest for recreation at all?

Naw, it's, it's not a recreation forest, it's a commercial forestry, there's no paths intae it. A mean, for all this talk o, o right of access an right tae roam an things, yer general public, a mean, bar yer very few, eh, fanatics, they want a path, they want a laid-out path, they want tae know where they're goin, they don't want to suddenly go up tae their thighs in a bit o bog or, eh, drop their mobile phone in there an think that's, ye know, curtains, eh − . . .

John and Edith Telfer's spoken memories about how they felt as a result of Whitelee Forest appearing on their doorstep were written down.

> *When Mr and Mrs Telfer had sold or swapped much of Carrot Farm to the Forestry Commission, they sold the small amount of remaining land to an English farmer who wanted to farm a small area. They left and moved to Stoneyhill Farm, near Dungavel. They were very pleased to leave Carrot Farm, which was such a difficult place to live and farm. Mr Telfer stated that he was not at all sad about the Carrot land being planted with trees and becoming a forest.*

Farm Pests

According to **Tom and Janet Grant**, foxes increased after the Forest was planted.

Pauline: . . . Who carries out the pest control?

Tom: *We shoot them. Well it's no me now it's ma son now he shoots maybe 50 foxes every year.*

That's a a fox a week virtually.

No. Aye, aye but it's condensed may fae October through

Foxes lived in the growing Forest, but came onto the farms to feed
Photo: Forestry Commission Picture Library

the winter. Ye could shoot some the whiles the just gaun aboot in fact Ah heard him say that there were some in his garden. She said he wis supposed tae be shootin foxes and she went oot an night and found three playin in her garden. (laughs) *But naw ye shoot them for the sake o the lambs. But there far more foxes now fae the forestry started…yaised tae be only see an oad [odd] fox but we had tae start an do something…an kill…an no lose so mony lambs. An they werenae too keen aboot a trapper an we couldnae get onybody tae keep shootin them so that is we started wirsel Ah got a gun and that hoo we started oorsels tae keep them down.*

David Findlay was also unhappy about pests in relation to Whitelee Forest.

Ruth: Is the land, um, looked after for, for game and, and pest control?

David: *No. Definitely not. Naw, n-, no in the Forestry anyway. Na, because the Forestry, they're never there. Ye get the, the forester'll come once-twice a year, eh, an that's about it really. Eh, the pest control's aw doun tae the like o us an the farmers.*

Right, right. So the Forestry Commission doesn't have anybody to do pest control?

Nn, they have, but there's, there again they're so big an organisation, they can't be everywhere, so they're only there at certain times, so

So that's why there are so many foxes and deer really?

Yeh, ay, ah mean the deer don't really do any harm, it's the foxes that's, that's out killin.

Foxes were also mentioned by **Matt Mitchell**.

Ruth: An I think you've already said that it doesn't, hasn't, um, had any real bad effect on pests and weeds coming onto the, to the farm

Matt: *Eh, the only thing I would say would be the foxes; foxes an deer, eh, it provides cover for aw them, um, so it wid be interestin to see actually, eh, when it is felled next tae our own farm, eh, juist what difference that makes, eh,* *whether it makes a sizable difference or no, eh, that's the only reason you can* [tell].

And Matt suggested that the species of weeds on his farm are determined by the type of ground conditions there and are not affected by Whitelee Forest.

Employment and Unemployment

An important aspect of the Forestry Commission's work was to assist rural employment. Several contributors commented on this aspect of Whitelee Forest.

Tom Grant explained that although the Forestry Commission did most things themselves, he got a few odd jobs when he was a young man.

> **Pauline:** Did you have any direct or personal involvement in Whitelee Forest ehm an could ye explain direct involvement other than sellin land…if ye took work wi the Forestry Commission or private companies or contractin or advisin them an giein yer own comments or lodgin workers.

> **Tom:** *Naw we never plantit nae trees oot. That wis only two three oors in the day …they trees oot Ah worked that wi the tractor maybe for three weeks for poaket money…We never had much either involvement with them so we didnae, for they had their ain men tae dae everything an yince they got startit right they broaght their ain men an they did everyhin thirsel the had heir ain tractors – they did everything thirsels – their ain plantin squads, ditchin squads they never employed anybody or very little people outwith at the finish up…*

Aye,

> *But it's jist hoo it's changed noo Ah don't think they've got anybody here . . . My first job. My first job. When Ah left the school wis [indistinct] a farm worker. That wis ma first job. Aw ma life…but ah did when the forestry started at Haptone* (Hapton) *Ah goat an odd day now and again Ah got sent wi a tractor an a transport box over tae Haptone an putting out trees for the forestry workers tae plant an then Ah had a wee while ..two or three weeks..plantin trees with Mr Malone he planted some o the trees at Haptone but generally speaking Ah wis a farm worker a shepherd an herded sheep at Brocklees. A farmworker* [indistinct].

And their son Young Tom earned some money at the pumps during a recent forest fire (see Chapter 10).

Employment in the Whitelee Forest area was not an urgent necessity to the locality. The nearby towns still had busy textile factories which employed people from far afield. There were often vacancies for Forest workers, which suggests that the locality was not short of employment. The full squad consisted of ten men.

Willie Malone's (the contractor) men worked for a few busy planting years in the mid 1960s; other contractors came on the scene occasionally. Prisoners from Dungavel prison came to assist with hand draining occasionally. The Whitelee Forest workers came mainly from the small towns of the Irvine Valley in Ayrshire, with none from bigger towns to the north and east (in Renfrewshire and Lanarkshire).

The tractor drivers were mainly existing Forestry Commission employees from elsewhere in Scotland, who travelled to whatever forest needed ploughing at any particular moment.

At its busiest, Whitelee Forest was a '2 forester unit' (one head forester and one forester) but after 1987 it supported a part-time, non-resident forester only. The forester grade personnel were not of local origin. The Forestry Commission sent them to Whitelee Forest (or any other forest in Britain) from their previous posting, so they did not fill local employment gaps.

Although during the twentieth century the number of local farm workers had been declining, there were still some shepherds working on the Whitelee Plateau in the 1960s. Low Overmoor had a shepherd when it was sold for forestry; he moved away when the sheep were taken off the land. Mr Willy McWhirter, father of contributor Dougie Mc Whirter, had run Carrot farm along with two shepherds, for Lord Weir since 1966. He and the other shepherds moved away after Carrot was sold by Lord Weir to the Telfer family (and later the Forestry Commission).

From the pool of over twenty families selling land for afforestation, only two farming sons and no farmer took work with the Forestry Commission (as its staff had optimistically envisaged). One of the two farm sons tenanted a Forest Workers' Holding which was the remaining inbye of his parents' farm, and the other drove tractors and diggers for a while.

James Mair emphasised to Ruth Tittensor that the Forest did not employ farmers.

> **Ruth:** Do you know whether the forest had other local effects, such as the building of new public roads, or any other public utilities or facilities?
>
> **James:** *I think none at all.*

Yes. So, in a sense you could say that Whitelee Forest has been sort of neutral. I shouldn't be asking you leading questions. (laughter)

I wouldn't like to say that, but... It's, it hasn't led to an improvement in roads. It has helped to reduce the number of people working locally in that area. And they haven't employed the people who worked there before. I mean the farmers haven't become forestry workers.

Farming and forestry are very different worlds, so it was possibly naive for the Forestry Commission to expect farmers to work as forest employees rather than decision-making managers of their own land. Several sons of families who had sold farms for afforestation saw it as an opportunity to get out of the endless drudge to which to they had been brought up, and found other jobs or careers off the land.

When the moorland of the Whitelee Plateau was planted with trees, gamekeepers were no longer needed to carry out all the duties connected with grouse, other game and pests. **Robin Chambers'** written memories explained how this affected the keeper on Lord Weir's estate, Iain Stewart.

> *But Mr Robin Chambers agrees with many people that the coming of the Forestry Commission was a lifeline to many farmers, as they got far more for selling their land than it was worth. It did, however, mean the end of work and jobs for moorland keepers in the area, and Mr Stewart retired.*

According to countryman **Jim Currie**, Whitelee Forest removed a lot of ad hoc employment that was important to the young people – well, the lads anyway – of his day, namely the possibility of earning money helping with all sorts of small jobs.

> **Jim:** *Yeh. Tattie howkers. Whit they used ti do wi the tattie howkers.* (Hoasts) *Ye hid, at certain seasons, where a lot. Where the locals come intae it. They come in for the, like, tattie pickin. We got off the school. We got a fortnight's holidays. An ye went tae aw the fairms an picked. An ye got paid fur it. Ken. Mean it wis aw the dunnerheids got aff the schuil ti go an pick tatties. An ye aw. But as faur as a'm concerned, that suited me away doun ti the grund. Gaun pickin tatties. An then. We got [??] Where ah wis they used ti. An the Manufacturers* hud their shoots. [?] feedin. An they aw hud shoots. They hud beaters. An aw, a mean. They'd mebbe come shootin fur three weeks. They mebbe hud three or four shoots in the week. A mean I used ti get ten bob. Well. Ten bob in thae days. An ye hid ten bob in the. An every. A mean. They'd mebbe thirty or forty beaters. An thae boys wid trample aw ower thae hills, down an dale. Up the back here.*

* [owners of towns' textile factories]

> **Ruth:** These were local boys?
>
> *Yes. Now that. Onyhing. That. I wid say, these wur the only two things that really bro(ch)t in a lot ae people. An it wis a. Definitely lik a seasonal thing. Ken. An. Like ah say, yer keepers wur there. But. A mean eventually, thay died out. Ken the keepers aw. But e- economically. It wis the economics o The Forestry destroyed it. There wis more money in it, but…*

Thirty or forty local boys and men working on game shoots several days each week in the season was a lot of local employment that disappeared.

Access and Recreation

Being an explorer on foot, **Bryan Simpson** had great difficulties actually traversing the new Forest in his quests for plant and animal life. He explained how he felt about the changing landscape.

Access became difficult and the view very limited!
Photo: Ruth Tittensor

So, I don't think I was too negative about it actually. I thought, well... I don't think then I fully realised, in fact I'm quite sure I didn't fully realise, the extent of the Whitelee Forest, what it was going to be eventually you know. That it was going to stretch for miles and miles and cover nearly all the hill country that I used to walk on. I

think I might have been a little less sanguine about it if I'd realised the extent of it you know. Losing all this peat bog.

Hugh Hendry said he also had trouble getting into the new forest.

Ruth: And at Whitelees, as you saw the forest growing did you carry on going up there and doing all the things you used to do?

Hugh: *Up tae a point but it then became very limited, because ye were limited really where ye could walk because it endit up basically that the only place ye could walk, in actual fact wis in the areas where they planned oot for their roadways so that they were like quite wide tracks that were left within the forest and that wis the only areas, in actual fact, ye could walk in and even at that there wi the growth o the vegetation it wis hard work. It wis hard work.*

Because there were no longer any sheep there grazing…?

That's right, another point, in actual fact, that there were literally no game – went void – that wis after the trees had like, formed a canopy. At the start, after the forest wis planted, once the various area within the forest wis planted – remember there wis quite large areas o the moorland left unplanted.

Matt Mitchell did not use the adjoining Whitelee Forest as a play area when a lad.

Ruth: Um, so you never went into, you never went into the forest apart from once to get a Christmas tree [so you] don't stray in it too often.

Matt: *No, no, it wasn't exactly a play place, no, no, they're jaggy, those trees. They're not for tree-huggers (Ruth laughs) although I believe some try.*

(Laughing) No I shouldn't think so – and so –

Huv ye no heard about that?

What, people hugging trees?

Ye wur talkin about Craigins*, ye wur talking about Craigins* earlier. That seems tae be a, a group that owned some trees up there that . . . Aa, they've a habit o comin *out on buses an, eh, shedding their clothes and jumping into the forest and hugging these trees.*

* [Craigends]

Right, right, well that's a new to me! (Both laugh.)

Well, if, eh, if it hud been a beech tree ye could understand it, but eh Sitka Spruce is not scuddy-friendly (laughs).

He reckoned that a burn was a far better playground for a child.

. . . y'know, there's a, there's a burn, a wee river runnin doun throu the, the meadow next to the house so a mean that wis far more invitin, y'knaw, playin in a wee burn wi the stones an dams an whatever.

Iain Hamilton bemoaned the loss of access to the meeting point of the three counties Ayrshire, Lanarkshire and Renfrewshire, but not the wet days lambing out on the moors!

The squad ensured the Watson family grave stayed free of trees
Photo: John Speirs

Hugh Maxwell next to Ben's gravestone
Photo: John Speirs

Well away at the tap end at Low Overmuir there ye could pit a haund in Renfrewshire a fit in Lanarkshire and anither fit in Ayrshire. There's no many place ye can dae that, three counties in wan. There's some stunnin views away fae the top end, ye cannae dae these things noo, I mean it's a physical impossibility. Ah think the last time Ah wis up Low Overmuir road end would be twa year

back an when Ah came back doon Ah had a tear in ma ee because Ah used tae walk they hills regularly but ye cannae dae that noo. Ah could take ye tae certain bits but Ah think even Ah wid get loast.

Ah find that a kinda bafflin thing tae ask aboot the views because ye canne do it [walk] anymore. Ah suppose the generation followin mine they cannae recollect these things, I can but when ye stert lookin back ye look at things through rose tintit glesses aye seem tae be better, it's no really. When yer walkin the hills wi dugs, a stick, a lambin bag oan a pishin wat day it's no a bit romantic. Ye unnerstaun whit Ah'm sayin?

Alec Fenton, squad worker and deer-stalker, spoke to Ruth Tittensor of the difficulties of walking even in the maturing Whitelee Forest.

Ruth: Yes. Yes. And if you walked through this Forest, what's it like to walk through?

Alec: *To be honest with you, I mean it was, although in some areas it was fairly flat and was fairly boggy underfoot, and, and some areas over to the west was sort of, a lot of rank heather, and it's, it's murder to walk through it, to be quite honest with you. (laughter) And,*

162

it's a bit soul-destroying to walk through. And, I mean people come in, a lot of people come in. When I was, when I was out at the deer-stalk there you get people out walking, you get people out cycling and stuff.

Planted in 1966, it was difficult to walk through even for a stalker used to rough ground Photo: Ruth Tittensor

Waterways and Fishing

Nearly 90 waterways flow off the Whitelee Plateau into the Rivers Avon, Clyde and Irvine. In often heated discussions, Whitelee Forest was sometimes blamed for changes to the waterways and the water-table of the Plateau.

Iain Hamilton described the effects of the initial forestry ploughing and the opening of the furrows into the drains or 'scheuchs'.

Pauline: Were there any changes in the water table or the flow o the burns or the fish?

Iain: *Oh Aye. Dramatically so. Obviously, because by the time they tied in aw their sheuchs. Ah always remember the moss it wis like a great big bit o blottin paper that soaked up everything and it wis a slow release intae the burns, Ah mean burns would take maybe five or six oors tae stert risin an they would be at ful spate for maybe a day and then it wid take twa days for a spate tae die back. But wi the comin o the Forestry watter levels rose that much*

quicker an the spate didnae last as long it run aff quicker, in that case ye would get an increase in river speed, in that sort o sense there wis a doon side, but Ah suppose they didnae waant their trees feet wat for too long or they wouldnae survive so Ah can unnerstaund the reason for them daein it.

Tom and Janet Grant also spoke about how the forest affected the local water flows – but not the midges!

Pauline: Dae ye notice any adverse affects on the weather or other than the so-called Global Warmin that we're having.

Tom: *Naw. This is juist a small part Ah wid say. The only thing it did do when it ….when ye got a lot o rain the burn went up quick it went doon quick whereas it took maybe a day tae get up it would go up in two or three hours an ye'd get a flash flood an then went back doon. That's the only difference we ever seen. We'd midges afore the Forestry wis there an we've still goat them yet an we'll still hae them when they're away.* (general laughter) *I don't like it. It's no made a lot o difference Ah don't think.*

Little Calder in spate, flooding more frequently after forestry ploughing Photo: Ruth Tittensor

163

The purity and constant flow of burns for drinking were what interested **Jim Currie**.

Ruth: (Still laughing.) Well, just carry on with what you're saying about the changes that, the changes that you've seen, as the forest was planted and developed.

Burns narrowed noticeably, affecting the fish populations
Photo: Ruth Tittensor

Jim: *Well. Yeh. An like ah say. The biggest. Ah keep comin back tae it. But the biggest thing ah wid say wis the rivers an the burns an aw that. Thae burns wid get wa-. They'd be rinnin aw year roun. Summer winter. Ye heard about drinks an aw this cairry oan. A mean I used tae walk there an. Ye always hid a billie can. There wis always a burn wi watter in it. But once they drained it aw an the forest wis – aw thae burns aw dried up in the summer. Ken.*

Lichenologist **John Douglass** has noticed the narrowing, drying burns and was concerned about 20 freshwater lichens which depend upon water flow and oxygenation, as well stable, water-covered boulders on which to grow.

Fisherman **David Findlay** reckoned that the forest affected local waterways, but that other factors like weather and farming made the situation complex to understand.

There is local agreement, from people with different interests, that Whitelee Forest has deleteriously affected the 90 burns of the Whitelee Plateau.

Catching Song Birds

Hugh Hendry wrote that as Whitelee Forest grew, people had to change how they caught song birds.

In the early autumn there were small songbirds – particularly bullfinches ('bulliss') and greenfinches – on the moors in droves. They fed on the heather seed.

Local people who kept budgerigars and canaries used to go and catch the wild songbirds to breed with the canaries and budgerigars. Before the trees were planted, they caught the wild birds in nets. When the Forestry Commission's planted trees started to grow up, the people put 'bird lime' on the trees' branches. 'Call birds' were brought with them – these were also usually bullfinches – and the call birds attracted the wild birds which landed on the sticky branches and stuck to the bird lime, ready to be caught by the local people.

Local Community

There were initial effects on local trade and particular economic benefits for those who now had steadings or flocks of sheep to sell, **Tom and Janet Grant** said.

Pauline: The effect of Whitelee Forest on the local community. Do ye know if there has been any benefits tae the Valleys, Strathaven, Eaglesham, Waterside and Moscow [can't be right]?

Tom: *Ah wouldn't think so Ah wid think there wis a big lot o benefit for…it's changed circumstances noo…now…it would make a wee bit difference tae start wi…markets, haulers wid loss a percentage o thir trade wi nae sheep tae take tae market the market wid hae no sheep tae sell, eh…eh…feed merchants an eh* [indistinct] *agents widnae be sellin as much wi the sheep that come offa here an the Whitelee Forest but the positive side is poabably where the Forestry boat the whole farm. At the finish up wi the Forestry…where they'd the whole farm they sold the house… the steadin tae a worker at the finish up maybe fifteen year ago maybe. When they boat Whitelee Hill they sold it tae the worker that wis in it that wis a condition…*

they got the farm...they got the holdin fae the Forestry at the finish up the Forestry sold the steadin an the grounds tae the worker now there very few o them left. They've made more money sellin it as a country home tae a good lifestyle body that wants tae stay in the country and it's worth more now for that than the whole thing wis put together. It's bringing mair money in that wey as it ever did than wi the Forestry Ah wid think.

When the workers of Whitelee Forest were made redundant and the forest office closed, **Richard Roberts** said it affected the local economy of Waterside.

Richard: *. . . I found it quite delightful that we were in this small rural Ayrshire settlement, but we had the Forestry Commission with a centre there, employing quite a number of local people. I used to see the crew bus turning up in a morning, the lads going off out with their tools, heading for Strathaven or wherever. There was always an office with, in fact, I can't remember the name, but, a lady from Fenwick was employed full-time in the office. So we had a little industry in Waterside.*

Ruth: Richard, do you think that the forest of Whitelee has had any effects of any kind on the local economy?

I think, I think it has, in, in the microcosm, the cessation of planting and, and really any effect apart from timber harvesting. The local shop in Waterside suffered very badly with...

Suffered badly?

Yes, well... when, when the planting ceased... suddenly there were fourteen or sixteen lads who weren't buying their papers and their cigarettes at Nellie Gibb's little shop . . .

He then mentioned the current, unforeseen difficulties of removing harvested timber – compared with just bringing in bundles of tree seedlings all those years ago. Residents on the west of the Whitelee Plateau are experiencing problems from forest on land originally sold by farmers to private forestry companies.

Ruth: Have there been any effects on things like infrastructure, roads, have...

Meikle Hareshaw sold its dairy herd to concentrate on sheep and beef
Photo: Ruth Tittensor

Laigh Hapton, once a small farm, was renovated as a modern residence
Photo: Ruth Tittensor

Whatriggs changed from mixed to sheep farming
Photo: Ruth Tittensor

Richard: *No.*

No. (laughs)

To, to put it mildly. And of course, the, the big problem now is that, it's easy to carry a sapling, you know, or a seedling, to be planted. It's a hell of a different matter, taking out logs. And, and, you know, this is one, one of the great problems around Waterside, how are we going to get these trees out? Because these roads are single-track roads. They're not designed for heavy vehicles. A lot of them along the greater part of the length are across peat bog. And, here we are now faced with a problem, how to get some return on all this land that was used for timber production . . .

You envisage some of it coming out towards Waterside [inaudible]...?

I... Well, well, there are, there are, because the Economic Forestry Group had a, you know, a few plantations and so on. And, there's still this problem of forestry vehicles coming out from, down Hemphill into Moscow.

That's already started, has it?

It's already started. And, one suspects in fact that there will be pressure on the Hairshawmuir road, dead end road from, from the A719... to, to get timber out from there. So, it's, it is a big problem, but... In a way, it's leading to a degree of sort of rural deprivation, because, you know, you're not going to be able to drive on a road that is fit to be called a road. Because of heavy lorries on, on roads that were never designed for the purpose, you know.

Yes. I've found that round on the south-east side of the forest, that the roads are deteriorating and the banks... on either side are... disappearing.

Disappearing, yes. I mean it's, it's getting like the old days of the stagecoaches and the wagons.

(Laughs) Yes.

You just move over another yard, you know, when one lot gets too boggy or broken down. So, you know, (laughter) it's nothing new under the sun, one suspects . . .

Mm. So how do the residents of Waterside and Fenwick view the forest?

Well they hate it now, because of the, the log lorries. Which, which are going to be quite a problem for quite a number of years. Because if you think, I mean, I'm not exactly certain when they did stop planting, but, I would think that it would be another twenty years before, you know, the last planted areas will be reasonably economically harvestable.

Right. So, so they and you were thinking of twenty years of, of lorries [inaudible word].

Of intermittent lorries trundling by laden with logs, on as I say, you know, single-carriageway roads.

Craigendunton is now a residence tightly surrounded by forest
Photo: Ruth Tittensor

Comment

Selling their whole farm allowed farmers to retire and their sons to get new, better-paid jobs. Or, if they sold only the farm's poorest land, they could use the finances to buy some better ground and improve their overall farm management. They put up with any practical disadvantages of forestry operations next door, and benefited from the shelter to which they were not accustomed. The midges remained, however!

To local communities who had frequently used the open Plateau, access became impossible on big ploughed furrows or amongst prickly treelets. People stopped going there. Sites of cultural significance could no longer be visited. Employment was generated on a small scale, but some skilled rural workers lost their jobs. People used to earning a bit in their spare time lost their fun and pocket money. Farmers, farming and rural life had, however, started to change for other reasons unconnected with Whitelee Forest. The European Union and its Common Agricultural Policy came to exert far-reaching influences on rural life and business.

What happened to the native residents of the Whitelee Plateau – the flora and fauna – when the Forest was planted and grew? In the next chapter, contributors describe what they observed.

CHAPTER 13

Ecological Changes After the Forest

Immediate Changes Seen By People

The black-headed gulls, whose eggs had been collected for food, changed their behaviour when forestry ploughing started. **Hugh Hendry** wrote about what happened.

> Eggs collecting started to die away when forestry ploughing to plant trees commenced and the birds started to move away from the main areas of the Hags and Lochfield Loch and nest in smaller quantities approx 10–20 pairs over a larger area including north-west of Croilburn Farm, east of Whitelee Farm and south of High Overmuir. Thus, after the Forest came, – to begin with – the gulls spread out (from their original few nesting hags) over the Whitelee Forest area to form lots of little colonies, such as at Flow Moss, where it is marshy.
>
> . . . then the gulls disappeared with the Forestry from these hills.

But he saw how the water which collected in the ploughed furrows attracted wild duck.

> When the Forestry Commission started ploughing the muirs it had bought at Whitelee, deep furrows and high ridges were formed. Until cross-drains were put in later, the furrows acted as deep-water channels in which rainwater collected. Sometimes the water level was quite deep, or even over the top of the ridges too. Initially, when there were no cross-drains, the water did not flow, unless the furrows were down the slope rather than across it. All these waters attracted wild duck, which increased a lot after ploughing.
>
> Thus an early effect of the new Whitelee Forest was to increase the number of wild duck. The duck were mainly mallard. When cross-drains were put in the water did not remain so noticeably in the furrows.

And he made another interesting observation on the reactions of birds to forestry ploughing.

> There were lots and lots of black grouse between Allerstocks and the Overmoor farms. There were also loads south of Pley Moss, where they nested in the heather. When Mr Hendry shot black grouse, and then opened them up, he always found their crops were full of rowan berries. This surprised him, because there were hardly any rowan trees south of Pley Moss. Rowans were most common towards Waterside (beyond the western boundary of Whitelee Forest). The black grouse season was very short . . .

When Whitelee Forest first started . . . the forestry plough turned over a long line of peat. What had been surface-vegetation was turned over and in, so that the heather was pushed under a ridge of the peat. Very soon afterwards, young heather started growing out of the side of the long line of overturned matter – then the black cock and grey hen increased considerably in numbers very soon after that over a wider area.

So the initial response by birds varied according to the species concerned.

Gradual Changes

Brian Speirs knew the Whitelee Plateau intimately from before the Forest until he left work in 1994. He had many memories of what he observed over the years.

Ruth: Can you remind me some of the most common birds you used to see up there?

Brian: *In the open hills – Curlews. Lapwings. Red grouse. Skylarks. Golden plovers. And that wes about the size of it, that wes about the bird population*

And were they common, were they common all of these?

They were very common really. Very common

And were they still there even after the trees had been planted?

The only thing that remained. Or the only bird that remained. Wes the curlew. It went on nesting until the trees were mebbe four foot high. And then it disappeared.

But the rest, no, they were away as soon as the – the operation started. They were away.

Yes. But did any new sorts of birds start coming to live in the – the new forest? Or in – or wasn't there anything that particularly liked...

No really. Once the trees were up. There wes a lot o different birds. But initially. Four–five foot trees, naw. Naw, there wasn't . . .

As we went over a hill with each new planting area, the wildlife there at the time was typical moorland wildlife, curlew, peeweet, golden plover, there wes skylarks, meadow pipits, the occasional hen-harriers, weasels, foxes. There was adders,

(Amused.) Oh, right.

There wes lizards, that wes about the extent ae it. As the trees grew up all that disappeared. Eh, but later on as the trees got bigger, a different type o wildlife come in which wes roe deer – right enough the foxes were still there, but roe deer, crossbills, robins, blackbirds, woodcock, doves – or, or pigeons – and occasionally pheasants, and that wes the different type o wildlife that come in as the trees got bigger.

Right. About how long did that take, how many years d'you think from first planting a...

The change from first planting, the change in the wildlife, would be approximately ten years, approximately ten years.

Lochfield Loch was a feature since time immemorial, but dried after Whitelee Forest was planted
Photo: Heather Scott

Alec Fenton saw and heard tawny owls in the growing Forest
Photo: : Michael Cruise

He said that rabbits on the surrounding farms came into Whitelee Forest through the fence to get some fresh eating (the ground was no longer being sheep grazed of course, so the vegetation could grow unchecked), but they did not burrow in the Forest and went back onto the farmland. Foxes were around but not common, he saw wild cats of some sort, roe deer and occasional sightings of red deer. Voles and mice were common. **Brian Speirs** very occasionally saw water voles.

> But that wes a situation if ye were down at stream or whatever. Ye had tae be there for a while. And bein quiet before you could see them.

> So I mean if you were down there an ye waded across the stream, the noise o that, you wouldnae see them, so very occasionally ye would see them, very occaisionally.

Several contributors spoke of a flock of self-sustaining sheep which went into the Forest when the trees were tall enough to cover them. Occasionally sheep do get into the Forest for a better or different bite. When this happens, the farmer usually manages to persuade them out with his collies, but the long-term sheep-flock is rarely seen and people like to think of them being permanent residents there.

Jim Leitch wrote about the bird life on the Whitelee moorlands and listed the changes he noticed.

> When the gulls were disturbed by egg collectors you could see a white cloud in the sky miles away. The grouse were plentiful with lots of heather for food. The Black Grouse were about but not in large numbers. The Skylarks were in large numbers. When you looked up you were likely to see a Skylark hovering high and singing its song. The Peewit were scarce on the hill, they preferred lower ground. The Curlew was a fairly common bird, laying an egg the same colour as the Peewit but much larger. Plover, Snipe, Pheasants, Partridges, Kestrels, Crows and Owls were seen regularly. There were a lot of White Hare on the hill. A hare shoot was often arranged for New Years Day, being the only holiday each year. Rabbits were about but only a few. Mr Fox would take a few newborn lambs at lambing time, or slip into the farms and take a hen from the henhouse.

Wildlife changed completely after the forest:

All gone: grouse, gulls, curlew, partridges, peewit, pheasants, plover

Nearly all gone: rabbits, skylark,

Still about: crows, kestrels, owls

Multiplied: fox

Newcomers: blue, coal and great tits, buzzard, chaffinch, hen harrier, peregrine, ravens (a colony emerged on Low Overmoor a few years ago), siskin, woodpigeon.

The siskin was also new to the Forest   Photo: Michael Cruise

Jim Currie spent many years as a joiner working on the Plateau farms and as an ardent wildfowler on Brocklees Loch. He described the more gradual changes he saw after afforestation.

> **Jim:** *But, when they started the forest an aw that, a lot o that ground aw got – eh – drained. An aw the rushes aw disappeart. An aw the rough grazin disappeart. Whit didnae disappear, the heather an that, they planted – they ploughed it aw up an that killt aw the, the moors, aw the heather. An then they plantit the trees, an aw the animals that – ye hud grouse, woodcock – aw these keena things – badgers. Ah don't think there'll be any badgers now, are there. The only thing ah would say multiplied wis foxes.*
>
> *Roe buck; roe deer. Ah wouldnae say mink. A'd say thay wur the two main* [searching for the word] *advan-, the two main, credit-, the two things that credited most wi it. Most o the ither – everyhing else – ah would say it wis detrimental to thaim. An aw yer wee birds an aw that. A lot o yer snow bunt… The bad weather. Ye hud snow buntins an goldcrests an aw thae… But. Thay aw disappeared. Gradually ewer the years thay juist got less an less.*
>
> **Ruth:** *Right. It wasn't sudden, it, it…*
>
> *Juist gradually. It juist… The whole – the whole character o the country changed. Ken. At one time when it wis aw heather ye could lie an ye got, like a summers day wi the breezes, an ye hud curlews. Ye could sit an…Ye could see for miles aw roun aboot ye. Ken. They planted aw the forest an ye could see thirty feet. Ken. Once the trees got up, a mean, they were like, it wis a desert. Ye hud. In between them aw. The only place ye seen any life at aw wis in the big rifts between the forests. The roads. Ken. In the forest[s] theirsel, even goin in them, even when we wur releasin pheasants. The pheasants went in there for cover an hidin. But naebody. A mean, most o yer pheasants preferred oot. Nihhin likes that kinnae stuff.*
>
> A mean you didn't get, uh, a lot, a big increase in mice and voles an that sort o thing when it started…?
>
> *O, a'd say we got less. Because. A mean the owls disappeart.*

But **Jim Currie** felt that many changes in fauna on and around the Whitelee Plateau were already under way when afforestation started.

> **Jim:** *A mean a've been up, been up, the knowe, four in the mornin, a've seen me sittin on the patio, an* [unclear word] *an sit doun an listen tae the dawn chorus. An a mean, ah could sit at night before 'The Forestry' came when they wur shootin ducks an ah could sit an ah could listen tae snipe drummin an ah could hear wee birds. 'The Forestry' came. They aw. Aw thae disappeart. There again, it wisnae aw Forestry's fault, becaus they drained. The biggest. One o the. The Forestry wis one thing, but the-, a'd say the secont biggest thing that changed the landscape wis drainin.*
>
> **Ruth:** The forest draining or farm draining?
>
> *Farm and forestry. Both ae thum. Ken becaus. Aw the farmers wantit. It wis aw wet an-, whit we caw boggy grund. Boggy grund suitit me cos ah could get snipe on it. Or ducks. But it wisnae guid for the farmin. Caus, a mean, it wis aw rushes an everyhin. An the cous got stuck in it, or the sheep got stuck in it. So thay, thay drained it oot. But that wis that rough shoot. Ah mean ah. Aw that environment for hares an rabbits an snipe an everyhin wis gone. Which is never gonnae come back. Unless ye block the drains . . .*
>
> *Mean, that wis one thing ye got a lot up there before the forestry, wis partridges. A mean, up in Brocklees an Burn Foot. Hughie Henry's bit. High Over-, High Huptone an that. A'd say he'd e* [?], *hauf a dizzen coveys o partridge. Fif-. Fifteen or twenty coveys o partridges.*
>
> These are the ordinary brown partridges?
>
> *Ay. An they. A mean they're aw gone . . . They wur aw wild. An. Once they'd. Once they'd drew aw the hedges an everyhing oot. Ken. A'd say they…*
>
> When did, when did that happen. The hedges. A mean…
>
> *Ah wid say aw a happened in the sixties. The fields wid aw be made bigger an…Ken. But. An, an. Once they drained. Whit wis aw, lik heather. What ye caw the muirs.*

Onced it aw got drained, they pushed the rushes back. They aw dis-. They aw died out. So, further up dried out. An the heather got gradually pushed back, an pushed back, an pushed back. An then they come in wi big machines an ploughed it aw up. An that wis it finished. That wis everyhing gone.

Fauna of the Maturing Forest

As deer stalker from 1997 to 1999, **Alec Fenton** was in the best position to observe the wildlife of the maturing Forest and he spoke about it.

Ruth: Alec, while you were out early mornings and late evenings stalking deer, what other wildlife did you used to see?

Alec: *Well your usual for that sort of area, rabbits and hares. There was also your raptors, there was merlin, sparrowhawk, tawny owl, and, areas adjacent to the Forest block, Drumduff Hill and places like that, you would see hen harrier. Because they nested in that sort of habitat.*

So, there was hen harrier. And then one occasion I actually caught an osprey flying overhead. I don't know where it was going, it was probably just heading somewhere, it could even have been heading for Aberfoyle, because it was going that, it was going in a northerly direction. (laughter) And it probably came from Africa, and it was just doing a fly, a fly-by over Whitelee Forest. So, yes. I never ever found goshawk. There was buzzard but not an awful lot.

What about mammals, like badgers, mink, otters?

Yes, there was badgers, there was otter, at Moss Mulloch there was often seen otter there. Badgers at High

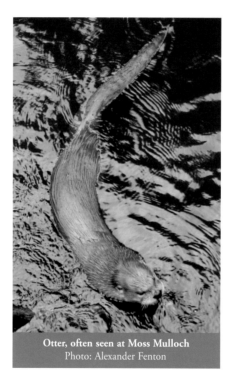

Otter, often seen at Moss Mulloch
Photo: Alexander Fenton

Overmuir. And obviously there was, there was foxes, a lot of fox dens throughout the whole beat. So there was.

Yes. Yes. And were there fish in the burns?

Well I couldn't recall, I couldn't recall any, any fish . . .

See, the way the Forest block was designed, Forest Design Plans now have changed, it used to be that if you had, you'd have a lovely burn, beautiful wee watercourse, and they would just plant Sitka right up to the, the edge of it. And you then got the sterile burn, or it could be a pond, and the same thing would happen.

Many contributors, particularly farmers, are adamant that Whitelee Forest has caused a big increase in the number of foxes which come onto their farms. This is said to be because the Forest provides cover, but also because the Forestry Commission did not carry out control of pest species except deer in the Forest.

One of the deer-stalkers was **Jim Newall**, who described the changing status of roe deer.

When Whitelee Forest wis planted it wis reckoned there wisnae a deer problem at it. For that reason there wis never at any time a full time stalker up tae Alec Fenton. Now, what happened wis, there were four o us worked together in Galloway. It wis normally two fellas by the name o Robin Henney an Ian White that done it, but occasionally a wid be asked to come up wi them, or maself, an dae some deer management in Whitelees. It wis a very kinna higglety-pigglety arrangement, but a always got the impression naebody wis really that bothered because they didnae think there wis a big roe deer problem. This went on for a number o years until the boundary changes came an Whitelees came under the new district Scottish Lawlands. By this time the deer numbers were out o control.

172

That's the bottom line o it, so they decidit they had to put a full time man on. His name wis Alec Fenton, he stayed in the village o Ga'ston*.   * [Galston]

Wildlife on the North Side of the Whitelee Plateau

The memories of **Robin Chambers** about how mammals and birds responded to changes in the environment were written as he spoke.

The coming of Whitelee Forest changed the whole bird population considerably. Both red grouse and black game have decreased considerably since Whitelee Forest was planted and grew. However, both species do still occur on Mr Chambers' adjoining open land. Roe deer, which were absent or very rare before the Forest, are now extremely common. Mr Chambers estimates that there may be as many as 600 roe deer in Whitelee Forest.

Foxes are very common nowadays both within and around the Forest, because they are not controlled within the Forest by the Forestry Commission or its shooting tenants. Weasels and stoats are commonly seen and Mr Chambers controls them on his own land (stoats eat grouse eggs). He has not seen the winter-white form ('ermine') of the stoat in recent years, but used to see them as a lad. He controls weasels and stoats with a Fenn Trap set in a tunnel in a stone dyke or old stone sheep pen.

He never saw mink until after the Forest was planted, but nowadays they come right near his home, where they have been known to eat through the mesh of a Larsen Trap and to kill and eat a Magpie within! Magpies and crows are very common and are classed as vermin.

Mr Chambers does not shoot pigeons at all – he leaves the pigeons as food for the peregrines which frequent the area, to save the grouse becoming peregrine food.

Badgers were not seen by Robin Chambers on the northern side of the area before the Forest, but nowadays they can be found in different parts of the Forest. There is still no evidence of water voles or snakes, but he sees frogs and

Puddocks live in moorland and Forest drains   Photo: Michael Cruise

toads frequently. They spawn in the wet places on the moor: there were always wet places on the moor (more wet places than dry places!), but for some reason he did not note them in his boyhood. Otters have been seen in the Forest recently: there may be more now than before the Forest, but they are still rare . . .

At the edges of Whitelee Forest there are lots of small birds, which of course did not occur previously. However, they do not occur in the middle of the Forest living in or on trees, as it is 'Black below'. The only species living under the trees are foxes and the roe deer – which sleep beneath the canopy. There are now a lot of hawks, cuckoos and a few woodcock: he sometimes sees woodcock at about 6 am gathering grit from the forest road from Carrot up to Myres Hill. Butterflies and bees are very abundant on the moors, wasps are nearer civilisation.

Half a Century for Plant Life Not Nibbled by Sheep and Cattle

As an experienced naturalist, **Bryan Simpson** studied the Whitelee Plateau from 1960 until the present day, so has an unparalleled knowledge of the changes that have occurred there. He described how the vegetation has changed without sheep and cattle eating it constantly.

Bryan: *I would stravaig, there's a good Scottish word, I would stravaig through the, the rides for miles through the forest and see what I could discover. But they can be very difficult, these rides, to walk through, because, grazing animals were being kept out of the forest plantings for like, upwards of twenty years. So, the heather and the moss all had a chance to grow in a way they would never normally have had. So become extremely rough terrain.*

Ruth: Yes, I found the same, yes. I once went out, last year I think, in May, and it took two hours to go a mile. Through that sort of ground.

That's right. If you're fortunate, you will find an animal track which is quite well beaten, where the foxes and the deer use it. And if you got one of them, then that helps you greatly to get through the rides, which I did quite frequently actually, find these, you know.

Yes. Can't imagine trying to get through it in the snow.

Oh it was pretty, pretty dicey. Because you couldn't see the ditches quite often when the snow lay on the, the rushes you know. And you put your foot and, swoosh, down a ditch you know.

Bryan then spoke enthusiastically about the new habitats created by Whitelee Forest and the beauty of it: it's not just a mass of trees.

Ruth: Yes. Yes. So, what, what do you feel about the forest nowadays? And what natural history do you see when you're up there?

Bryan: *Well, things have changed from the point of view that, I think probably one of the, the biggest gains is the fact that, the forest being there, you have an increase in the number of lichens. You don't have an increase in the number of species of mosses and liverworts and bryophytes and what, but you have an increase in the number of lichens, because you've got the trees there, and they accumulate. Oh they do accumulate a few bryophytes as well. But, the fact that the grazing animals were being kept out of there is one of the most important things.*

What has happened over twenty-odd years is, you've got these

Mountain pansy on a rocky outcrop   Photo: Andrew Tittensor

Mosses form huge hummocks along brakes   Photo: Andrew Tittensor

Moss *Polytrichum commune* **with capsules, Munzie Bog**
Photo: Andrew Tittensor

wonderful cushions of common mosses... growing, sometimes three feet in height... golden, golden green cushions.

And there are several different species that form these cushions, your common Polytrichum form big deep green masses there. It's wonderful. And when they flower, which is not really a flower... when they come up with all their different colours you know, it's quite a sight, it's quite an interesting sight.

Along the edge of the forest, you also get quite a variety of fungi there... associated with the trees I suppose. And, also, quite a variety of different types of lichens like to grow on the forest edge. Especially on the edge of the track where it's all gravelly and rotten. You get this wonderful mix of lichens and bryophytes . . . they've had over twenty years to establish themselves and they've done a really good job of it you know. And, it's, really attractive and very interesting to study these things at the side of the tracks on the edge of the forest.

So, yes, the forest's not just a, a mass of trees, like people tend to think. It's much more than that. And also the bird stock is very interesting. There's a very wide variety of birds up there. And there seems to be quite a substantial number of ravens in the forest. And I presume, they may be nesting in the trees there you know. Although they're generally rock-nesters, maybe... Because, everywhere I've been in the forest, I've seen and heard ravens.

And you get the whole swatch of the usual birds, you know, robins and blue tits and coal tits and song thrushes up there, and blackbirds, so on, but you also get the occasional visitors, interesting visitor like crossbills, we've seen, I've seen them once only. Crossbills. And redpolls. And bullfinches, flocks, small flocks of bullfinches. So all these things...

Which wouldn't have been there before, all these things?

Probably not. You probably... I never saw them in the early days. No, I can't remember ever seeing them in the early days . . . And over the little lochans up there, swifts, you often see swifts in the summer time. You know, after the things there . . .

175

Lichen *Ramalina fastigiata* on rowan in Dickman's Glen
Photo: Andrew Tittensor

Lichen *Evernia prunastri* on rowan in Dickman's Glen
Photo: Andrew Tittensor

Lichen *Usnea subfloridana* on rowan in Dickman's Glen
Photo: Andrew Tittensor

And, also, with these lochans being there, you'll get quite a variety of dragonflies as well, mainly, I think what they call black darters, they seem to be exceedingly common up there. But you get the large blue, the common blue, and the damselflies, the common red damsel and the common blue damsel. You get all these hanging about where there's water you know.

So, all in all, the ecology is really quite interesting. And, although we have demeaned modern forests in the past, I think there's less inclination nowadays, now there's more known about it.
He also said,

So, they're really quite nice actually to walk through, these rides, and some of them go on for hundreds of yards. And to be in there on your own, especially if the evening's just coming in, it's quite magical. You've got the scent of the forest and you've got this immense silence. This immense silence, broken only by the sound of, sometimes small birds, finches you know, redpolls, whatever, twittering away in the treetops. And it's really... I think, to me it's, it's quite magical. I've enjoyed many many hours just walking through these, these rides in the forest on my own.

Black Darters range over the Forest's new ponds   Photo: Andrew Tittensor

Lichen Flora of the Whitelee Plateau

John Douglass spent many happy hours studying lichens in Whitelee Forest
Photo: Courtesy John Douglass

Lichenologist, **John Douglass** has studied the lichens of Whitelee Forest and adjoining areas during the past seven years, and talked enthusiastically about them.

Ruth: Can you explain to people listening what lichens are?

John: *Well lichens are a, well they're classed as a 'symbiosis' which is like a, a unity between algae and fungi. Where the algae actually provides the nutrients for the fungi, and the fungi provides the environment to live in sort of thing. Because the, the algae can't actually live separately, on its own . . .*

And in Britain, there's about 1700 known species, and in Scotland, maybe about 1400 of them actually live in Scotland . . . So you find them basically everywhere, and if you just look out on your garden wall or your garden fence or a local tree, you see a little crusty growth, a grey thing or a yellow thing, or, you know, that'll be a, that'll be a lichen more than likely . . .

. . . things like that the dogtooth lichen, Peltigera is the genera for that, then they will grow pretty fast and they can grow maybe two or three centimetres in a year . . .

Whereas the crusty growths, things like the map lichen, that's a common crustose, crusty lichen which grows on stone dykes or, well any rock surface, usually in, tends to be upland situation, or you get them in churchyards and that, and that would maybe grow only tenths of millimetres, or up to a millimetre or so in a year.

He then described how lichens fit into ecological systems.

Ruth: Can you explain to people what eats lichens? Do they, do they start food chains?

John: *Oh absolutely. Well, because they're at the bottom of the food chain, they are producers, they'll, you know, they... they do have a lot of things associated with them, and maybe to start out with, you've got things like bark lice, which are things called psocids [two s's, long o] or psocids [pronounced like sockid], you pronounce that. And then... So these are minute little creatures about a millimetre in length. And you've got other things called oribatid mites, and they're, they will also live on and feed on the lichens . . .*

Or they'll munch around on the surface of the lichen. And they use it as an environment, as a habitat, they'll grow, they'll live underneath them. Quite often if you take a lichen off a tree or peel a bit back or peel some of the lobes back, you'll find hundreds of these little mites just living and mooching around under there. So it's an entire little world, a little ecosystem. There's various spiders associated with them, there's moths and caterpillars. Some caterpillars actually eat lichens, others, the moths are very good at using them as camouflage . . .

So, you know, there's various ways in which animals are associated with it.

Other animals, mammals and things, and, well, if you go to the birds, birds use them in their nests, you know, use them as nesting material, which helps to camouflage the nest.

And then if you're moving on to mammals and stuff, reindeer and red deer, all sorts of mammals will actually eat lichens, and, they reckon that some reindeer will maybe eat about three kilograms of lichen in a day.

Mm. So it sounds as if they're a very important part of the natural world.

Oh aye. I mean, in terms of carbon cycles and carbon sinks and stuff like that, and nitrogen cycles, they're very, very much, useful, well they're very much... a good part.

177

The March Fence between Ardochrig and Cleughearn farms remains in the Forest. Witch's Hair Lichen (*Alectoria fuscescens*) shares it with other lichens
Photo: Andrew Tittensor

John explained that Bryan Simpson introduced him to the Whitelee Plateau and they subsequently spent much time there – for very good reasons.

Ruth: . . . what sort of places or habitats do lichens grow in Whitelee Forest?

John: *Basically anywhere. And, as soon as you go in, it depends what area you go into, but I mean, you start off on the Tracks, you'll find mainly on the track-sides, you know, areas that haven't been disturbed too much... you find them there. And you'll find them on the, the cut peat areas, you know, where they've dug the trenches out and stuff. And you'll also find them on, even on the Sitka spruce and on the... on the branches and stuff. But the ones that grow on the spruce are usually pretty, pretty common things, like Hypogymnia physodes, Hypogymnia tubulosa . . .*

And then, I mean when you're moving into the open areas, you've got your fences and fence posts, there's a lot of, there's a lot of stuff grows on there, a lot of Cladonia species, and... There's a couple of species at the new county records I think, there's a thing called Protoparmelia oleagina, I think that's the name, I think I'd better check. But that's a thing that was, we found recently, and that's a nationally scarce thing. Another thing called Ochrolechia microstictoides, which is a white-looking thing with little powdery structures on. So, so that's the, I mean the fence posts can be really good. It depends when they've been put in.

And then, moving into the, the sort of, the prime habitats, there would be like, Blanket Bog, I mean there's some really nice stuff on the blanket bog. A lot of Cladonias, the Reindeer Lichens, the Cladonia arbuscula, Cladonia portentosa, Cladonia ciliata. Then there's also little mushroom lichens called Omphalina, and they're, oh well they're just, they're the shape of a mushroom, but they've got an associated algae to them . . .

So you've got your peatlands. And then the other, the other main areas of lichen interest are the burns and gulleys.

And along there you've got your, it's the rock exposures, and also boulders, they're in large boulders that area in streams

Myxomycete *Badhamia lilacina* on stems of cotton grass near Browncastle Burn Photo: Andrew Tittensor

Lichen *Cladonia bellidiflora* Ardochrig Hill
Photo: Bryan Simpson

Milkwort and Tormentil on rocks near Munzie Well
Photo: Andrew Tittensor

or nearby streams. So these rock faces, some of these areas have dry underhangs, and you get particular lichens associated with them, things like Enterographa zonata and Rhizocarpon, oh what's the name of that now? Er?

Another habitat would be the Boulder Field which you mentioned before. And that's particularly good. It's got about three or four nationally scarce lichens on there. Some really nice, really nice diversity of things. It's got a thing called Ophioparma ventosa, which is actually, well, I think it translates as like, blood clot, or, blood clot lichen, because it looks like little blood clots, the spore bodies look like little dots of blood on a very pale, the plant body which is called the 'thallus'. So that, that's a, a nice thing...

Grey Hair Moss *Racomitrium ericoides* **on the Boulder Field**
Photo: Andrew Tittensor

And then, in terms of other rock habits, you've got these sheep fanks and the drystone dykes which are really good. We found a number of interesting things there, again, two Stereocaulon species, one called Stereocaulon delisei, and that tends to associate with metal-rich areas. So there's obviously some metallic thing going on there. And another thing called Stereocaulon leuco, leucoflavia I think it's called. Hold on, I'd better check that. (laughs)

I think this thing's called Stereocaulon leucophaeopsis, but I may be wrong. So that, yes, I mean these, these rock habitats have been around for a long time, these, some of these stone walls obviously have been there for, since before

the trees were planted. So they've had time to develop these lichens, and usually it's the case that the longer the habitat's been there, the greater the diversity of species and, you know, usually the greater number of rarities you'd find there as well . . .

Well it sounds as if there's a big variety of lichen habitats in Whitelee Forest which one wouldn't sort of think of straight away, because everybody thinks that blankets of Sitka spruce make the ecology of an area, they just get rid of everything, but obviously there is an awful lot still there from before the forest on the, on the stone walls and peat bogs and so on.

So, has the, has the forest, have any of those habitats, have any habitats actually been added when the Forest came, I mean has the Forest added to the biodiversity of lichen?

. . . it is possible that the, you know, certain things associated with Sitka spruce have added things, but, I think in general, you know, the forestry, putting forests in large areas of prime Blanket Bog is not really a good idea, because, because of the habitat, it obviously takes thousands of years to get going and these, you know, the trees will eventually dry the habitat out and degrade it in terms of, you know, you know, there's not much light getting underneath, so there's, there's not much of the active bog or Sphagnums and stuff going on.

But certainly in the rides and in the fire breaks and along the tracks. And there are good, good areas that are still there, I mean like Flow Moss and Corse Hill Moss . . . But I mean in general, I don't think it's a good idea to keep putting these trees onto good quality Blanket Bog.

Right. So that, it doesn't totally destroy everything straight away, but, particularly if areas of blanket bog are left open and unplanted, but in the long run it's likely that the, the area will dry out and the peat will stop growing and so the habitats for the lichen, the original habitats for the lichens will gradually worsen and maybe disappear?

Aye . . .

So, you know, some of these areas, it's sort of, fragments of, remnants of the ancient habitat that was there. So I mean it, you know, would be a good idea to remove some of these trees and allow, open the place up a bit more and in theory the species that are still there will start to colonise other areas and stuff . . .

I think there's a lot of evidence to say that, that some of it will come back, but there's a lot of evidence to say that it will be damaged for a long, you know, a long time like.

Yes. So, you'd be very happy if these remaining peat bogs in the Whitelee Forest area were kept pristine and allowed to develop naturally without any further interference?

Aye, definitely. I think it's absolutely vital that these areas are left. I mean there's certain areas like Flow Moss and Corse Hill bog which are excellent representatives of, you know, active* blanket bog, you know, and this stuff is really amazing.

* [active bog is growing every year]

When you go out and have a look at some of these things up at Corse Hill, you've got these huge peat hags and they're just, just like prehistoric landscapes, it's incredible.

And the, you know, the, the diversity of species, not just lichens, you've got, you know, all the different types of Sphagnum and, you've got all this and else growing on there, you know, the invertebrates, I mean, umpteen number of spiders, I wouldn't have a clue at naming them, you know.

It's just, it's hooching with life.

Comment

'Hooching with life' is a very beautiful and encouraging description by John Douglass of the life of the active peat bogs within and adjoining Whitelee Forest. His plea to conserve them, as relict habitats and 'prehistoric landscapes', will hopefully be heard. John's dedication to lichen identification and ecology adds significantly to our understanding of Whitelee Forest ecology.

The studies by Bryan Simpson are valuable because they have been long term, starting before the first parcel of land was bought by the Forestry Commission. This means he has noted ecological changes going on while Whitelee Forest developed. He is positive about these. 20 to 50 years without sheep and cattle grazing has been significant, allowing lichens to accumulate in number and amount. Both spruce trees and the variety of new habitats provided by the Forest are important from this point of view. The shelter from drying winds has encouraged mosses and liverworts as well as lichens. Large areas of huge 'golden green' moss cushions are obvious effects. These dynamic 'hummock and hollow' systems have developed since the 'no-grazing' regime. The long stability of the environment, without sudden or major change, has been another important ecological factor for flora and fauna. Bryan's 40 years of field note-books contain many details of ecological interest.

The species described by local people were important in their lives. It is not surprising that the observed declines of animals such as grouse, blackcock, snow buntings and skylarks, were a source of dissatisfaction. The newly-arriving species like roe deer and siskins, and the increase in raptors do not seem to give equivalent satisfaction. Nor do foxes or grey squirrels!

All the observations – from all the observers – when put together and analysed, provide a picture of the dynamics of the ecology of the Whitelee Plateau. Every observation is important, and adds to the fund of knowledge of the ecosystems and how they react to changing land-use.

'Hooching with life': one of the Forest's 'prehistoric bogs'
Photo: Andrew Tittensor

181

CHAPTER 14

The Present and the Future

Depletion of Forestry Commission Personnel

The 6,000 ha Whitelee Forest was completely planted by 1992. Communities nearby had seen numbers of on-the-spot Forestry Commission personnel declining for some years. They knew that the four left in the squad often worked in other Ayrshire forests or on the Isle of Arran. And they knew when the squad was finally made redundant, because the workers came from local families.

After that, people saw few happenings in Whitelee Forest. Adjoining farmers and others did not know why there was no ongoing management. They saw broken fences, windblown trees, and felt the effects of foxes and deer coming out from the Forest onto their land.

Management from Afar . . . And Obscurity

Apart from the remaining farmers and a few shooting tenants, Whitelee Plateau Forest drifted into obscurity. The trees continued to grow, however!

Tom Grant noticed the change.

> *Basically it's dead ground, yeah. Yaised tae be ye wid get a lot o bikers through. Used tae be but ye never see them noo. Ah don't know what's happened tae it. Used tae see, regularly ye seen bikers but ye never see a soul noo. But naebody ever walks there..Ye used tae get them come up ower the hill an come oot through on their bikes but Ah never see a soul noo. Havenae seen them for a while. Why it stoaped Ah don't know.*

People who had lived, worked or enjoyed themselves on the Plateau or worked in the Forest took new work, recreated elsewhere and became elderly. Whitelee Plateau and Forest no longer provided local employment, ad hoc jobs for youngsters, recreation, or a subject for discussion. It became the norm for farmers and farm wives to take on extra work away from the farm. The time came when farmhouses and steadings were sold to part-timers, non-farmers or developers. Fewer, but large, agricultural units became usual. The computer age enticed young people to indoor work.

Whitelee Forest became almost forgotten by nearby communities who had used the land for so many purposes in the past.

Rural communities felt the initial change away from a mainly familial and local network of owners (farmers) of the Whitelee Plateau. Such owners could be spoken with easily, casually, informally. The new single, distant, institutional owner (the Forestry Commission) could also be spoken with while foresters and workers lived in local communities. When the Whitelee Forest office had closed and resident foresters gone, people could no longer speak directly with the representatives of the Forest's landowner. **Norman Gibson**, living in an enclave in the Forest, felt strongly about this.

Ruth: . . . So did you ever meet anybody working in the forest, or any of the foresters in charge?

Norrie: *Yes, we did, because, at that time, there were people employed by the Forestry Commission... who would be in charge. There was one particular, there was a fire out here... many years ago. And we reported it, and actually helped them, with the Fire Brigade when they came here. And getting them out there. And we got a wee commendation from the Forestry Commission. But we knew the guys involved, so we knew who to phone. And that was, the personal touch then. If there was any incident, you could get* *in contact with somebody right away.*

Latterly there was someone else who was here, and, well, that was many years ago, when they were spraying crops, spraying all the, the Forestry.

So, so what's the situation now, do you have a local person that you can...?

Not at all.

You don't know anybody?

No. No all we ever see, activity from the, the Forestry Commission, is, putting up signs saying 'Whitelee Forest'. And they will come up and they'll cut the grass round about the sign. That is all we ever see. But it's not the Forestry Commission any more. I haven't a clue. Scottish Woodlands? It's all into private, private companies. We haven't a clue who's in charge of it all now. If there was a fire here, we'll just phone the Fire Brigade.

Right. So you don't actually know anybody in the Forestry Commission, or the local Forestry Commission office?

None at all.

Do you know where it is?

Well I believe there's some... The last dealings I had with them, I wanted to buy a bit of ground off them just in front of the house here. And, it was down, Borders direction.

The institutional landowner's relevant representatives had become unknown faces in an unknown office, in an unknown place, who rarely visited the Forest and who worked to rules unknown to the local population. The system of resident foresters managing individual forests was replaced by one of specialist foresters, each managing all of a District's forests from a distant District Office.

Whitelee Forest sign, Caldergreen
Photo: Ruth Tittensor

James Mair also had strong views about modern institutional ownership and management of rural land when he spoke to Ruth Tittensor.

Ruth: 'Yes. And what would you yourself like, personally?

James: *The folk, the residents don't seem to benefit as well as they should. They don't seem to have investigated how they'd have worked in Switzerland or Norway with regard to people owning pieces of forest, piece of land, how the agricultural, fisheries and forestry all combined in – er – individual ownership. And by that method, keeping people on the land.*

It's all decided of course by economics. If the large-scale economics they can see in this old-fashioned system of the economies of scale, then, you have no, you can't, you can't yet get the better of that. If people are determined to carry on on that basis, then you can't win. But if they were to look at alternative methods of using the land and the fisheries, and, then, improvements could be made. But it's maybe too late in the day for all that, because folk have been talking about that for 100 years.

The New 'Scottish Lowlands Forest District': Revitalising Neglected Forests

Without local people realising, the Forestry Commission's plans for forests in lowland Scotland moved forward. Whitelee Forest was placed in the new Scottish Lowlands Forest District where the management of a number of neglected forests (including Whitelee) was the priority.

Malcolm Crosby
Photo: Keith Hobley

Malcolm Crosby, a Planning Forester, said that he especially wanted to come and work in this new Forest District.

Well I've always been a Forester, I started off by supervising harvesting team. So there was quite a bit of being out and about and, you know, moving things around and that. But, over time, things have been much more, you know, foresters were indoors more, and that you had other staff. So eventually, in Borders*, when I was supervising the planting side of things, and also forest management as it was called, that was gradually, you know, eventually I got a foreman who did the sort of running around, day-to-day stuff.

* [Scottish Borders District]

Which means that you're left to do more of the, the paperwork, computer work and all the rest of it. And then, round about 1998 I changed on to doing forest design plans full time. And I've been doing that ever since.

And that's one of the reasons why I wanted to move to 'Lowlands', because with... And the District was set up to try and take back into management all these areas in central Scotland that had been neglected under the previous political regime where they were all, a lot of them were on the disposals list.

And, I felt that this was a very important aspect of the, the work, trying to, you know, get these things going again. You know, a lot of social aspects and all the rest of it. That's something I've been very keen on.

Malcolm explained that Whitelee Forest will contribute to the timber industry, still the primary role of state forests, but that other outputs or uses are now important.

And that is our business, we're in the business of producing timber and selling it. But, it's not our only business, and certainly over the last ten to twenty years we've increasingly been, been diversifying away from pure conifer forestry, just for producing timber . . .

Over the, all the time we're producing four or five million tonnes a year, but that is, and that's going up, but the actual amount of money we get for that isn't going up, because the price is constantly going down. But as I say, we, we are not just in the business of producing timber, it still accounts for a very large proportion of our income, but in the last public expenditure settlement, I mean the Government made a commitment to provide us with money for various other things than just timber production . . .

Now, the...Whitelee is still young yet, so it hasn't made much of a contribution to the forest industry in, you know, the west of Scotland, but, the other forests around about have enabled the private sector, not just the Government but the private sector, to set up some very large timber-using factories. There's the plant just outside at Auchinleck, there's one at Irvine. And all these things are using timber from the forests in Ayrshire and Galloway and, and all that sort of thing . . .

Now, as I say, Whitelee is some of the poorest ground we've got in, in soil quality and productivity terms. But there is still going to be timber produced from it . . .

The Modern Remit of the Forestry Commission

Fulfilling social needs is nowadays an important role of forests. **Jim Smalls** came into the Forestry Commission after 20 rural years with Strathclyde Police. He now works as a community environment ranger. Jim explained how modern forestry is divided into three types of work: Planning, Operations and Community.

Jim: *Well, if you look at forestry, you can literally split it into three separate sections. You have the planning side of the forestry . . . they actually work out where the trees will be planted. In the past they would just go in and plant big* square blocks. Whereas nowadays, it's planted to take into consideration the contours of the land, to make it look good.

Then you have your operation side of the forest, who will do the, forest maintenance more or less though. They'll go in for, when the planting starts. They'll go back in a few years later and they'll check on, have there been any more, have any of the trees died? And they'll what they call beat up, they'll replace the dead trees. And then after about ten years they'll go in and they'll thin the trees out. Because they'll plant two and a half thousand trees to a hectare. Well by the time they get to ten years old, they're squashing, and you literally need to take out, like every second tree, to allow expansion. So you have your planning side, your operation side, and then you have your community side.

And we will, not so much work for them, for the planning or the operation side, but we'll work towards the community aspects of things, or the environmental aspects.

So we'll go into a forest and, our entrance, we'll strip the branches off the bottom of the trees that allows light through, and it makes it more appealing for people to walk through the trees.

We'll make sure the litter's cleared up. If there's any... if there's problems in the area, it's not nice but we'll put barriers up, because, in a big forest like Whitelee, we had a problem at one point with people burning cars out.

So you put, heavy steel bars are up. On one occasion a barrier lasted twenty-four hours. So, you literally have to keep the area secure. It's not that you want to stop people going in; you just want to stop the, the anti-social side. But still leave access for the community. So we work towards encouraging people and making sure that when they go in that it's safe, but at the same time, operations will help us out; if we have something ongoing, then we will help operations out . . .

Ruth: . . . So, the skills and the sorts of tasks that you're doing now and that you've been telling us about, did your previous job as a policeman, has that helped you in the work you're doing now, or not particularly?

To a certain extent I would say yes, because, when you're working in a rural community you're, you're working with farmers and gamekeepers, and you're working with, with rural people. And a lot of the people round about Whitelee are rural people. You get used to going to schools and speaking to schoolchildren. As a result of that, if you can go and speak to a class of schoolchildren, you can literally speak to anyone. And we do get invited to go to rural groups, Scouts and Guides.

I wouldn't say it was that much different, you're going out there, you're patrolling an area, as I would have done with the Police. You're looking to see if there's any problems, and doing your best to solve them.

Litter on Windshields Moor　Photo: Ruth Tittensor

Integrating Community, Conservation and Recreation

Community involvement, conservation and recreation are important functions of the modern Forestry Commission. **Rena Tarwinska** is district forester for community and environment in the new Scottish Lowlands District. She discussed her work in relation to Whitelee Forest.

Rena Tarwinska
Photo: Forestry Commission

Rena: *The Forestry Commission in Scotland is, has developed significantly in the last five, six years in trying to involve local people more, [or] interest people, whether they're local or not, in the workings of a forest, and, essentially, trying to explain why we do things the way we do, and also, just as important if not more important, to integrate people's opinions and ideas and thoughts into any planning that we do and any management that we do. With that in mind, whenever we develop a Design Plan, we put it out to consultation, and always hold our meeting advertised to local people, held in a local village hall, or school or whatever, and invite people to come and, and have a look at the plan, and, well, as far as we have developed it, we try and involve people right at the start; obviously we, we don't want to spend a lot of time working on something and then say, "Well, this is it, like or lump it".*

What we try and do is say, "Well look, these are our thoughts so far; this is what we know about the place. Come, you know, let us know how you use it, and..." Some of these have been very successful, particularly often the ones where we have communities that are adjacent to the forest and are already using it or, you know, it's very much an important part of their lives anyway.

In Whitelee, one of the issues that we found is trying to get a handle on the local communities. Because if you look at the map and look at where Whitelee is, I've mentioned [it's] already, it's at the top of a plateau... (laughs)... and there's no obvious village, and no obvious town which is the place associated with that forest.

Recreation in Whitelee Forest   Photo: Ruth Tittensor

You know, there are several villages and towns round about. So, in a way the, the local population live, in relative terms, distant to the forest. So, you know, it just means that when we, when we do organise our local meetings, we'll probably have to have several.

Ruth: Yes. So you haven't had any such meetings at Whitelee yet?

We haven't had anything so far. But, I gather from some of the other conversations that you've had with people that there are opinions out there. And we would certainly want to know what they were, and, and take them on board.

Great, great. And there's knowledge out there as well... as I am finding.

Yes. Yes. And I think your report and, you know, and the information that you're gathering and people's memories and past knowledge and present knowledge will be hugely important to us in, in developing our thinking for Whitelee. Because I think if you just... If you just look at it out of context, you just think, it's a forest in the middle of nowhere, you know, who could possibly have any interest in this? Someone, someone might think, but, you're finding absolutely differently, and, you know, we want, we want to be able to build that information into the future plans.

The community and wildlife aspects of forestry are integrated with the main aim of producing timber, as **Rena** explained.

Ruth: But forestry is still the main, the main remit for Whitelee, is it?

Rena: *Yes, it will always be, it will always be a forest... but, I think, it can be a bit misleading I think to, to imagine that a forest is nothing but trees. And in a way I, when people ask me what I do, I sometimes explain that my colleagues manage the trees themselves, and I manage the spaces between the trees, and there's a surprising amount of space between trees in the forest. The open space for deer, from glades that we design in, and roadsides, and general open space for keeping viewpoints open, and that's,*

"Deer Lawn" at Snab Bent
Photo: Isobel Cameron

that's all really important, and most species and habitats develop as a result of the open space and the, an interface between the forest and the open space.

So, although we refer to the whole, whole area as 'a forest', it's actually a huge complex matrix of different habitats and, habitat types and species opportunities. So, it can be quite a complicated organism in itself.

And I think people will find that interesting, to know that, because the public tends to think of the recent forests as masses of conifers with nothing in between them, you know.

Mm. Yes, but that's, it's actually not true because the more you look, the more you find, and... [Noises interrupt conversation] Leaking room pipes and Land Rovers and things. (laughs)

Rena. Now what about ecology and conservation, how does the... does the Forestry Commission carry out any conservation activities in these forests at the moment? Does it have somebody who is involved with that sort of thing at Whitelee?

We have a couple of rangers in the district who are particularly well-versed in conservation issues. One ranger specialises in habitat types, and the other one focuses more on the actual species themselves.

But between them and the general sightings that we get from the various other staff going around, and also what they hear from local people who report them to rangers when they see them, we keep a record of all those . . .

So we have our own record system where we're almost informally recording sightings and noting, noting things as they appear. And we also have these more formal studies which are done, sometimes as part of our proposed development, other times they're taken on as part of a national study on a particular issue, such as, red squirrel or black grouse or whatever, so...

Yes. Right. Right. So in the Design Plan that's being, the new Design Plan that's being prepared at the moment, all these, this information and these issues will be part of that?

Yes. We, we would flag up as part of the Plan what species, what nationally important and regionally important species there were known in Whitelee and around about.

Certainly, because Whitelee is on an upland plateau, the species of importance in the general area tend to be the upland species, and these tend to prefer large areas of open space, or be adjacent to the fringe of the, the forest . . . The idea is that, that we integrate all these objectives into the forest plan, into the Design Plan.

The First Harvesting of Whitelee Forest

The job of District Forester for planning and implementation in the Scottish Lowlands District is undertaken by **Frank Jackson**. He described how the ground conditions affect when trees can be harvested.

Frank Jackson
Photo: Forestry Commission 2006

Frank: *. . . We, at the same stage Whitelee came within our banner as well, and that was my next contact with Whitelee. By then, in '99, Whitelee was, or sections of Whitelee were up, were ready now for clear-felling, that is, because of their age, you know, trees can just grow to a specific age. It's Sitka spruce in the main which is planted on Whitelee.*

And by the time they get to age thirty, thirty-five, they're needing to be clear-felled, because of reasons already mentioned, that a certain amount of wind blow, it's a high wind risk area is Whitelee, and very exposed, and the ground conditions are not terribly suitable for establishing deep-rooting trees. Because of the peats et cetera.

So, by then, the western section of Whitelee, which is the oldest section of Whitelee, was becoming ready, becoming ready for clear-felling. We produced a Design Plan for Whitelee, which is the Forestry Authority wing, that's approval of what we were going to do, as far as management's concerned, which starts with the felling fees, and the areas we're felling are called coups . . .

But to do anything in Whitelee, first of all we had to have access to it. Our main access, or in the past, had been from the west end. But, that was... Waterside through... Yes, Waterside and Moscow et cetera, through in. Well we had, the biggest difficulty trying to access from that end was the problems with the roads, the public roads.

And, our concern was for our neighbours and the traffic that would be travelling down these roads and breaking up the roads, which were not built to withstand timber lorries of forty-five tonnes et cetera coming down at any

great quantity. So, we worked on that, we planned on that, and, eventually got the funds through to put the road through from the east through to the west, which is from Ardochrig right through to the west end at Whitelee Farm.

Ruth: You're talking about a road within the forest?

Within the forest. Roads kept to the forest, and then access and on to the Ardochrig Road at the east end, which takes you through to East Kilbride . .

Somebody listening might say, well, didn't you think about these things, or didn't someone think about these things when Whitelee was first planted? . . .

I'm afraid in those days, Whitelee was planted, as a lot of other forests were planted, because of government diktats, because of the need for a timber reserve in case there was another world war . . . these areas are planted up, with the best will in the world, with a lot of professionalism, and a

The Whitelee Forest road, vital for timber harvesting and extraction
Photo: Ralph Tittensor

Contractor's abode, Green Knowe, 2001
Photo: Robert Graham

Harvester in Whitelee Forest. Its 'harvesting head' fells the tree, cuts off the branches, cuts it into lengths and gives a GPS position.
Photo: Forestry Commission Picture Library

lot of goodwill by the people that did it, they put a lot of energy and expertise into these things. If they didn't do these things now, then, we wouldn't have a timber industry in Britain nowadays.

OK? And for those reasons, you've got to applaud them. They did a lot of work, and they put their heart and souls into it. So we have the likes of Whitelee Forest.

And no, they did not think about access, but there was access. But it certainly wasn't access that could withstand the timber weights that we're putting out nowadays. Things have moved on, you know? And then we're fifty years on, we're further on.

Yes. So it's no longer a horse extraction and single, single logs being hauled out.

No. No, I'm afraid not. It's, it's forty-five-tonne lorries, and all the harvesting is done by machinery rather than men.

Then **Frank** spoke about the actual harvesting techniques in Whitelee Forest.

Ruth: So I suppose that comes to the next question then, who, who did and does the harvesting?

Frank: *Right. The harvesting started back in, once we'd got the road in, we started clear-felling the first areas in 2001. The harvesting is sold on a standing sale basis.*

Which means?

Right, OK. The timber area, if it's a coup, or it's a volume, let's say it's 10,000 tonnes, we put it to the market... yeah, we have market sales four times per year. And, merchants, timber merchants put in for it. And so, the one with the

Forwarder at High Hapton picks up logs and stacks them on its trailer, 2000
Photo: Robert Graham

190

highest bid, like any of these, gets it. Now he employs, or they employ, their own contractors to do the work. They employ their own haulage contractors to take it away. And they either take the log material, which is the best part of the tree... the big part, away to their sawmills, if they've got a sawmill, if they're that type of group, where they cut it into boards for housing et cetera et cetera. The rest of the tree, the smaller end of the tree (coughs), excuse me, goes to either the pulp markets, like, Irvine being one, or export pulp.

And there is quite a marketplace for that. Or, if it's degraded timber, drier timber et cetera, and it's maybe not Sitka spruce, (coughs) excuse me again, it might be [inaudible] Lodgepole pine or larch, which there is some of in Whitelee, then that goes down to Auchinleck*. So, they're the people that work the forest.

*[Egger (Barony) Ltd mill, which produces chipboard]

OK. So once you've sold it, that's it really, they get on with it?

They, they get on with it, but with our management control. We inspect the sites, make sure that all the health and safety regulations are being adhered to and that they're working the site in an environmentally sensitive manner as well. I am in charge of that. I have foresters who look at the site, keep an eye on things.

Right, OK. OK. OK, right, and what are they called, these foresters, they're...?

Operations Foresters.

Tracked Digger bogged down, High Hapton, 2000
Photo: Robert Graham

Frank Jackson then went on to explain that modern mechanical forest harvesting has not just ousted the individual workers: for a start, nobody wants to work in the conditions suffered by the Whitelee squad any more.

> **Ruth:** Frank, you said that forestry nowadays, or particularly the harvesting side, is done by machines and not by people any more, which to me seems very sad, so, can you explain why and what sort of machinery is used, particularly with reference to Whitelee?
>
> **Frank:** *Yes, I certainly can. And, it does seem sad, and,*

The Forwarder stacks logs by the forest road, 2000
Photo: Robert Graham

having worked through forestry from '69 up to the present day, and with the Bucleuch Estates forestry at that stage where it was very manually-orientated and, there's one guy with a chainsaw and the rest of us snedding with axes behind him, and extracted by horse, we're now to the stage where at Whitelee the harvesting operation is done by one machine, the felling of the trees, a harvester it's called, harvester.

Now, the machinery, the harvester can either be an excavator-based type machine, which is a Crawler, with, instead of having a bucket on the head of it, it has a harvesting head, which... These harvesting heads et cetera were, in the main they come from Scandinavia; you get some coming from North America. But they've had years and years of experience and aptitude, and they have got machinery down to a fine art. And with the machinery you get a better output, you get a more, more, what's the word to use?

Uniform?

Thank you. (laughter) Something like that. You know what's going to happen, you know that the machine can produce, in these sites in Whitelee, up to ten tonnes an hour, because of the tree size. We're talking an average tree size at Whitelee, .25 cubic metres*, so about, .2 of a tonne*, something like that. And so, they can produce ten tonnes an hour. And a man with a chainsaw, you'd need a group of men with chainsaws, oh you'd need a gang of thirty men to do the same work. So, that's the reason why we've got machines. And men... And it's not just that, it's not just that the machines have come in and done the men's, man's work away.

* [that is 0.25 and 0.20]

The men were becoming less and less adaptable to working in the type of climate that we have in this country, and, working the hours, going away at the end of the week with aches and pains, which only now begin to show up with bad backs et cetera, and in the early days with chainsaws, there wasn't anti-vibration dampeners on them, so, a lot of people have ended up with white finger et cetera. So, they had these complaints. And then the Scottish climate, you've midges all summer. Nobody wants to go into that, they'd

rather go into an office, they'd rather go on the dole, they'd rather do anything rather than do this.

So the machinery part of it is a blessing in disguise, and it allowed us to make sure that we had a steady supply of timber all year round at that same rate. And... That's the felling. Extraction is done by a forwarder, which is a purpose-built tractor with a trailer on the back. I use 'tractor' loosely but it's a tractor unit with a trailer which is attached to it as well. It's, it's all pretty well hydraulically tied up. So, this thing extracts fifteen tonnes on it, and it takes to the roadside. So, our horse extraction could never manage that either, so we'd have to have four or five teams of horses doing that sort of work, and they wouldn't be able

Stack of shaved logs on Allerstocks Moor
Photo: Ruth Tittensor

Trailer of logs awaiting a timber lorry in Whitelee Forest
Photo: Ruth Tittensor

Good quality Sitka spruce used as roof spars
Photo: Forestry Commission Picture Library

Clear-felled coup with branches left to lie giving tree seedlings shelter from browsing
Photo: Ruth Tittensor

Nowadays tree seedlings are planted on Mounds or 'Dollops'
Photo: Forestry Commission Picture Library

to work eight-hour shifts, extracting that amount of timber . . .

You've got to bring these machines in I'm afraid. So, that, that's where we're at, and that, that is the harvesting part of Whitelee, and we're doing about 12,000 tonnes a year at Whitelee.

That's a lot is it?

In the shape of things, it's, it's not enormous in south Scotland scale, but it's a, it keeps Whitelee moving along. It works within the Design Plan that we've created, and it's... Because the Design Plan, as I said before, breaks down the area into coups, felling coups, and we know at Whitelee that we can manage on about 12,000, 15,000 tonnes a year. And it can work through like that for the next thirty, forty years quite easily.

The Next Generation Whitelee Forest

The exceptionally hard work carried out with such vigour and professionalism during the planting years are now coming to fruition.

Felling and harvesting have been followed by replanting: the 'second rotation' of Whitelee Forest has started. Modern methods of planting trees are different from the 1960s too.

Frank: *After it's, we are moving on quite a bit, and we have made a lot of inroads now into Whitelee, the harvesting part of it, but we've also started replanting areas that we first felled, and so, we've now planted up at least fifty hectares of Whitelee again. And, and the crops themselves have been established by a different cultivation technique, it's one I touched on before.*

Instead of ploughing, we're now going in with a Backacter to, to cultivate the site. And with the Backacter we're creating dollops, which is the spoil, what comes in the bucket when the Backacter digs. Spoil drain. And on either side of the spoil drain, he throws out a dollop, which is a mound of earth. And, we're planting up to 2,700 plants per hectare on these evenly-spaced dollops.

Which is more, or, or, slightly more than original . . . Tighter spacing creates a better form tree, it creates a tree with less branches, less whorls on it so less branches. So you get less knots. And it's that type of timber that our marketplace needs. They don't need trees with lots of knots, because it's not stress-gradable, you cannot use that in building.

The Wind Farm

The future of Whitelee Forest seems to be assured. However, only half a century after the first huge change in land use, there is a second big change in progress on the Whitelee Plateau. A wind farm of over 200 turbines is being built in and beyond the northern part of Whitelee Forest.

But **Frank Jackson** seemed to be pleased about this development.

> **Frank:** *The future of Whitelee is, I think, I think in my own mind is quite exciting, because, there will be a wind farm established on Whitelee, probably starting next year, 2006.*

> *And, with that it, I think, will open up the rest of Whitelee dramatically to the, the general public. Because, the wind farm people, Scottish Power, will have to put roads in to, a) to put in their wind turbines, and b) to connect the wind turbines to each other, and to a centre where they can actually start putting that electricity into the main grid. So, which will open up Whiteleee more and more for walkers, for mountain bikers et cetera et cetera, I feel.*

Ruth: So, can you explain how a wind farm is going to be integrated into a commercial forest?

Part of the 'Whitelee Wind Farm' on Bught Knowe, 2008
Photo: Ruth Tittensor

Right, OK. Now the wind farm in Whitelee is just going to take over, or take up I should say, take over, it'll take up a specific area within Whitelee.

The wind farms at Whitelee, or the wind farm at Whitelee, will comprise about eighty wind turbines within the forest area. Now, the wind turbines themselves... This doesn't mean that the whole of Whitelee where these wind turbines are going to be situated, or the section where the wind turbines in Whitelee are going to be situated, is going to clear-felled.

The only areas that's going to be clear-felled are the areas round about the wind turbine, the base of the wind turbine, and the roads that connect the wind turbines to each other.

Our plan is to re-establish a crop, Sitka spruce, again in the areas where we can plant, with the wind turbine cuts. This has been agreed with Scottish Power, and it was part and parcel of the deal that we had to establish a wind farm there. Now... And so in that sense, the ground will be replanted, but the only criteria to that, instead of the crop reaching, growing on for about thirty, thirty-five years of age, we will fell it at, top height twelve, thirteen, which will probably be about year twenty of age.

The reason behind that is that, if it gets too tall, then it'll affect the wind through for the turbines themselves, there'll be too much turbulence and it will, it won't be... it isn't what's required for the wind turbines themselves.

OK, right. Now, this is obviously going to affect your, your Design Plan and your forest management. Will you have smaller coups, or, how will, how will it affect...

Yes, it will, it will affect it to a certain extent. Some of the areas, there will be smaller coups established, just because of where the turbine is situated, and because of what I've suggested just now, that the trees have got to be felled slightly earlier than normal . . . The only effect on the look of Whitelee will be the wind turbines themselves; you'll still have a forest floor, the forest will be retained as it is, but...

But with little holes and... for the turbines... sticking out of the holes.

Absolutely.

And **Jim Smalls** was enthusiastic about the wind farm too.

. . . I would rather see a wind farm on a hill than see one of these big globes for a nuclear power station, or a big chimney belching smoke out.

So, I thought it was going to be beneficial. I can understand that people will have objections to them, because, if they're living too close and there is a noise, that's fine, they have every reason to object. So my only... I can't really say, don't do it because you're going to upset these people, or do it because it's going to benefit the area for electricity. My only opinion on it can be, if it happens, it will open up the forest.

And if it opens the forest up, and it puts in roads and paths, and it allows the communities in East Kilbride and Strathaven and Darvel and Galston, and Eaglesham and all these places round about, to go in there and make use of that land, then I think that would be a good thing.

And if they can find some way to balance it so that no one is affected by noise from the turbines, while still putting them in, and still giving both sides the benefits, it would be a fantastic thing to happen.

Everything we can do to get people out into the fresh air is a good thing.

What do non-Forestry Commission people think about the 'forest-with-wind-farm' prospect? Ruth Tittensor spoke to **Karen Bruce**, who lives with her young family close to the wind farm which is being built.

Ruth: How do you feel about the wind farm?

Karen: *Yeh, it doesnae really fuss me. We have to find other ways of power, you'll, of getting power and things we canna just keep relying on earth* (laughs) *also, sort of thing, but I don't know I'll wait and see what happens once it's started, how sort of, different it makes things and* (indistinct words) *what happens.*

But there are, you haven't, you won't actually see any from here?*

*We will. We will see, I think mebe (pause) a dozen**

As many as that?

*I think we're gonna see the tops of them. At the time Scottish Power did give us a, what we would be able to see, y'know a sort o' picture of what we'd be able to see and we could see about a dozen of them** . . .*

* [wind turbines]

It would be behind us and to the left of the house. It will be, we'll see them round that way . . .

But there will be a lot of roads being built, so that will increase the access into the Forest.

There will be, again not from here though. I don't think there's much access from here, it'll all be Eaglesham side, they'll be comin in from. But, we'll wait an see.

You don't feel it'll take away the sort of remoteness or feeling of being out in the country?

N-not here. I think it will for a lot o' places. I think it will change the way they feel, but mm, I personally like bein out in the middle of nowhere (laughs).

Tom Grant felt happy about the wind farm.

> **Tom:** *Ah wid say Ahm for it. Ah'd say we have the roads for it, for the wind farm the foarestry would get the trees back oot so it's servin a double purpose* [indistinct] *an they wind farms Ah think they blend in, the blend in ye get yaised tae them bein there.. If that's the wey tae make electricity it's maybe better daein that than burnin coal. Ah widnae be against it.*
>
> **Ruth:** Would you have them on your land?
>
> *Yes! It widnae bother me, no'*

In 1986, a small group of experimental wind turbines were built on Forestry Commission land at 330m altitude in an unplanted area of Whitelee Forest. The National Engineering Laboratory and engineering firms carried out research and produced electricity and heat from them.

Norman Gibson and his family have lived for twenty-one years within 300m of these experimental turbines. So he knows, more than anybody else in the area, what it feels like to live in close proximity to a wind farm and he described some of the drawbacks.

> **Norrie:** *We have a pretty hard time constantly when anything ever happens with wind turbines. It's not just a case that they're there, that they're noisy, and they cause...*
>
> **Ruth:** They are noisy aren't they.
>
> *They are noisy, yes. Regardless of what anybody says. They're annoyingly noisy, it's like a cement mixer in the sky . . . The other problem we've had with the existing ones up here is lightning strikes.*

Mhm. Yes, can you tell me about that?

The first time it happened we thought it was just a one-off. And all the phones, all the phone lines, all the phone sockets were destroyed. We got all that replaced. And it happened again. So when we started, any time we hear lightning, we all take out all the phone sockets. One time it happened, we've had four so far, four lightning strikes...

Last time, one of the times it happened the computer was plugged in, and the modem, and it destroyed the computer. All that is an act of God according to the insurance companies. Every time we've just replaced phones, we just buy cheap phones now. Fax machines, like that, we just buy anything that works. Nobody... people don't use fax machines much now anyway. But the close proximity of the wind turbines attracts lightning. It has destroyed a lot of their stuff themselves, although they won't, they won't admit it.

Right. Right.

At any time I've brought this up in conversation with wind turbine companies, they say, **"Oh it won't happen with our company"** *. . .*

What we do get disturbed with, which is another thing that nobody seems to bother about, flickering. Our bedroom is on this side, and on a sunny morning it's just chop-chop-chop-chop-chop-chop-chop-chop-chop, with the light coming into the room.

Yes, that's never been mentioned, that sort of thing, has it?

No well they say, unless you're, unless you're subject to... epilepsy, and it's only photo, photosynthetic epilepsy I believe, that it affects people that way, but again they just, pooh-poohed all that sort of stuff, it doesn't exist. It doesn't happen to us.

Mhm. Well I suppose with so many wind farms being built, we'll discover whether all these things...

Yes indeed.

He then forecast what it will be like with a very large wind farm around his house.

Ruth: And how... I mean, are you going to be surrounded by wind turbines?

Norrie: *Yes. Completely surrounded by wind turbines, yes.*

Mhm. Mm. Rather as you were surrounded by forest. [looking at map]

Virtually... I'll be able to see quite a lot of them.

So when you go out of your house, you will see lots and lots and lots of wind turbines? And you'll hear them, and...

The experimental wind turbines on Myres Hill in the 1980s. Plantation on Loch Hill (left), Drumduff Hill heather (right)
Photo: Courtesy Robin Chambers

You will hear them, and that's one thing for sure. They are very noisy. You can actually, if you listen to all the bumf there on the television, you can actually, actually go and have a conversation with somebody underneath them. It's quieter when you're underneath it than it is half a mile down the road. Sometimes you're sitting and you'll hear something like an express train coming.

This is when it shuts down. Feathers itself against the wind to stop, and change direction. It's like an express train coming in. It gives you a fright sometimes . . .

Yes, you must be one of the few people around who has experience of these things.

Yes. Unfortunately, nobody listens to me.

John Douglass had reservations about the Whitelee wind farm due to its potential ecological effects.

Ruth: . . . how will that affect the populations of lichens, and how will it affect the peat, the remaining peat bogs?

John: *. . . I don't necessarily have a problem with turbines and wind farms. If they put them in the right areas. I mean if they, if they fell the Sitka spruce and just put them in the areas where the, the habitat has already been degraded, that's not necessarily a problem; it's when they start putting them on blanket bog which is prime, active blanket bog, you know, that's been there for thousands of years, and they put these things in, piling thousands of tonnes of concrete, and that's going to change the, the whole structure of the place really, it's going to degrade the, the peat. And when, when peat is exposed, it will oxidise, which means it just tends to sort of, well, crumbles up. And then when it gets wet it just turns into a mulch sort of thing, it's like a, you know, like quicksand, it's like a bog, you know, if you put your foot in there, you're just [?killed]. It's like a soup. And quite often you can, you find that nothing can colonise that. In certain areas we've noticed that these sort of soupy areas, nothing's able to colonise, because it's just so unstable . . .*

And what about the wind farm improving the habitats?

Could they make new habitats for lichens, could lichens grow on the turbines, on the stalks of the turbines, or on the concrete bases?

Oh aye, I'm sure there will be winners, winners and losers in every game. Aye, I'm sure there'll be things that will grow on the concrete. But usually, stuff that grows on concrete, and if it's only been there for, you know, if it hasn't been there for that long, it's not going to be a particularly rare species, or, commonish stuff, and that'll be replacing the, the ancient indicators you know.

While **Robin Chambers** discussed his own attitudes to the wind farm, his ideas were written down.

Whitelee Forest is very close to Glasgow (only half-an-hour from the city centre). It will be opened-up by the Wind-Farm development, so lots of new access is inevitable. Mr Chambers sees this as an opportunity to educate people to enjoy countryside access without spoiling what they have come for. The population on the Forest's doorstep is enormous, the views are still fantastic, lots of people already use it and will use it more. He thinks the proposed Visitor Centre is a very good idea, so that local schoolchildren can be taken there to learn about the Covenanters, the Forest and other subjects of interest. The idea of a route for disabled people is good.

Mr Chambers likes his privacy, but also likes meeting people and explaining about the Forest to them; he likes to explain to them to wear suitable clothing, to bring maps, to realise that Whitelee Forest can be as remote as anywhere in Scotland. He explains to people that they should tell someone else where they are going. Finally, Mr Chambers sees Whitelee Forest as being very important in providing clean energy close to a large community.

Comment

A group of resident forestry professionals and workers who lived in local communities, represented the new institutional owner of the Whitelee Plateau from June 1961 onwards. Although ownership was no longer in many local families and access was difficult once the Forest had been planted, some of the communities still knew what was happening, knew the staff personally and kept an eye on things.

When forestry employees were gradually reduced, then the Forest office was closed and finally the remaining squad no longer needed, Whitelee Forest was lost into obscurity. Community feelings of interest, of 'belonging' or 'ownership' had declined: they could no longer use the land due to access difficulties and could not affect its management as it was owned outwith the locality. Older people had long since gone elsewhere for their work and recreation, and the younger generation hardly knew of the Forest's existence.

In due course, the new Scottish Lowlands Forest District was formed by the Forestry Commission; its express purpose was to revitalize a number of forests in the same situation as Whitelee, which had, at one time, been on the 'Disposals' list. Whitelee Forest was 'placed into this new District. This coincided with the very first plantings becoming mature enough for harvesting, and with the new Forestry Commission remit to integrate social purposes into forestry.

Modern Forestry Commission staff involved with Whitelee Forest are as professional and motivated as earlier staff and workers who had established Whitelee Forest. Their tasks are to oversee the timber harvest and replanting, to make Whitelee Forest welcoming to people and to oversee mitigation of the ecological impacts of the wind farm.

Future silvicultural plans include increasing 'biodiversity' by 'opening up' the forest into small management units. It is worth asking, however, whether there are sufficient data on the current ecological structure of Whitelee Forest to decide whether its diversity needs increasing, how, and by how much? Could its conservation value have been equally served by continuing earlier management styles and maintaining an un-fragmented Forest? Complex ecosystems and large home-ranges for top predators require long-term stability of environmental conditions and large areas of habitats.

However, the new Whitelee Wind Farm (was the potential for a wind farm the reason that Whitelee Forest was not actually sold in the 1980s?) adds complexity in putting any modern forestry policies into practice. What is done will be visible to many more people. And the long-term ecological results can only be guessed at.

The Whitelee Wind Farm will not be discussed further because it is part of the next phase of the history of the Whitelee Plateau. Perhaps someone else will record what does actually happen to Whitelee Forest, the flora, fauna, local economy, and people's feelings about it.

CHAPTER 15

Issues Important to People

Whitelee Forest: Part of a National Process

Successive governments during the twentieth century pursued the policy and process of afforesting suitable British uplands. The Whitelee Plateau was a late and relatively small contribution to this in Scotland. Contributors to the Whitelee Forest Oral History Project have shown that the transformation of landscape and changes in land ownership and management have been significant for its communities, the locality, and in a wider context. There have been significant ecological changes too.

Contributors described how difficult it was for the Forestry Commission to fulfil its remits: ensuring large-scale home-produced timber supplies by planting as many hectares as possible, creating rural employment and contributing to local economies. Tree-planting was very successful, but contributors agreed that little employment was needed in the locality at that time. Whitelee Forest provided some economic benefits in the form of an initial inflow of cash to over 20 farmers and wages for six to 14 forestry employees over the years.

Changes in Farming and Farm Families

Hardy upland breeds of sheep and cattle disappeared from the landscape when farmers sold their moorland habitat, to which they were well adapted. Clydesdale horses, retained on some farms long after the Second World War, had almost gone as traction animals. The loss of stock breeds is still felt keenly by local farmers, even though they know it was inevitable and would have happened eventually even without Whitelee Forest .

A decrease in cultivation was another inevitable change when sheep farming was forced from the moorland 'downhill' to the better ground where larger breeds and hybrids could be raised with help from bought-in fodder.

With fewer farm workers employed after the Second World War there had been increasing dependence on farm wives and families. There were still at least six full-time shepherds on the Plateau when Whitelee Forest was started. Only a few part-timers continue to have employment on the remaining farmland.

When parents sold all their farmland to move to better land or retire, some young people eagerly took the chance to leave the world of farming to make a living elsewhere – though the links with farming were kept.

Some farm families benefited greatly from the sale of a proportion of their land, and were able to carry on farming. The younger generation could then remain on the farm, initiating updated managements or diversification into new businesses. Some nevertheless still left farming but, with great resourcefulness, carried on making a living in other ways connected with the rural estate.

The strong agricultural tradition associated with an intensely social, but very hard-working way of life and close familial links with local towns and villages, lessened, much to the sadness (and sometimes bitterness) of people who missed the close comradeship of the moors. The coming of the Forestry Commission merely hastened agricultural changes which were in the offing, but which happened later here than in other parts of Britain.

The view of Forestry Commission managers that they were helping some of the farming community with an input of capital was well founded. Their idealistic hope that farmers who sold all their land would be only too happy to get work

Jimmy Leitch with crook and collie Spot, Gateside 1940s
Photo: Jim Leitch

George Graham and collie Jen on quad bike, Bransfield 2008
Photo: Ruth Tittensor

Ayrshire cow, main dairy breed Mossgiel, in 1960s
Photo: Ruth Tittensor

Holstein-Friesians, main modern dairy breed, Bransfield 2008
Photo: Ruth Tittensor

in forestry was possibly a naive view: farming and forestry are as different as chalk and cheese. A farmer, a resourceful businessman used to making his own decisions, is unlikely to want to work as a forest worker (or even tractor-driver), unable to make any personal decisions on the nature of his daily or seasonal work. Only two farm sons (from over 20 farms sold) came to work in Whitelee Forest. Even farm workers like shepherds are independent people used to working on their own. Redundant shepherds from the Whitelee Plateau found work on other farms elsewhere, not in the Forest. The redundant gamekeepers retired when forestry took over their patch.

Technology and the Workforce

Afforestation of the Whitelee Plateau was regarded by the Forestry Commission managers in 1961 as at the limits of their technical capabilities, because of its extreme environmental conditions – particularly the deep, wet peat and all-round wind exposure. They went ahead nevertheless. Suitable tractors, ploughs and other items were available to use on the Whitelee Plateau because they had been, and were being, developed on deep peats in places like Flanders Moss. Firms like Cuthbertsons and Clarks were important partners in developing the double-mouldboard ploughs which made it possible for trees to grow better roots and therefore be less likely to windblow. The experienced tractor drivers who had developed their skills ploughing difficult terrain over large parts of upland Scotland were also very important to the success of the Forest. The fact that their machines sometimes sank in the peat bogs, shows what difficult conditions they faced on the Whitelee Plateau.

Harvesting the first tranche on time, after exactly 40 years, shows that both the technical capacities and the abilities of the original squad were up to scratch for the task of establishing the forest. The motivation and skill of a long-term squad whose members worked at many tasks during the 33 years of afforestation is testimony to what was achieved. Their work was physically hard and sometimes hazardous. They worked long hours, in remote places, without radio

contact until later years, in weather that could be difficult at any season, and seven days a week in the fire-risk time of spring and early summer. Five of the squad also ran Forest Workers' Holdings of about 100 acres, with lambing no doubt coinciding with spring fire-watch.

It is difficult to imagine how they did it, except that their wives and families helped them. Life was very different to that of the present residents of the Holdings several of which have become modernised country dwellings.

Although machinery which was advanced for its time was used for ploughing and initial digging of huge drains, the squad used hand tools throughout. Some of the hand tools, such as the border spade, rutter and howk, were taken over from similar agricultural tasks on the previous moorland. Helicopters were the only form of mechanisation of the squad's work, used for spraying fertiliser once the trees were too thick and prickly for men to get through them. A resident squad and its hand tools are now an old-fashioned idea: most tasks are nowadays carried out by one or two people with an extremely expensive machine. However, tree-planting itself is still manual.

Few women were employed by the Forestry Commission at Whitelee Forest. Part-time secretaries worked in the forest office at Waterside. The daughter of a head forester and her friend worked on squad duties for a summer vacation. In the late 1990s a woman forest district manager based at Straiton had Whitelee within her compass. Without testimony from these women, there is unfortunately no feminine view of working for Whitelee Forest.

Foresters and their Role

Acquisitions officers were the first Forestry Commission staff to make contact with people on the Whitelee Plateau. They forged good relationships, as did most subsequent head foresters and foresters. One forester forged such a good relationship that he married the daughter of an adjoining farmer. The foresters were both practical men and managers of their workforce and budgets. They could turn their hand to squad work or tractor driving if necessary. They had been trained in a profession requiring many practical skills: a knowledge of geology and soils, tree biology, markets, budgeting, mensuration and personnel management.

The more senior staff such as district officers, (district managers as they became), conservators and senior executives who were involved with Whitelee Forest all expressed considerable interest and a positive attitude towards their past involvement. They had been very motivated for the success of Whitelee Forest just as much as the men on site. Of course they (and the Forestry Commission) also cared about their careers, which is why their relationships with Whitelee were often short or broken by service elsewhere. Their job was to provide scenarios whereby governments' remits for the Forestry Commission were put into place for a variety of forests, but also to think about employees and problems at individual sites.

People and Change

The coming of Whitelee Forest changed the lives of those people living on the Plateau, and using the Whitelee Plateau regularly for the many purposes which have been described. The difficulty of access due to new fencing and closely-packed, prickly trees, the lack of open moorland to walk across or camp on at will, the disappearance of game and food species and the cost of Forestry Commission shooting leases all caused local users of the Whitelee Plateau to look elsewhere for their needs.

During the 1980s, the Forestry Commission realised it needed to build a forest road to link the forest interior with the outside world, for harvesting. People once more started to use Whitelee Forest when that forest road gave an access point from a public road. But the sort of people using the Whitelee Plateau, and where they came from, had changed. They were, in the late 1990s, members of the 'leisure' society from East Kilbride and the urban centres of Lanarkshire. They came on their mountain bikes and horses, or by car with their children and pet dogs. A few, who could afford Forestry Commission shooting leases and the cost of stalking training, continued with the tradition of shooting: but deer not grouse, snipe and hares.

Whitelee Forest and the Local Economy

At the start, incoming funds were paid to landowners selling land for Whitelee Forest. Most of these were individual owner-occupiers, but there were two tenanted farms.

At that time, local industries were busy. Textile factories, Ayrshire coal fields, Kilmarnock engineering firms and the electronic industries of East Kilbride supplied most of the employment needed, so forestry was not as vital in providing employment as in other parts of Scotland. Contributors stressed, however, that it gave men who wanted employment outdoors and not in factories, that opportunity.

The Forestry Commission supported the small business of moss-picking in Whitelee Forest. But contributors' testimonies show that Whitelee was regarded by senior managers as a 'farmed forest', primarily for pulp production.

Previous money-producing uses of the Whitelee Plateau became, of course, gradually impossible and ad hoc employment declined to nil. The comradeship of the moors evaporated leaving comradeship of the forest workers to develop. The Plateau's rich, varied and accessible base of natural resources was reduced to tree-cellulose production only. The cellulose had, and has, more distant benefit when private enterprise built a pulp mills at Irvine and a chipboard mill at Auchinleck, both about 20 miles away. The peat, which caused a problem from the start of the Forest, is still a problem now, at harvesting time. The Caledonian Mill at Irvine, built with Whitelee and other west coast Scottish forests in mind, apparently finds the Whitelee timber too contaminated with peat to be used as pulp for good quality paper.

In the 1980s, engineering firms and the National Engineering Laboratory at East Kilbride leased some unplanted land in Whitelee Forest for experimental wind turbines. This presumably brought income to the Forestry Commission but probably not to the locality. Nor did shooting leases bring income to the locality, as they had done 'Before the Forest' when the farmers themselves profited from the game one way or another.

Continuation of the wind turbine experiments on Myres Hill was jolted by sudden possibility of a derelict barytes mine being opened up again (and presumably mining under the turbine site). However, this came to nothing. This small-scale research sparked the possibility of a much bigger, economic turbine development in due course. A commercial wind farm is now being built within Whitelee Forest and on moorland to its north.

Ecology

At the time that the Forestry Commission bought lands on the Whitelee Plateau, its staff reported on the Plateau's environmental conditions, to recommend which tree species be planted there. Professional ecological research on land destined for new forests was not part of statutory forestry land acquisition and management at that time. However, contributor Richard Toleman and others later carried out soil surveys of Whitelee Forest as part of a national scheme of soil studies in forests. In the 1980s, the forest district manager had a quantitative assessment of the timber crop carried out. The first known collection of data on flora and fauna by the Forestry Commission was carried out by Alec Fenton in the late 1990s when he was full-time ranger and deer stalker in Whitelee Forest. New wildlife rangers have recently later followed suit.

This oral history project has shown that the communities on and around Whitelee hold a large reservoir of knowledge on the past and present flora and fauna of the Whitelee Plateau. This information is distributed within many testimonies and a selection has been presented here. Several contributors to this project had already written their own reports on the flora and fauna of the Whitelee Plateau, for their own satisfaction or for wider dissemination (see Bibliography).

Some local contributors have negative feelings about the ecological changes they observed because of the obvious big declines in species important to their lives. This is wholly understandable.

However, there is much that is positive and exciting. A fruitful result of years of 'leave-alone' has been the new dynamism of some plant communities. For instance, 'Hummock and Hollow' systems are developing on a huge and beautiful scale along many miles of brake. To see this phenomenon (and to struggle through it) is a great experience. The several large peat bogs left unplanted because they were too soggy and treacherous for either ground preparation or tree growth, have also had decades without grazing, peat-digging or other human use and are in an 'active' state.

The linear brakes and unplanted peat bogs are what remain of the pre-Forest moorland 'blanket bog' ecosystems and landscape. They have been neither ploughed for forestry, nor grazed for decades, nor driven over by vehicles and are scarcely walked on. The lines of wooden posts as well as some stone walls along some brakes are the earlier March Fences marking boundaries between the original farms. They too are ancient habitats with their own specialist flora of great beauty.

Long-term stability in the little-used, developing forest ecosystem has given a period without human contact and interference. This would be important to animals which need large territories (such as roe deer, badgers and and raptors) or are shy of human contact (such as water voles, otters and dippers).

The Forest has also provided shelter (which was definitely not there previously!) for certain lichens, which are relicts of much earlier Whitelee Forests: they have been able to grow into their real biological form rather than their stunted 'exposed' form. Another effect of lack of sheep and cattle grazing for an extended period has been the regeneration of native trees and shrubs like willows and rowan. Some, and the amenity broadleaf plantings of the 1990s, provide suitable habitats for many epiphytic lichens and mosses. They are specialist ecosystems developing naturally in the sheltered spots. New habitats provided by the Forestry Commission, such as forest road verges and small road-stone quarries, are important as homes for newly-arrived species (as noted by observant contributors).

The thick, dark, tree canopies characteristic of twentieth century planted conifer forests are the subject of much public criticism for their apparent lack of flora and fauna. However, contributors at Whitelee have noted the features of Whitelee Forest which have actually allowed the development of a rich botanical array. A rich botanical array provides a basis for many food-chains and therefore fauna. More, big, attractive animals will come in due course (indeed, have probably already come) if large enough parts of the Forest are left with minimal interference to develop.

The pool of ecological information given by contributors is a time-capsule picture of the plants and animals living on the Whitelee Plateau during one half century of its long history.

Knowing the history of the Whitelee Plateau and its ecology makes it possible to start to understand the changing ecological patterns and dynamics of its ecosystems. These

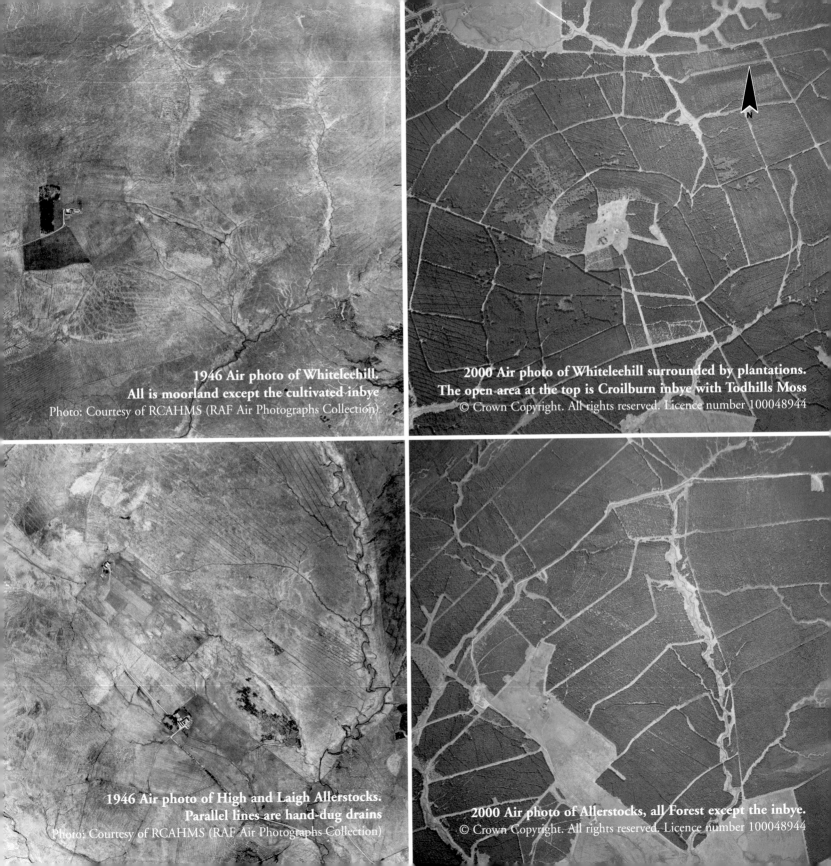

1946 Air photo of Whiteleehill.
All is moorland except the cultivated inbye

Photo: Courtesy of RCAHMS (RAF Air Photographs Collection)

2000 Air photo of Whiteleehill surrounded by plantations.
The open area at the top is Croilburn inbye with Todhills Moss

1946 Air photo of High and Laigh Allerstocks.
Parallel lines are hand-dug drains

Photo: Courtesy of RCAHMS (RAF Air Photographs Collection)

2000 Air photo of Allerstocks, all Forest except the inbye.

features – the *processes* of ecology – are far more important to conservation and other land management than mere 'biodiversity' and promoting a few, selected species.

Reflecting on Forestry Commission Perceptions

In the early days of Whitelee Forest, the Forestry Commission perceived the Whitelee Plateau as empty, boring moorland with run-down farms, whose owners would benefit from an input of capital from the sale of land. This last belief was true, but there was little perception at that time of the many ways in which the wider population made use of the landscape, nor how it might be possible for locals to continue using it within the forestry framework. At that time, it was not the Forestry Commission's remit to take such wider issues into account.

The landscape was perceived as having little beauty or value; it was invisible from outside, except from parts of East Kilbride to the north-east. It was compared unfavourably with the famous Forest Parks of Scotland: the Queen Elizabeth, Argyll and Galloway Forest Parks, with their well-known and accepted beauty and tourist status. What was not seen were the stupendous views from the Whitelee Plateau: the 360° panoramas which have been so eloquently described by many contributors to this project. Whitelee Forest lies within one hour's driving distance of the homes of about 40 per cent of Scotland's population. The population residing within one hour of the Galloway Forest Park is much smaller.

These perceptions and their resulting attitudes affected the whole history of Whitelee Forest as described by contributors.

In the early 1960s, archaeology, ecology, landscape and conservation of the natural and cultural heritage were neither an important component of the Forestry Commission's remit nor were they part of the world view of many foresters.

Growing as much timber as possible, over as large an area as possible (forced by government policy to be always in unsuitable conditions for tree-growth) was their job. And they were exceptionally good at it. It took the public outcry at afforesting the famous Caithness 'Flow Country' to alert some professional foresters to these other possible facets of land management on Forestry Commission land, as Gordon Cowie described in Chapter 6.

As the twentieth century wore on, the cultural aspects of the Whitelee Plateau were as yet not recognised. Once planted and growing, Whitelee Forest came lower on the list of priorities than other forests in the region. Staff were, of course, doing their primary task of producing a continuing cellulose resource for paper pulp. Ploughmen and planting squads had left untouched the human graves and the boulders which had been Covenanters' meeting places: they knew their significance. But these and other sites special to local people became hidden within the growing forest, without access.

The historic living and non-living landscape became tree-covered. Older local residents remembered its earlier significance and integrity. The Forestry Commission appointed staff to the new Scottish Lowlands District at the turn of the century. They started to collect data on several aspects of Whitelee Forest, including flora and fauna.

In the early twenty-first century a wind farm started to be developed. The windfarm developer was legally obliged to have experts and professionals carry out surveys of archaeology, ecology, geology, history, hydrology and landscape. It is sad that the knowledge of local people in some of these disciplines was not tapped. There is much information – useful, verifiable information – in the minds of participants to this oral project and other residents in local communities. This project has shown how important is a knowledge of history in understanding the structure and functioning of a landscape.

The Forestry Commission's early perceptions and its policy that Whitelee Forest would be for 'farm forestry' alone, made it convenient for it to be placed successively in four different administrative districts in the twentieth century. Its last placement, along with other forests which had been on the disposals list, was into the new Scottish Lowlands District. The role of the new district was to re-connect with each locality and instigate active silvicultural management in the forgotten forests.

Whitelee's apparent sparseness of living and non-living historic heritage made it possible to justify first a forest and then a very large wind farm on-site. Nowadays, Forestry

Commission staff discuss potential and actual changes to the previous 'No-Thin' (no management) policy. They talk with enthusiasm of creative and prolonged activity: silvicultural restructuring, planting more variety of tree species, encouragement of recreation and public use, and the possibility of deliberately increasing the biodiversity. It is interesting that these same themes were discussed between squad and foresters twenty years ago, in the hope that they could develop an alternative to the factory-forest Sitka-spruced Whitelee Forest. It was with pleasure that some of the squad planted broadleaved trees in parts of Whitelee Forest and improved the Weavers' Trail in their final working years.

Between 1961 and 2001, Whitelee Forest had 40 years to grow unhindered by disturbance from machinery, human access, silvicultural management decided on from afar, other land uses, or a wind farm also decided on from afar. What a luxury for the floral and faunal residents of the Forest! They could live as components of a large, developing, forest ecosystem unhindered by external scientific theories on biodiversity and recreation and by human disturbance.

Issues Important to Local People

The issues felt by the people involved or watching how the Forest was bought and developed from a farmed moorland were: the end of a way of life associated with hill and moorland farming; impossibility of using the Plateau ever again in their lives for previous normal activities by plateau residents and nearby communities; the rather sudden loss of moorland wildlife including game species; the apparent great increase in deer and foxes coming from the growing forest onto farmland; redundancies at planting-end; loss of local Forestry Commission contact after planting-end; the apparent and unexplained silvicultural neglect of the growing Forest; that the Forest seemed to have been forgotten; its seeming to be 'dead ground' not being used by the Forestry Commission nor the public; the lack of recreation facilities or encouragement for the public to use the Forest; the lack of a 'Balance Sheet' for Whitelee Forest to demonstrate its economic usefulness (or not); the apparent lack of interest in later years of deleterious happenings like windblow or broken

fencing. Not knowing the location of the relevant office nor the name of any personnel was frequently mentioned by people living in adjoining properties.

The Value of Information from Oral Sources

Matthew Mitchell discusses farming with Ruth Tittensor
Photo: Susan Anderson

The whole of this book is from oral information given by participants in the project. It shows the vast reservoir of knowledge that can be held in the minds and memories of communities. So far as I know, the detailed story given in this book is not available in print. Most of it is has probably been recorded only in people's minds until now.

This Whitelee Forest Oral History Project was set up to research a change in land use which was of comparable significance to the Scottish Clearances and Agricultural Revolution. The process of afforestation of the Scottish uplands in the twentieth century, has not previously been described by any people who actually carried it out or were involved, although the political background has been described and analysed frequently (see Bibliography for examples).

The interest and enthusiasm of about 60 participants, whose memories, knowledge and feelings were recorded, written down or which they wrote themselves, has not only made this possible, but has shown that it was long overdue. More people contributed photographs, maps and objects, gave time to discuss or explain, help with multi-media, with taking photographs, finding places or obtaining information.

I am the facilitator bringing what they have to say to the public gaze. Afforestation in Scotland is unlikely to be done to the same extent or in the same way again. The previous landscapes will not return, and people accept that.

The previous agricultural methods of working the land are obsolete. The early afforestation methods described here are obsolete too. So, in half a century, two major methods of land use, their machines and their tools have disappeared.

The results of this oral history project could be viewed as just another factual history to add to the archives. However, I believe there is much, much more to it than this, more that is of immense relevance to institutional land management.

When Whitelee Forest started, forestry staff formed good relationships with the people from whom land was bought, with adjoining farmers and communities. Local people could see what was going on when the forest was young, there was still unplanted moorland which could be accessed, some nearby people worked for 'The Forestry' in the squad or office. The foresters lived in the community and their children went to local schools. Some contributors argued and discussed afforestation with the foresters.

This all changed dramatically as employee numbers were reduced, eventually to none. The forest office was closed and Whitelee Forest was managed from afar. Local residents had to guess what, if anything, was happening. Whitelee Forest became 'dead' in local minds. Then, after apparently blank years, forestry rangers with a wider remit than fox and deer control started to visit the Forest. They discovered that some people were actually using it. Rangers noticed and noted wildlife and archaeology. When first harvesting became a reality and a wind farm more certain, the Forestry Commission carried out more detailed surveys of Whitelee Forest so as to integrate these and other uses into the future management of Whitelee Forest.

Experts and professionals seem not to have asked local people, such as those who contributed to this project, if they had knowledge, information or ideas relevant to the proposed changes in use. Yet they could have been helpful and useful to specialists in archaeology, ecology, geology, history and tradition, and would have plenty of suggestions for the future forest.

The contributors to this oral history project are not just elderly people with rose-tinted spectacles, remembering times now gone. As past users and current residents, they too are interested in the future of Whitelee Forest. Their knowledge of Whitelee Forest is based on long years of observation, which new, young staff and experts do not yet possess, however, keen they are. On the same theme, history is what produced the present: its relevance is still with us. I would expect people who have lived and worked long in any locality to have similar sorts of detailed knowledge to those of the Whitelee Plateau area.

Nowadays, many staff (those who work in offices which are distant from a forest) are certainly at a disadvantage: they have to balance the tensions of fulfilling their modern paper-and-procedure-biased work load with visiting the forests and contractors within their jurisdiction. However, communicating with people around those forests can save time in the long run, provide a good example of practical social forestry and be very fulfilling.

I commend to all who are interested in, involved in, or work in the Scottish countryside, the memories and feelings of the many contributors to this project.

Changes in how Whitelee Plateau was used during the second half of the twentieth century are summarised in Table 8 (page 212).

Mathew Mitchell, Farmer
Photo: Ruth Tittensor

Last Words

The last words go to three local people who have seen and lived with what happened on the Whitelee Plateau during the second half of the twentieth century. One is a farmer, one a forest squad worker and one an historian.

Mathew Mitchell spoke about the farming point of view.

Ruth: Okay, now, Mister Mitchell, you're President of

the (Matt laughs) Loudoun and Galston Agricultural Association so you know a lot about farming and the farmers round here, so if they were to look back to the period of the sixties to the nineties, um, do you think they would have been glad to have sold that land, or could they now be making a good living from the hills that were open at that time, could they be making a living from it now?

Matt: *Augh, that's hard tae tell, that's hard tae tell, the guys that – a lot o them that were around in the sixties probably arnae even around any more.*

Eh, they're probably pushin up the daisies themselves, but a think they would be very glad to have sold it, a don't think there's – well, it's one o these things in farmin, ye, ye make a decision, ye do it, ye can't spend yer time lookin back sayin a should have done this or a should have done that, ye move on and, eh, aa, no, a think the bulk o them would be glad to do it, it would open up opportunities at the time – certainly if they had held ontae it an they had made it throu, but, eh, a mean actually there's, that's anither wee sayin o ma father's, a mean the'r no use plannin for the long term if ye don't survive in the short term, so, ehh, if they had survived the short term until the long term, certainly under the recent C.A.P. schemes* they probably would have made a fair livin out ae a, a big enough hill farm, but likes o these farms that were five-hundred, a thousand acres, ye said previously, they would ha need to have been halfed, a mean they would ha need to have been a thousand and two-thousand acres now tae make a livin, eh, for like everythin else, it's, a lot o them have to go oot for the, for the rest tae survive, an, em, they, they, they mebbe could have made a livin but the'r no use really speculatin too much about it, eh, it's in trees,

An, eh, it disnae go, it disnae go back the way.

* [Common Agricultural Policy of the European Union]

The feelings of **Brian Speirs** about Whitelee Forest (of which he planted over 1 million trees) becoming the home of an enormous wind farm were written down as he spoke them at the very end of the project.

Brian Speirs, retired from the Whitelee Forest Squad
Photo: Ruth Tittensor

Everybody involved at Whitelee Forest, everybody (the people who bought it, the foresters and squad) were under the impression that they were creating a working Forest for generations to come. It was, for me at least, it was more than just a job, it was satisfaction doing a thing like that. That's the point. I gave personal input to creating that, pride I think, more than just a job anyway.

The way things have turned out, I would say everybody who was involved would be very disappointed that… I don't know how you would describe… them, the Forestry Commission, Scottish Power, the Government, whoever it is, they've decided that the Forest comes secondary, comes secondary to wind farms, unnecessarily as far as I'm concerned. See there's other sites round about especially the edge of the Forest. Purely on ethics it seems a big mistake, doesn't it.

I would imagine that everybody would feel the same. I dunno. I know it's all money isn't it. I dunno. It is all money.

James Mair, Archaeologist, Historian and Teacher
Photo: Joyce Mair

Historian **James Mair** spoke to Ruth Tittensor about the future of Whitelee Forest at a time when a windfarm was not in the public domain.

Ruth: Mr Mair, you've seen the Whitelee Hills when they were open moorland. You've seen them with young trees on, not long planted, and nowadays you go up there in your car, and you walk in the open rides. If you had the ears of the Forestry Commission and some say into what the future of this particular forest would be, what advice or what ideas, and what things would you like the Forestry Commission to do with this large area of mature forest?

James: *I don't think they should do much at all really, because it's established forest now, and it should maybe continue as an established forest. I don't see any reason why not. The day of open moorland and the sheep farms, that's passed, and now it's, it's used for forestry, it's an established forest. And so you cut the trees and you replant them, the area. So, OK, we just accept it now as a, as an established forest.*

The benefits, I don't know, there may be benefits, there could be... They could do away with... Say for instance there was a communal... a collective view of the harmful sides of forestry... among the various people who live in the area, the Forestry Commission could look at these and consider if they are valid criticisms, and try to ameliorate them somehow or other. Or they could look at what folk think is good about it, and advance ideas to improve even more the fact that they have an established forest on their doorstep.

Now we don't want them to... I wouldn't visualise the idea of ever clearing it all away again... and try to establish peat and peat moss.

. . . would you suggest to the Forestry Commission that they have some public consultation in the area to find out what the local people would like on their doorstep?

That's always a good idea. If they carry it through, and if they take them on board, that's a good idea.

Quite often these are just public relations deals, but, if they do really, are interested in finding out what local folk are wanting, or would like, and they are willing to take these on board, and consider them and implement them, well that'll be fine.

It's always better to do that.

END

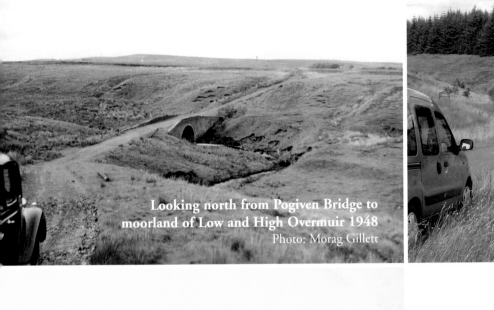

Looking north from Pogiven Bridge to moorland of Low and High Overmuir 1948
Photo: Morag Gillett

Looking north from Pogiven Bridge to moorland of Low and High Overmuir 2008
Photo: Ruth Tittensor

Brocklees Loch 1960s
Photo: Jim Currie

Brocklees Loch 2005
Photo: Ruth Tittensor

Ridge and Furrow ready for tree-planting, Kielder Forest 1950s
Photo: Courtesy Norman Davidson, Forestry Commission

Mounds ready for tree-planting, unknown forest 2000s
Photo: Forestry Commission Picture Library

Table 8: Changing Land-uses with Afforestation

FARMING

People or Use	Before Forest*	After Forest**
Full-time farm families	19	c. 6
Part-time farm families	0	3
Steading no longer a farm	0	6
Not known	0	4
Farmers also contracting	Occasionally	Most
Employed Shepherds	8 Known	2 known
Employed farm workers	Many but declining	None known
Employed game keepers	2	None known
Seasonal farm workers	Irish turnip thinners and drain diggers, local tattie howkers	Lambing and fencing
Hill-sheep raising	All farms: hundreds per farm	c. 6 farms with sheep
Hill-cattle for sale to lowland farms as heifers	Most farms	None known
Single-suckler beef cattle	A few	Most working farms
Pigs kept	Common	None known
Muir burning	Common	Declined to nil
Beekeeping	Unsuccessful attempts	Unsuccessful attempts
Peat digging for fuel	Very common	Reduced to one by 1960s
Farmland fires	Occasionally	Not known
Draining inbye	Frequent but declining	Not known
Draining moorland peat	Hand-dug open drains, later use of tile drains	Forest open drains, finished 1992
Fertilising	Ash, slag, manure	P, K granules by hand; N from air
Tree-planting	Few shelterbelts of beech, Sitka spruce	Almost all Plateau, Sitka spruce

FORESTRY

People or Use	Before Forest*	After Forest**
Resident foresters	None	1961-1987, 1-2 men
Forest Workers	None	1961-1994, 6-12men; stalkers occasional except 1997-1999
Forest Contractors	None	For short periods of planting; post-2001 for harvesting
Forest fires	None	Several

*   *Before 1960*   **   *1960s onwards*   *Source of data: contributors, observations*

Table 8: Changing Land-uses with Afforestation

COUNTRY SPORTS

People or Use	Before Forest*	After Forest**
Unkeepered syndicates	Not Known	Several adjoining Forest
Large, keepered shoots	2 Known	None known adjoining Forest
Ad hoc or on-farm shoots	Common	Few
Forestry Commission shooting leases	None	Forest shooting leased to few tenants
Pheasant-rearing to shoot in situ	Common	None known
Wildfowling	By locals	None known
Pest control	Widespread: foxes, hares, rabbits, stoats, weasels	Forest none; foxes, stoats, mink on nearby farms
Deer culling	Very rarely	1980s FC stalking; now all leased to syndicates

COLLECTING

People or Use	Before Forest*	After Forest**
Collecting birds' eggs for food	Very common	Declined to nil
Collecting wild plant foods	Common	Almost nil
Collecting Bog moss	Occasional (medical)	Horticultural firm 1980s
Collecting 'medicinal' plants	Common	Almost nil
Poaching	Common	Declined, now increasing
Collecting wood	Farmers for fencing	Becoming common
Collecting Christmas Trees	None to collect	Occasional

STUDY AND RESEARCH

People or Use	Before Forest*	After Forest**
Archaeology	Few studies	Many research projects
Taxonomy and Ecology	Several naturalists	Naturalists, FC staff recently
Soils	Not known	FC surveys 1970s,1982
School group study	None	1 local school met forest workers
Weather recording	3 rain gauges known	Rain-gauges gone; Corse Hill radar & meteorological station 1991-2008
Wind and turbine studies	None	Myres Hill Experimental Site 1980s

* *Before 1960*   ** *1960s onwards*   *Source of data: contributors, observations*

Table 8: Changing Land-uses with Afforestation

RECREATION

People or Use	Before Forest*	After Forest**
Fishing	Very common	None known in Forest burns
Guddling & Girning	Common for boys' fun	None known
Swimming in pools	Common	Quite common
Rover Scouts & Boys Brigade	Common	None known
Horse-riding	Heavy-horses working on farms	Pleasure riding common
Walking between farms for socialising	Common, across the moor	Impossible through Forest, nowadays by car
Rambling	Locals on minor roads, rambling clubs on Weavers' Trail	Rambling Clubs and other walking now increasing
Natural History	Occasional	Becoming more common
Ornithology	Locals (1 bird-watcher with hide)	Common: amateurs and professionals
Cycling	Workers on farm access roads	Initially impossible, now recreation on forest road
Motor cycling	Not known	Surrepticiously (prohibited)
Recreational dogs	Greyhounds exercised	Families with pet dogs
Feral dogs	Quite common	Occasional
Working dogs	Many per farm	Few working farms
Catching song birds	Common	Occasional

OTHER USES

People or Use	Before Forest*	After Forest**
Police	Checking dog licences	Not known
'Travellers'	Beggars in barns	Occasional lost people
Council Workers	None (no bin collection)	Planning officers perhaps
Vets	Frequent visitors	No stock within Forest
Water supply	Wells, burns and pumps	Wells, aquifers and pumps
Digging stone	Farmers, small-scale	FC for forest road
OS mapping personnel	Ground- surveys	(From the skies)
Utility workers	Attending poles	Attending pylons and poles
Military training	During War	None known
Burial	5 sites known	None known
Courting	Not known	Common
OS Trig Points	2	Derelict

* *Before 1960* ** *1960s onwards*   *Source of data: contributors, observations*

214

Norman Adam
Shepherd

Robbie Allan
FC Tractor driver

Susan Anderson
Graphics Designer

Madge (Bell) Andrew
Women's Land Army

John Andrews
Multi-media

William Barr
Farmer
(now deceased)

Michael Chalton
Saughall Meteorological Station

Robin Chambers
Country sports

Gordon Cowie
FC Conservator, Acting
chief executive

Malcolm Crosby
FC Planning forester

Anna Currie
Resident nearby

James S. Currie
Country sports

John R. Douglass
Lichenologist

Alexander Fenton
FC Squad, Senior ranger

David Findlay
Country sports

Norman Gibson
Whitelee Plateau resident

Morag M. Gillett
(née Loudon)
Whitelee Plateau resident

Janet Grant
Farmer

Thomas Grant
Farmer

Roy Harvey
FC Ploughing forester

Hugh Hendry
Country sports

Keith Hobley
Photographer

Frank Jackson
FC District forester

Alister Jones
FC District officer

Jim Kennedy
Farmer

Jim Leitch
Farmer

James Loudoun
Fisherman

John Mackie
Artist

James Mair,
Historian, teacher
(now deceased)

Bill Meadows
FC Forester

Susan Meadows
(née Semple)
Farm family

Ann Miller
Resident nearby

Robert Miller
Resident nearby

Archie Mitchell
Farmer

Mathew Mitchell
Farmer

Jim Newall
FC Squad, Senior ranger

Grant Peter
FC Squad, Forest Workers'
Holding

Richard Roberts
Resident nearby

Kerr Robertson
FC Head forester

Tom Semple
Farmer

Stan Share
FC Trapper

Bryan Simpson
Field naturalist

Jim Smalls
FC Senior ranger

Christopher Smout
Project instigator,
environmental historian

Brian Speirs
FC Squad, Forest Workers'
Holding

John Speirs
Childhood on Forest
Workers' Holding

John McI. Struthers
Farm family

Margaret Struthers
Farm family

Bill Sutherland
FC Acquisitions/district officer

Rena Tarwinska
FC District forester

Andrew Tittensor
Photographer

Ralph Tittensor
Photographer

Richard Toleman
FC Surveyor, project instigator

Elizabeth Watson
Farm family Whiteleehill (now deceased)

Jim Watson
The Meteorological Office, Edinburgh

Appendix 1: Contributors to the Project, no photographs available

Pat Armstrong: FC Resident head forester
Karen Bruce: Whitelee Plateau resident
William Clark & Son (Parkgate) Ltd: Plough manufacturer
Fred Cowie: Resident head forester (now deceased)
Susan Cowie: Forester's wife
James A. Cuthbertson Ltd (Biggar): Plough manufacturer
Aileen Ferrier: Resident nearby
Robert Graham: Forest-harvesting contractor
Iain Hamilton: Farm family, Fencing contractor
William Hunter Snr.: Photographer
P. A. Innes: FC Chief acquisitions officer

Bob Logan: FC Senior ranger
John W. MacKinnon: Photographer
Dougie McWhirter: Farm family
Margaret Richards: Place-names survey
Gavin (Guy) Ross: Farmer (now deceased)
John R. Speirs: Milk lorry driver
Edith Telfer: Farmer
John D. Telfer: Farmer
George Young: Tree-planting contractor

Photos courtesy: Contributors, Isobel Cameron, Keith Hobley, Ruth Tittensor

ENGLISH and SCOTS	*LATIN*
Mammals	
American Mink	*Mustela vison*
Badger	*Meles meles*
Bank Vole	*Clethrionomys glareolus*
Mountain Hare/Blue Hare	*Lepus timidus*
Brown Hare	*Lepus capensis*
Brown Rat	*Rattus norvegicus*
Cattle, Domestic	*Bos taurus*
Common Shrew	*Sorex araneus*
Fallow Deer	*Dama dama*
Ferret (domesticated polecat)	*Mustela putorius*
Field Vole	*Microtus agrestis*
Fox	*Vulpes vulpes*
Goats, Domestic	*Capra hircus*
Grey Squirrel	*Sciurus carolinensis*
Hedgehog	*Erinaceus europaeus*
Mole	*Talpa europaea*
Mouse	*Apodemus sylvaticus*
Muntjac	*Muntiacus reevesi*
Otter	*Lutra lutra*
Pigs, Domestic	*Sus domesticus*
Pine Marten	*Martes martes*
Polecat	*Mustela putorius*
Rabbit	*Oryctolagus cuniculus*
Red Deer	*Cervus elaphus*
Red Squirrel	*Sciurus vulgaris*
Roe Deer	*Capreolus capreolus*
Sheep, Domestic	*Ovis aries*
Sika Deer	*Cervus nippon*
Stoat	*Mustela erminea*
Water Shrew	*Neomys fodiens*
Water vole	*Arvicola amphibius*
Weasel	*Mustela nivalis*
Wild Cat	*Felis sylvestris*

ENGLISH and SCOTS	*LATIN*
Birds	
Barn owl	*Tyto alba*
Blackcock	*Lyrurus tetrix (male)*
Black grouse/Black game	*Lyrurus tetrix (both sexes)*
Blackbird	*Turdus merula*
Black-headed gull	*Larus ridibundus*
Brambling	*Fringilla montifringilla*
Bullfinch	*Pyrrhula pyrrhula*
Buzzard	*Buteo buteo*
Canada goose	*Branta canadensis*
Capercaillie	*Tetrao urogallus*
Carrion crow	*Corvus corone*
Chaffinch	*Fringilla coelebs*
Coot	*Fulica atra*
Corn bunting	*Emberiza calandra*
Corncrake	*Crex crex*
Cuckoo	*Cuculus canorus*
Curlew	*Numenius arquata*
Dipper	*Cinclus cinclus*
Duck, Domestic	*Anas platyrhynchos*
Fieldfare	*Turdus pilaris*
Geese, Domestic	*Anses anses*
Goldcrest	*Regulus regulus*
Golden eagle	*Aquila chrysaetos*
Goldeneye duck	*Bucephala clangula*
Golden plover	*Charadrius apricarius*
Goldfinch	*Carduelis carduelis*
Goshawk	*Accipiter gentilis*
Grey goose	*Anser species*
Greenfinch	*Carduelis chloris*
Grey goose	*Anser species*
Greylag goose	*Anser anser*
Grey hen	*Lyrurus tetrix (female Blackcock)*
Grey partridge	*Perdix perdix*
Hen, Domestic	*Gallus (domestic)*

ENGLISH and SCOTS	LATIN	ENGLISH and SCOTS	LATIN
Hen harrier	*Circus cyaneus*	Siskin	*Carduelis spinus*
Heron	*Ardea cinerea*	Skylark	*Alueda arvensis*
Hobby	*Falco subbuteo*	Snipe	*Gallinago gallinago*
Hooded crow/Hoodie	*Corvus corone cornix*	Song thrush	*Turdus philomelos*
House martin	*Delichon urbica*	Snow bunting	*Plectrophenax nivalis*
House sparrow	*Passer domesticus*	Sparrowhawk	*Accipiter nisus*
Jack snipe	*Lymnocryptes minima*	Starling	*Sturnus vulgaris*
Jackdaw	*Corvus monedula*	Stonechat	*Saxicola torquata*
Jay	*Garrulus glandarius*	Swallow	*Hirundo rustica*
Kestrel	*Falco tinnunculus*	Swift	*Apus apus*
Kingfisher	*Alcedo atthis*	Tawny owl	*Strix aluco*
Lapwing	*Vanellus vanellus*	Teal	*Anas crecca*
Linnet	*Acanthis cannabina*	Tit, Blue	*Parus caeruleus*
Magpie	*Pica pica*	Tit, Coal	*Parus ater*
Mallard duck	*Anas platyrhynchos*	Tit, Great	*Parus major*
Meadow pipit	*Anthus pratensis*	Tit, Long-tailed	*Aegithalos caridatus*
Merlin	*Falco columbarius*	Whaup or Wap	*Numenius arquata*
Mistle thrush	*Turdus viscivorus*	Wheatear	*Oenanthe oenanthe*
Moorhen	*Gallinula chloropus*	Wood pigeon	*Columba palumbus*
Moor owl/Short-eared owl	*Asio flammeus*	Woodcock	*Scolopax rusticola*
Moss cheeper	*Anthus pratensis*	Wren	*Troglodytes troglodytes*
Partridge, Brown	*Perdix perdix*	Yellowhammer	*Emberiza citrinella*
Partridge, Red-legged	*Alectoris ryla*		
Peewit/Peeweep/Peezer	*Vanellus vanellus*	**Amphibia and Reptiles**	
Peregrine Falcon	*Falco peregrinus*	Adder	*Viper berus*
Pheasant	*Phasianus colchicus*	Frog, Common	*Rana temporaria*
Pied wagtail	*Motacilla alba*	Grass snake	*Natrix natrix*
Ptarmigan	*Lagopus mutus*	Lizard, Common	*Lacerta vivipara*
Quail	*Coturnix coturnix*	Newt, Common	*Triturus vulgaris*
Raven	*Corvus corax*	Puddock/Paddock	*Rana temporaria*
Red grouse	*Lagopus lagopus*	Slowworm	*Anguis fragilis*
Redpoll	*Carduelis flammea*	Toad, Common	*Bufo bufo*
Redshank	*Tringa totanus*		
Redwing	*Turdus musicus*	**Fish**	
Ring ouzel	*Turdus torquatus*	Eel	*Anguilla anguilla*
Robin	*Erithacus rubecula*	Bairdie	*Gasterosteus aculeatus*
Rook	*Corvus frugilegus*	Baggie Meenies/Mennan/Mennaw	*Phoxinus phoxinus*
Sand martin	*Riparia riparia*	Brown trout	*Salmo trutta*
Sandpiper, Common	*Tringa hypoleucos*	Minnow	*Phoxinus phoxinus*

Rainbow trout	Salmo gairdnerii
Salmon, Atlantic	Salmo salar
Sea trout	Salmo trutta
Siller/Silly/Silver Willies	Salmo trutta (parr)
Stickleback	Gasterosteus aculeatus

Insects

Cleg (horse fly)	Haematopota pluvialis
Dragonflies: Black darter	Sympetrum danae
Common hawker	Aeshna juncea
Damselflies: Common blue	Enallagma cyathigerum
Common red	Pyrrhosoma nymphula
Honey Bee	Apis mellifera
Midge (Highland Biting Midge)	Culiciodes impunctatus
Red Admiral Butterfly	Vanessa atalanta
Wasp	Vespula vulgaris

Flowering Plants and Conifers

Alder	Alnus glutinosa
Ash	Fraxinus excelsior
Beech	Fagus sylvatica
Bent (grasses)	Agrostis species
Bilberry	Vaccinium myrtillus
Birch	Betula pendula, B. pubescens
Bird cherry	Prunus padus
Blackberry	Rubus fruticosus
Blackthorn/Sloe/Slew	Prunus spinosa
Bluebell	Hyacinthus non-scriptus
Bog moss	Sphagnum species
Bog cotton /Cotton grass/ Hare's tail/Draw-moass	Eriophorum vaginatum
Bog myrtle	Myrica gale
Bramble	Rubus fruticosus
Broom	Cytisus scoparius
Bugle	Ajuga reptans
Cherry/Gean	Prunus avium
Chilean beech	Nothofagus nervosa (procera)
Claytonia	Claytonia or Montia species
Cloudberry	Rubus chamaemorus
Cowberry	Vaccinium vitis-idaea
Cow parsley	Anthriscus sylvestris

Cranberry	Vaccinium oxycoccus
Crab apple	Malus sylvestris
Cross-leaved heath	Erica tetralix
Crowberry	Empetrum nigrum
Damson	Prunus domestica ssp. instititia
Dock	Rumex obtusifolius
Earthnut	Conopodium majus
Elder	Sambucus nigra
Elm	Ulmus glabra
Fir	Abies species
Flote-grasses	Glyceria species
'Gentian'	Meum athamanticum
Gorse/Furze	Ulex europaeus
Groundnut/Grundnut/ Pignut	Conopodium majus
Hard grass	Nardus stricta
Hawthorn	Crataegus monogyna
Hazel	Corylus avellana
Heather	Calluna vulgaris
Horse chestnut	Aesculus hippocastanum
Hybrid larch	Larix x marschlinsii (eurolepis)
Japanese larch	Larix kaempferi
Jointed rush	Juncus articulatus
Labrador tea	Rhododendron groenlandicum
Lady's mantle	Alchemilla species
Ling	Calluna vulgaris
Lodgepole pine	Pinus contorta
Marsh violet	Viola palustris
Milkwort	Polygala vulgaris
Mountain pansy	Viola lutea
Oak, Pedunculate	Quercus robur
Oak, Sessile	Quercus petraea
Norway spruce	Picea abies
Primrose	Primula vulgaris
Purple/Blue moor-grass	Molinia caerulea
Ramsons/Wild Garlic	Allium ursinum
Raspberry, Wild	Rubus idaeus
Reed	Phragmites australis
Rhododendron	Rhododendrum ponticum
Rose, Wild	Rosa (likely R. canina)
Rowan	Sorbus aucuparia

Rush	*Juncus* species
Sallow	*Salix caprea*
Scots pine	*Pinus sylvestris*
Sitka spruce	*Picea sitchensis*
Sloe	*Prunus spinosa*
Sourocks/Sorrel	*Rumex acetosa and R. acetosella*
Spignel/Bawdmonnie	*Meum athamanticum*
Stinging nettle	*Urtica dioica*
Sycamore	*Acer pseudoplatanus*
Thistles	*Cirsium palustre, C. pratense, C. vulgare*
Tormentil	*Potentilla erecta*
Tufted hair-grass	*Deschampsia caespitosa*
Water crowfoot	*Ranunculus aquatilis*
Western hemlock	*Tsuga heterophylla*
Wild pansy	*Viola tricolor*
Wild plum	*Prunus domestica ssp. institia*
Willows	*Salix species*
Yorkshire fog	*Holcus lanatus*

[Mosses, Liverworts and Lichens are normally known by Latin names only]

Appendix 3: Glossary of Scots and English Words (as used by Contributors)

Ayrshire	A large, maritime county in south-west Scotland
Ayrshire (cattle)	Breed of brown-and-white dairy cattle with rich milk
Afforestation	Planting a forest on previously bare ground
Bairdies	Sticklebacks (small fish with spines on back)
Baggy Mennan/Mennaw/Meenies	Minnows (small shoaling fish)
Barytes	Aluminium ore used in the oil industry
Beater /Beating	Boys (usually) who traverse an area noisily to flush game
Beating-up	Infilling gaps in plantations where tree seedlings died
Beasts	Cattle
Blackface	Breed of hardy sheep common in upland Scotland
Blaeberries	Blueberries or Bilberries (*Vaccinium myrtillus*)
Blue-arse flies	Flies which lay their eggs in the guts of sheep
Blue-gray/Blue-grey	Hardy hill cattle from a cross between Galloway and Shorthorn breeds
Bog cotton	Cotton Grass or Hare's tail (*Eriophorum vaginatum*)
Bothy	Farm attic, small room or outbuilding where workers lived
Brake/Break	An unplanted way between forest blocks for access
Braxie	A fatal disease of sheep
Bryophytes	Mosses and liverworts (small plants without flowers)
Buchts	A fenced or walled enclosure with internal compartments for separating sheep
Chain	Measurement of length used in forestry: 22 yards (20.11 m)
Check	When small trees and tree seedlings stop growing
Clearances	Periods of mass removals of tenants by Highland landlords and their replacement with sheep-flocks
Clipping	Cutting or shearing the wool from sheep
Clydesdale	Breed of large, grey-brown working horse from Clyde Valley
Covenanters	Adherents to the National Covenant which defended the Presbyterian faith (God, not monarch is church head, and worshippers, not bishops run the church)

Cowpies/Cowping	When a sheep gets stuck on its back (or a machine sinks)
Doric	Form of the Scots language spoken in NE Scotland
Draw-moass	Hare's tail (*Eriophorum vaginatum*)
Dunnerheids	Dunderhead or stupid person
Earthnut	Pignut (*Conopodium majus*)
Epiphytic	Plant which grows on another plant, not as a parasite
Flitting	Moving house or elsewhere
Gentian	Spignel (*Meum athamanticum*)
Girning	Catching river fish with a snare
Groundnuts/Grundnuts	Pignut (*Conopodium majus*)
Guddling	Catching river fish by hand
Hag/ Hagg	Exceptionally soft peat with deep gullies
Hay park	Part of the enclosed inbye for growing hay
Heft	Area of pasture on which a group of sheep is permanently established
Heifer	Young female cow before the birth of its first calf
Hird	Shepherd
Hirsel	Outlying small farm or shieling on a big farm
Hoast	A bad cough or coughing
Hogg/Hogget	Second year non-breeding female sheep
Hooching	Bursting (with delight)
Heuk/Hock/Hook/Yock	Short-handled, circular-bladed, cutting tool (like a billhook)
Holstein-Friesian	Modern black-and-white dairy cow with high milk yield
Howk/Hawk	A fork with its three prongs at right-angles to the handle
Inbye	The enclosed, cultivated and hay land near a farm steading
Inbye park	Field within inbye
Knowe	Knoll or small hill
Laigh (Laich)	Low; low-lying ground
Lambing park	Enclosed field in inbye for lambing some ewes
Lime	Artificial fertiliser made from calcium deposits
Manure	Effluent from cattle used to fertilise fields (organic)
March Fence	Boundary line, fence or wall between farms
Mat/Mats	Platform of bolted timbers on which a digger stands
Mennans/Mennaws	Minnows (small shoaling fish)
Mensuration	Measuring lengths and volumes of trees and timber
Moss	Bog moss (botanical Musci); a peat bog; very soft ground
Mule/Scotch Mule	Large sheep from Blackface x Bluefaced-Leicester cross
Oilskins	Very heavy rainproof clothing
Outbye	Uncultivated farmland not enclosed
Parr	Salmon and trout up to 2 years old
Parritch	Porridge
Parrocks	Sheep pen for giving a ewe an orphaned lamb

Peeweep, Peezer	Lapwing, peewit
Piece	Food eaten at midday away from home
Piecework	Work that is paid according to the amount, not time, done
Pinkie	Smallest finger on each hand
Pit Props	Upright timbers supporting roof and walls of coal-mines
Pooch	Pocket or purse
Puddock/Paddock	Frog or toad
Rock phosphate	Artificial fertiliser used to encourage growth of young trees
Rig/Rigs	Raised lengths of ploughed land separated by furrows
Rigs/Riggs	The sheep of poor quality in a flock
Runrig	System of joint tenure where every tenant was annually allocated a selection of rigs to cultivate
Rutter	Large, sharp, triangular spade for clearing turf or drains
Schooch/Schoch/Scheuch	A drain; placing bundles of tree seedlings in a wet drain to await planting
Scuddy/Scuddie	Naked or with only one garment
Scythe	Long-handled tool with long blade for cutting hay or cereals
Shearing	Cutting the wool from a sheep
Shrub/Sprig	Tree seedling awaiting planting
Siller/Silly/Silver Willies	Very young sea trout (parr)
Slag/Slang	Artificial fertiliser made from factory effluent
Snedding	Cutting off the branches from a felled tree
Sourocks	Sorrel (*Rumex acetosa* and *R. acetosella*)
Spean	Lamb being weaned
Sprit grass	Rushes (*Juncus species*)
Squad	Team of men working in a forest
Stay	Reside in
Steading	The working farm buildings and farmhouse
Stravaig	Roam, wander
Tattie Howker	A person who works at lifting potatoes
Taxonomy	Classification and naming of living organisms
Ten Bob	Ten shillings (half an 'old pound')
Teuch	Tough, persistent
Toggle	Coarse or rough wild grass
Tuggle	Pull about roughly; feel harassed
Tup/Tuip	Fertile male sheep
Web	Length of cloth woven on handlooms
Weeding	Removing long grass from around tree seedlings
Wether	Castrated young male sheep
Yowes	Ewes (fertile female sheep)

Source of information: Scottish Language Dictionaries (Edinburgh); The Shorter Oxford English Dictionary; Contributors

Oral Histories

Anon (2002 & 2003) *Hanes y Goedwig (The Story of the Forest)*. Two brochures produced by the Welsh Forest Oral History Project. Forestry Commission Social Forestry Team, Aberystwyth.

Brown, H. (2003) *A Life on the Land: Farming in Angus 1934 – 1994*. The Pinkfoot Press, Balgavies, Forfar & Angus Council, Brechin.

Bryan, E., Forster, A. & Mitchell, H. (1999) Midlothian: *Voices, Faces, Lives*. Midlothian WEA Salt of the Earth Project. Booklet of oral history recordings on CD and transcripts. WEA Scotland, Edinburgh.

Clark, H. & Carnegie, E. (2003) *She Was Aye Workin'*. White Cockade, Oxford.

Donati, C. (1994) *The Monklands House-Book*. A booklet of transcripts of stories, songs and poetry by the residents of Monklands House. Project Ability (Strathclyde Regional Council), Glasgow.

Evans, George Ewart. (1970) *Where Beards Wag All: The Relevance of the Oral Tradition*. Country Book Club, Newton Abbot.

Lotz, J. (2005) *Green Horizons: The Forests and Foresters of Nova Scotia*. Pottersfield Press, Lawrencetown, N.S., Canada.

MacArthur, E.M. (2002) Iona: *The Living Memory of a Crofting Community*. 2nd edition. Edinburgh University Press, Edinburgh.

MacLellan, A. (1997) *The Furrow Behind Me*: The Autobiography of a Hebridean Crofter. Birlinn, Edinburgh.

Martin, S., Emery, M. & Dyke, A. (2006) Wild harvests from Scottish Woodlands: an exploration of the health and well-being benefits of non-timber product collection and use. *Scottish Forestry* 60:3 (21- 26).

MacDougall, I. (2000) *Voices From Work and Home*. Mercat Press, Edinburgh.

Neat, T. (1996) *The Summer Walkers: Travelling People and Pearl Fishers in the Highlands of Scotland*. Birlinn, Edinburgh.

Ó Crohan, T. (1929/1937/1978) *The Islandman*. Originally published 1929 in Irish, with later translations. This edition translated from the Irish by Robert Flower & published in 1978 by Oxford University Press, Oxford.

Watson, M. (2003) *Being English in Scotland*. Edinburgh University Press, Edinburgh

Oral History Textbooks

Perks, R. & Thomson, A. (1998) *The Oral History Reader*. Routledge, London.

Howarth, K. (1998) *Oral History Handbook*. Sutton Publishing, Stroud, Glos.

British Woodland and Forest Histories

Jefferies, R. (1945) *The Wood from the Trees*. The Pilot Press, London.

Linnard, W. (2000) *Welsh Woods and Forests*. Gomer Press, Llandysul, Ceredigion. 2nd edition.

McCracken, E. (1971) *The Irish Woods Since Tudor Times*. David & Charles, Newton Abbott .

Porter, V. (1994) *Tales of the Old Woodlanders*. David & Charles, Newton Abbott.

Pringle, D. (1994) *The Forestry Commission: The First 75 Years*. Forestry Commission, Edinburgh.

Rackham, Oliver (2006) *Woodlands*. Collins New Naturalist No.100. HarperCollins, London.

Ratcliffe, Derek (2007) *Galloway and the Borders*. Collins New Naturalist No.101. HarperCollins, London.

Ryle, G. (1969) *Forest Service: The First Forty-five Years of the Forestry Commission in Great Britain*. David & Charles, Newton Abbot.

Shaw, D. L. (1971) *Gwydyr Forest in Snowdonia: A History*. Forestry Commission Booklet No. 28. H.M.S.O., London.

Simmons, I. G. (2001) *An Environmental History of Great Britain: From 10,000 Years Ago to the Present*. Edinburgh University Press, Edinburgh.

Smout, T.C. (Ed.) (2002) *Scottish Woodland History*. Scottish Cultural Press, Dalkeith.

Smout, T.C. (Ed.) (2003) *People and Woods in Scotland*. Edinburgh University Press, Edinburgh.

Smout, T.C., MacDonald A.R. & Watson, F. (2005) A History of the Native Woodlands of Scotland, 1500-1920 Edinburgh University Press, Edinburgh.

Background

Anon (2004) *Forestry Statistics*. Economics and Statistics Section, Forestry Commission, Edinburgh.

Darling, F. Fraser and Boyd, J. Morton (1964) *The Highlands and Islands*. Collins, London.

Hart, E. (2004) *Hefting in Practice*. Edward Hart, Ludlow.

Hendry, George (2003) *Midges in Scotland*. Mercat Press, Edinburgh.

Lee, J. R. (1933) *The Flora of the Clyde Area*. John Smith & Son, Glasgow.

MacGregor, M. & MacGregor, A. G. (1978) *British Regional Geology: The Midland Valley of Scotland*. 2nd edition. H. M. S. O.. Edinburgh.

Macpherson, K.A.T., Smith, R. A. & Akhurst, M. C. (2001) *Geology of the Kilmarnock District*. British Geological Survey, Nottingham.

McClure, D. (2002) *Ayrshire in the Age of Improvement: contemporary accounts of agrarian and social improvement in late eighteenth century Ayrshire*. Ayrshire Monographs 27, Ayrshire Archaeological and Natural History Society, Ayr.

Mair, J. (1996) *Cessnock: An Ayrshire Estate in the Age of Improvement*. Ayrshire Monographs No. 18. Ayrshire Archaeological and Natural History Society, Darvel.

Robinson, M. (Ed.) (1997) *The Concise Scots Dictionary*. Chambers, Edinburgh.

Wheeler, D. & Mayes, J. (1997) *Regional Climates of the British Isles*. Routledge, London & New York.

Peat

Ashworth, Nancy (2004) *Voices From The Peat: An Oral History of the Avalon Marshes.* Somerset County Council, Taunton.

Brunning, R. (2006) *The Avalon Marshes: a Peatland Story.* (CD) The Dog Rose Trust and Somerset County Council, Taunton.

Godwin, H. (1978) *Fenland: its Ancient Past and Uncertain Future.* Cambridge University Press, Cambridge.

Hingley, R. & Ingram, H. A. P. (2002) *History as an Aid to Understanding Peat Bogs.* In Smout, T.C. Understanding the Historical Landscape in its Environmental Setting. Scottish Cultural Press, Dalkeith.

Lindsay, R. (1995) *Bogs: The Ecology, Classification and Conservation of Ombrotrophic Mires.* Scottish Natural Heritage, Battleby.

Sutherland, P. & Nicolson, A. (1986) *Wetland: Life in the Somerset Levels.* Michael Joseph, London.

Whitelee Forest

Blair & Cadell W.S. (1921) *Ayrshire: The Estate of Loudoun. Particulars and Plans ... (... which will be offered for sale on Wednesday 2nd November 1921...).* Modern Copy of Sale Particulars.

Bousfield, N. & Spernagel, M.R.T. (1982) *Site Survey Report: Carrot Exchange (Carrot 1 and 2) Block, Whitelee Forest W (S), Western Midland Valley Site Region; Carrot 3, Appendix 3.* Report to the Forestry Commission, Edinburgh.

Boyd, J.M. (1999) *The Song of the Sandpiper.* Colin Baxter Photography, Grantown on Spey

Douglass, J. (2002) *Ecological Comments on Scottish Power's Proposed Windfarm Development at Whitelee.* Report to South Lanarkshire Council.

Douglass, J. (2004) *The Lichens of Whitelee Forest.* British Lichen Society Bulletin (94) pp.17-19.

Douglass, J. (2004) *A Lichen Survey of the Upper Boulder-Fields (Proposed Borrow Pit Site V) Whitelee Forest.* Report to South Lanarkshire Council.

Douglass, J. (2005) *Whitelee Forest Lichen and Bryophyte Survey. With recommendations for the proposed wind-farm development.* Report to British Lichen Society and South Lanarkshire Council.

Leitch, J. (2006) *Memories of the Whiteleehill Area Before and After The Forest.* Whitelee Forest Oral History Project archives. Scottish Life Archive, National Museum of Scotland, Edinburgh.

Macallister-Smith, E. & Wilson, J.D. (1977) *Soil Report on Avondale Block etc Whitelee Forest, Central Southern Upland and Western Basalt Classification.* Report to the Forestry Commission, Edinburgh.

Mair, J., Johnstone, A. & Hearns, G. (1996) *An Archaeological Field Survey of The Irvine Valley, East Ayrshire.* Association of Certificated Field Archaeologists (Glasgow University) Occasional Paper No. 23.

Malkin, J. (1981) *Sir Alexander Fleming: Man of Penicillin.* Alloway Publishing, Ayr. pp. 4–5.

Michie, C. (Date not given) *The Covenanters.* Booklet produced by The Lochgoin and Fenwick Covenanters Trust. Available at The Museum Room, Lochgoin farm, Fenwick, Ayrshire.

Tittensor, R.M. (2005) *Whitelee: Word o Mooth o a 20th Century Scots Wuid/The Oral History of a 20th Century Scottish Forest.* Project Brochure, Countryside Management Consultancy, Darvel.

Tittensor, R.M. (2006) *Whitelee Forest Oral History Project.* Consultancy Report to the Forestry Commission, 60pp.

Tittensor, R.M. (2008) *An oral history of a 20th Century Ayrshire Forest.* Scottish Forestry, 62 (1): 3-8.

Toleman, R. (1972) *Reconnaissance Soil Survey for Whitelee Forest Western Basalt Classification.* Report to the Forestry Commission, Edinburgh.

Web Sites

http://www.nationalarchives.gov.uk
National Archives website

http://www.old-maps.co.uk
1st edition 1:10,000OS maps 1850s and 1860s

http://www.ohs.org.uk
Oral History Society website

http://www.rcahms.gov.uk/index.html
Royal Commission on the Ancient and Historic Monuments of Scotland site, for scheduled archaeological and historical websites

http://www.scan.org.uk/index.html
Scottish Archive network website

http://www.oralhistoryscotland.org
Scottish Oral History Group website

http://www.arohascotland.org
Aberdeen and Region Oral History Association website

http://www.benlawers.org.uk/OralHistory
Ben Lawers Historic Landscapes Project, Oral History

http://www.scotlandindex.net/peat.htm
Peat digging methods and tools in Sutherland

http://www.forestry.gov.uk
Forestry Commission website

http://www.forestresearch.gov.uk
Web site describing Forestry Commission research projects

http://www.touchwood2007.org.uk
Oral contributions by the Forestry Commission to the '2007 – Scotland's Year of Highland Culture'

Geology Maps

British Geological Survey (1993) *Hamilton. Scotland Sheet 23W. Drift Geology. 1:50 000*. British Geological Survey, Nottingham.

British Geological Survey (2002) *Kilmarnock. Scotland Sheet 22E. Solid & Drift Geology. 1:50 000*. British Geological Survey, Nottingham.

Modern Maps

Ordnance Survey (1957 & 1959) *[Sheet name not known] 1:63 360 Sheet 60*. Ordnance Survey, Southampton

Ordnance Survey (1962) *Ayr. 1:63 360. Seventh Series Sheet 67*. Ordnance Survey, Southampton.

Ordnance Survey (1963 & 1965) *Glasgow 1:63 360. Seventh Series Sheet 60*. Ordnance Survey, Southampton

Ordnance Survey (2001) *East Kilbride, Galston & Darvel. 1:25 000. Explorer 334*. Ordnance Survey, Southampton.

Ordnance Survey (2000) *Glasgow. 1:50 000. Landranger Sheet 64*. Ordnance Survey, Southampton.

Ordnance Survey (2004) *Ayr, Kilmarnock & Troon. 1:50 000. Landranger Sheet 70*. Ordnance Survey, Southampton.

Ordnance Survey (1994) *Lanark & Upper Nithsdale. 1:50 000. Landranger Sheet 71*. Ordnance Survey, Southampton.

List of Illustrations

Page numbers in **bold** type indicate illustrations   * refers to contributors to the Project, see Appendix 1
† for Latin names of organisms, see Appendix 2   § see the glossary of Scots and English words in Appendix 3